Astronomy and Spiritual Science

The Astronomical Letters of Elisabeth Vreede

physically-conceived orbits with inner spiritual experience of the planets. But an important thing for the reader to see confirmed here is that Ptolemy's old-world, traditional Venus was the same planet as Copernicus' Venus of today.

In the Letter of July 1928, Vreede discusses the slow movement of the Sun's spring position round the zodiac of fixed stars, which is measured in thousands of years. Astronomically this movement is called the precession of the spring equinox. If the zodiacal constellations are all considered to be relatively the same length along the Sun's path, then today the spring position will move (westwards) through one constellation in just over 2000 years. Such a length of time is said to mark out the significant years of particular cultures, such as the Ancient Indian, Persian, Egyptian, and Babylonian. However, it is important to note, as Vreede does in her next Letter and in the one of July, 1930, that the *beginning* of a cultural period should be measured from when the spring Sun is in the *middle* part of a constellation. This reckoning is particular to anthroposophy, and offers an explanation as to why Steiner speaks of the beginning of our modern age (the age of the consciousness soul, as he terms it) taking place in the fifteenth century, when the spring Sun was well within the conventional fixed-star constellation of Pisces.

Here the reader should be cautioned when studying details of the long-term dating of events, such as early cycles of cultural periods, movements of the Earth's perihelion point through the seasons, ice ages, etc. It has to be considered that, depending on the context, the twelve sections of the zodiac can be measured from the beginnings *or* centers of each of the following: 1) equal divisions of constellations; 2) the conventional unequal divisions on star charts; or 3) somewhat different un-equal divisions (to the conventional ones) based on indications by Rudolf Steiner.

While explaining the slow movement of the Sun's spring position in the Letter of July 1928, Vreede is drawn into an inevitable discussion of the difference between the traditional astrologer's zodiac (tropical) and the astronomer's zodiac (sidereal). The traditional astrologer's zodiac has the Sun's spring position as its starting point. It is a Sun zodiac, oriented to the cycle of the seasons of the year, festivals, and the relationship of Sun to Earth. It marks out twelve equal "signs" round the sky, behind which lie the "constellations" of fixed stars. The Sun's spring position, along with the twelve "signs" attached to it, slowly pass, in thousands of years, over the fixed background of the constellations of the star zodiac. Today's astronomer calculates that the leading spring point of the Sun at the head of the tropical zodiac of "signs" takes about 2,150 years to traverse 30 degrees of the star background (i.e., one twelfth of a zodiac which is divided into twelve equal parts). Therefore, once in about 25,800 years the two zodiacs coincide, Aries on top of Aries for example, which was the case around the time of Christ. Since then the Sun's spring position, and the Sun zodiac along with it, has moved almost all the way across the star constellation of Pisces and close to its conventional, modern star-chart boundary with Aquarius. [It will cross this boundary in A.D. 2597.] So the two zodiacs differ by about one constellation or sign, the Sun "sign" of Aries today lying on top of the star constellation of Pisces.

Because the two zodiacs no longer coincide, it could be said that one of them is valid and the other not. In discussing this, Vreede at one point seems to express herself in a burst of feeling, claiming that whoever continues to describe the "sign" Aries as the beginning of the zodiac denies the Christ impulse and the spirituality of the stars. Later she refers to the first edition of Rudolf Steiner's *Calendar [Kalender] 1912/13* which contained, besides a *Calendar of the Soul* of 52 weekly verses beginning at Easter, zodiacal illustrations, and calendar notes—indications about the positions of the Sun and Moon throughout the 12 months. She says that this first edition confined itself entirely to the zodiacal constellations.

However, although the first edition of the *Calendar* places the Sun against the background of star constellations, it places the Moon in the astrologer's tropical zodiac perhaps inadvertently. Vreede herself also points to the fact that Steiner did use tropical (seasonal) zodiacal designations (e.g., Aries for the beginning of the zodiac) in some of his work.

Ptolemy used both zodiacs (the tropical one for astrology) though he knew the difference between them by his calculations. Vreede calls this zodiacal distinction an error. Yet each of the two zodiacs has its own rationale. The fact that they have separated since the time of Christ, as they were also separated before that time, is meaningful. But we should let Vreede have the last word on this—a word with which one can readily agree. In the Letter of July 1928, she writes of the placement of the spring Sun (or beginning of the "sign" Aries) in the star constellation of Aries, and the connection of this with the wonderful balance of Greek culture. With the crossing of the spring Sun into Pisces, this harmony was destroyed—it had to be destroyed, she says, through the Christ impulse; and with the moving on of the Sun's spring position, new forces were released . . .

This theme of the spiritual role of Christ in humanity's future and the changing relationship of the human being to the stars, is frequently brought forward to center stage in this book. In all three years of the Letters, such questions are boldly confronted.

✦ ✦ ✦

APART FROM HER STANDPOINT that the methods of early astrology are out of place today, and apart from her disapproval of modern popular astrology, Vreede does not discount that there is meaning in the stars for the human being. But she does not hesitate to quote Steiner as saying that no-one but the most experienced occultist, who stands at the end of his or her path, can really make use of astrology. She also quotes Steiner as writing that the real astrology was an intuitive knowledge and required the development of higher supersensible powers which, he said, can be present in very few persons today.

Then Vreede explains, in the same Letter of October, 1928, that since the Crucifixion human beings must gradually become free from the cosmos; they no longer stand in the same relation to the stars as before. In the centuries following Christ, what could be predicted about a person on the basis of the birth horoscope, or of their destiny on the basis of star positions later in their life, harmonized less and less with the actual facts. She quotes Steiner on how the reading of horoscopes brings dangers for persons who are striving toward esoteric development. Such astrological activity involved a refined egoism and, just when a person strives for inner development, they can easily arrive at such self-seeking, which is the more dangerous because it works subtly.

In this context of human/cosmic relationships, Vreede then brings up the important question of the activity, as taught by Steiner, of the archangel Michael—a being which has been described as a great Fire or Mercury spirit. This "Michael mystery" can only be understood in the light of a human evolution passing from receptivity to activity, from compulsion to freedom, from past to future. It is explained that what gives the human being a real foundation for action in freedom is what the being Michael brings as connecting forces out of the starry and planetary system—forces which can no longer be compelling, for they do not penetrate into the world of nature. Steiner is quoted on the incarnation process in present times and how Michael keeps the world of stars united, *through the human being,* with the divine. Today, which is a time when the course of the stars is only a continuing of the manner in which the divine worked in the past, this harmony cannot exist unless the human being seeks for it. It could be added that this free creation of harmony with the cosmos also applies to the human being's rise through its own activity into the spiritual worlds during life. A consequence of such harmony would be that the human individuality could then be inspired directly out of the spirit, passing beyond the stars.

Elsewhere in these Letters, Vreede goes on boldly to convey some dramatic spiritual pictures. For example:

○ the ideal that the human being can overcome the karma which expresses itself in the horoscope;

○ how Steiner's book *How to Know Higher Worlds* (Anthroposophic Press, Hudson, NY; 1994) contains instruction for becoming independent of the cosmic forces in the right way—and while a person finds himself or herself at home on Earth according to their star positions, they must find the forces which make for independence in the right way from these star positions;

○ how forces which rain down from the zodiac as a sacrifice must also reascend from the Earth, for through human evolution a new zodiac shall arise.

In contemplating the whole span of this book, one is made aware of the extremely alive yet paradox-like nature of the phenomena which confront the human being when experiencing the evolving universe. In the first pages, mention is made of the stars revealing themselves as colonies of spiritual beings. Two years later, mention is again made of this, with the rider that these spiritual beings are no longer directly united with individual stars. A star is visible to us just *because* it is no longer the dwelling place of a spiritual colony. The individual stars, she says, are the forsaken bodies of the gods. According to Steiner, stars are the bodies of gods whose souls carry on their activities in a new manner in the world, independent of these bodies.

Then again, while discussing Copernicanism in the Letter of May, 1930, it is said that just for materialism, astronomy has always been the pioneer. Even so, at the beginning and end of her text, Steiner is quoted as saying that astronomy is that science which, sooner than all others, may be restored to spirituality.

Elisabeth Vreede was a faithful starry messenger and pioneer of such a restoration in this resounding word-symphony of astronomical teachings.

★   ★   ★

NORMAN DAVIDSON (1933-2007), originally from Scotland, was a journalist in the U.K. for ten years before taking a teacher training course at Emerson College, Sussex. He was then a Waldorf teacher in England for 16 years, specializing in astronomy, projective geometry, ancient history and literature. He emigrated and joined Sunbridge College, Spring Valley, New York, in 1986 and was Director of Waldorf Teacher Training for 10 years. He is the author of *Astronomy and the Imagination* (Routledge & Kegan Paul, UK; 1985) and *Sky Phenomena: A Guide to Naked-eye Observation of the Stars* (Lindisfarne Books, Great Barrington, MA; 2004).

INTRODUCTION

The science of astronomy is that science which, sooner than all others, may be restored to spirituality.

—*Background to the Gospel of St. Mark*
LECTURE BY RUDOLF STEINER

THE ATTEMPT WILL BE MADE by means of these Letters and on behalf of the Mathematical and Astronomical Section to carry out what Rudolf Steiner, in his Letters on the "Free School of Spiritual Science," stated to be the particular task of the *Vorstand,* namely, "to bring to those who want it such results of his work as they may desire and as may be possible."

"The share that the whole membership can take in the work of the Goetheanum will be the best guarantee for the welfare of the [Anthroposophical] Society. And the *Vorstand* will endeavor to make everything that takes place through the members an integral part of the Society."

These words already imply that the present form of these Letters is only a preliminary stage and indicate a possible extension of their scope. But the Astronomical Section feels itself justified in beginning to give out some general information to those members who desire it.

Rudolf Steiner's whole work contains a grand cosmogony. This stands in contrast to that impoverished mathematical-mechanical view of the world living in the general consciousness of humankind, a view created by the modern astronomical worldview. But there exists in the healthy human soul a craving for knowledge of cosmic law and order that will help people to feel united with the cosmos. Human beings today long to experience their life as bound up with that of the cosmos. Rudolf Steiner, in his incomparable way, has given us the guidance toward such a feeling of "self-unitedness" (*Sich-Einfuhlen*) in his *Calendar of the Soul*

(*Seelenkalender*). Everything that takes place in time has its own life within the cosmos, as have the seasons of the year.

Thus, in order to become acquainted with these temporal events, one must first feel oneself connected with the forces that are at work. The knowledge of the universe rises upward through three degrees: from astronomy to astrology, and from astrology to *astrosophy*. But every one of these realms of knowledge is today more or less bewitched. *Astronomical science* is devoid of spirituality, but must once again be permeated with it. *Astrology* preserves an ancient spirituality that no longer has the same value for our own times. True astrosophy is at present surely not to be found outside Rudolf Steiner's spiritual science. Astrosophy is at one and the same time the goal of an anthroposophical science of the cosmos and its starting point. Hence we will commence these letters with a concise review of that wonderful lecture cycle Rudolf Steiner gave at Helsingfors in 1912, *The Spiritual Beings in the Heavenly Bodies and in the Kingdoms of Nature.* There exists no better and more comprehensive introduction than this to anthroposophical astronomy.

The fact that we turn our attention to the active beings of the cosmos links us especially with the significance of the moment when these letters first begin. The festival of Saint Michael is near at hand. Michael, the messenger of the Sun and of the Christ, has very special functions to perform in the celestial worlds. When he wields his starry sword the dragon of the summer's heat vanishes. When a human being is born, the world-will of Michael dwells in the constellation ruling at the birth. If it were not for Michael's activity, humanity and the world of the stars would have been parted asunder. He works in such a way through astrology, and he gave us astrosophy, inasmuch as spiritual science was able to arise during his era.

In the next Letter we will speak in more detail of the world rhythms and the constellations of the stars.

With friendly greetings,

E. VREEDE (PH.D.)
*Leader of the Section of Mathematics
and Astronomy
Dornach, September 1927.*

YEAR ONE

September 1927–August 1928

Astronomy and Anthroposophy

RUDOLF STEINER'S spiritual science has given us a cosmology that is in accordance with spiritual law, and through which humankind is once more placed within the world-picture, and heaven and Earth are again united. He repeatedly attempted to establish the connection between this spiritually-based knowledge and that of modern scientifically-based astronomy. The necessity of establishing such a connection springs from the very foundations of spiritual science—the idea that the external world is maya, or illusion, and that spiritual science seeks to penetrate to the reality that lies behind it. Where and how maya and reality meet with one another is the great question. It was this question that Rudolf Steiner addressed in his cycle of lectures in Helsingfors [Helsinki], Finland (1912), *The Spiritual Beings in the Heavenly Bodies and in the Kingdoms of Nature.*

A close study of this cycle reveals to us the way from external maya to inner spiritual reality. If one wishes to find what has resulted from this reality one must go back to the past. "The world of physical heavenly bodies represents the remains of the past deeds of the various beings of the hierarchies, and the aftereffects of their deeds extend into the present."

Thus the world of stars is as much an illusion or maya as the rest of nature, and what is more, it is a maya of the past! But if one penetrates behind this maya then the stars reveal themselves as "colonies of spiritual beings." One is led to contemplate the beings of the higher hierarchies that are raised above humankind in nine degrees, and who are all in one way or another connected with the world of the stars and its cosmic evolution. This is more closely described in Rudolf Steiner's *An Outline of Esoteric Science.*

Above the human being there is, first of all, the sphere of those angelic beings we call *angels* or *angeloi,* who are the guardians of individual human beings and accompany them from incarnation to incarnation. They live in the sphere of the Moon, although they do not actually carry out their activities upon the Moon itself. For that greater powers are necessary, which are only to be found among the *archangels* or *archai*. These beings, who, together with the angels, compose the first or lowest hierarchy of the spiritual world, guide the nations of the Earth and the great epochs of time. The archangels are at the same time folk-spirits and the archai, spirits of time. Thus this hierarchy, which extends as far as the Moon, is primarily concerned with the historical life of individuals and of whole peoples.

Further, in the Sun we find those beings whom we designate as the second hierarchy; to these belong the *spirits of form,* the *spirits of movement,* and the *spirits of wisdom.* In a certain sense these beings have their habitation on the Sun, but from there they work upon the planets and send their forces from the planets down to Earth. The spirits of form give the planets their outer configuration. The spirits of movement cause the inner mobility of the planets—not their movement through space, but the alterations and transformations that take place within them over the course of centuries and millennia, for example, those that take place on Earth through the ebb and flow of tides, through volcanic eruptions and earthquakes, and through meteorological and climatic influences. It is different with regard to the spirits of wisdom. These beings work from the Sun itself, and are the mediators who convey the forces of the Sun throughout the planetary system. While the inner configuration and inner mobility of each planet is different in accordance with the individual forces of the active spirits of form or spirits of movement, the efficacy of the spirits of wisdom is the same for every planet.

We can trace the uniform workings of the spirits of wisdom most easily in the plant kingdom. The forms of the plants are all different; their stipules and tendrils show varieties of spiral regularity. In these are reflected planetary forces that come either from spirits of form or spirits of movement who have their respective planets as the starting-points of their activity. But there is one thing that is common to every plant, namely, the vertical direction of its stem, from Earth to the Sun. This is for every plant the expression of the uniformity of the work of the spirits of wisdom. It is a kind of universal, simple form of consciousness of the entire planetary system, somewhat as in all human beings there is a universal similarity of feeling and inclination that rises out of the subconscious. The spirits of wisdom are not only to be found upon the Sun, but also upon every one of the fixed stars, so that the first commonality of the entire world of the fixed stars is to be sought in these spirits of wisdom. Hence they are also described as the doorway for the inflowing of the Christ, whose light, in a certain sense, shone through the spirits of wisdom into the Sun during the time previous to the Mystery of Golgotha before he united himself with the Earth.

In the first hierarchy are the most sublime and lofty of all the beings of the cosmos, the *thrones, cherubim,* and *seraphim,* as they have been called in the ancient esoteric wisdom. It is the thrones, or spirits of will, who create the movements of the planets through space, while the cherubim regulate the different movements and bring about definite relations between planet and planet. They are the messengers for the planets, as the angels are the messengers for the human world. The seraphim have a similar task in respect to the entire world of the stars. They bring about a mutual understanding between the Sun and the other stars, between fixed star and fixed star, bringing the whole universe into a single harmony.

We come thus to the following scheme:

Seraphim	
Cherubim	*Comets*
Thrones	
Spirits of Wisdom	*Fixed Stars*
Spirits of Movement	
Spirits of Form	*Planets*
Archai	
Archangels	*Moon*
Angels	
Human Being	*Earth*

We must also mention the comets as being a special sphere for the activity of the seraphim and cherubim. It may appear surprising that the sphere of the comets, who are the rebels against the general order of the cosmos, should be allocated to the highest of the hierarchies we have mentioned above. In order to understand this we must try to enter still more deeply into the relation between maya and reality.

What we have just described contains, as it were, the divine universal plan that the beings of the higher hierarchies (and particularly the first hierarchy) receive from the divine world spirit and bring to completion during the course of the whole stupendous evolution of the cosmos. But during this process a great deal has entered in that has brought the spiritual reality into the state of maya we all live in today. In this connection we include, above all, the fact that the movements of the planets and of the fixed stars (and here we mean the apparent so-called movements of the latter) are carried out in so regular a manner that a modern person might well ask: What can the thrones and the other beings still have left to do in regulating the external movements of the planets? Everything is taking place according to strict mathematical laws!

But it was not always so, and indeed in a certain sense neither is it the case today. The comets are an exception, and one can begin to understand that their movements need to be directed by the very loftiest beings.

We must now observe that the universe has gone through various stages of development that are called, in Rudolf Steiner's *An Outline of Esoteric Science,* the "Saturn," "Sun," "Moon," and "Earth" periods. To this we must add what was given in his "Leading Thoughts" (*News-Sheet* 1.43). During each one of these periods the whole world of stars was different. On Old Saturn there were only spiritual beings—those whom we have mentioned just now. But they did not yet express themselves in the form of a starry firmament, but rather as a general inclination or "hint" of stars. During the "Sun" evolution, however, the stars were there as revelations of the spiritual beings. In their movements and so on they were a direct expression of the beings who dwelled on them, in the same way that the human physical body is a direct manifestation of the movements and expressions of the indwelling spirit. In the next stage, that of the Moon, the spiritual beings could only pour their effective working into the heavenly bodies. They gradually withdrew themselves more and more. In order to make this a little clearer, we will briefly describe the historical progress of Earth evolution from this standpoint.

Earth represents the fourth of these stages, and Rudolf Steiner described it as a *finished work,* inasmuch as what was set forth at the beginning of this letter has now been realized. But during the historical ages, humankind again lived through the earlier evolutionary periods of consciousness. In the ancient Indian civilization, for example, human beings' attitude toward the world of stars was such that they did not notice them at all (this was at a time previous to the Vedas), but instead looked up to the spiritual beings themselves. In the ancient Persian civilization Zoroaster received the revelation of the being of the Sun. (The Sun itself at that time moved, of course, in accordance with the same laws as today, whereas in the Old Sun condition it was still a direct expression of the Sun spirit. Therefore the ancient Persian experienced an earlier condition at a later age.) The Old Chaldeans and Egyptians realized with special force the *effective working* of the spiritual beings in the heavenly bodies, and hence they had such a wonderful astrological science in their time (which, however, cannot be applied in the same form by humanity today). Theirs was a kind of recapitulation of the Old Moon condition. They saw the beings connected with Sun, Moon, planets and stars, but these beings were no longer solely those of the higher hierarchies. The forms of the Egyptian gods—human bodies with animal heads, or complete animal forms, which appear in the Egyptians' world of stars—do not belong directly to the beings of the hierarchies mentioned above. But they are their offspring-beings that the hierarchies have separated off from themselves. It is these beings, then, who in a certain sense continue the activities from which their creators, the hierarchies themselves, have withdrawn, now that the plan of the movements, orbits, and so on of the planetary system has been established. There are numbers of effective lesser gods of this kind in the universe. The Egyptians or the Chaldeans, especially of later times, who could no longer raise their perception to the gods of the stars themselves, contemplated instead the working of these lesser beings. These offspring of the various hierarchies regulate those things that human beings today believe "go of themselves." In order that the human being should develop in freedom, it was necessary that the higher beings should withdraw themselves from the starry worlds and from the whole of nature and leave these to a mechanism apparently without spirit. (We will speak in more detail about the meaning and manner of this withdrawal later on.)

Nevertheless, in this mechanical celestial world, as in every phenomenon of nature, the spiritual beings who are the offspring of the higher hierarchies continue to work.

The sprouting of the plants out of the Earth in spring, their flowering and fruiting, their decay in autumn, the coming of spring and the blossoming of the plants at the other side of the world when we have autumn here—this is brought about by those nature spirits, the sylphs, undines, and gnomes who are the descendants of the third hierarchy (angels, archangels, and archai), and by the salamanders (fire-spirits) who have been "separated off" from the spirits of form. They carry out this work under the guidance of the spirits of the revolutions of time, who direct them here and there over the Earth, and who also turn the Earth upon her axis, while others guide the Earth and the planets around the Sun on their regular orbits, and so on. The spirits of the revolution of time are the descendants of the highest hierarchies, of the seraphim and cherubim. The spirits of movement, wisdom, and will have as their offspring those beings we can call the group-souls of the animals, plants, and minerals.

We can set down in a schematic form which beings have been separated off from the different hierarchies as their offspring:

Hierarchy	Offspring
Seraphim, Cherubim	Spirits of the Revolution of Time
Thrones	Group-Souls of the Minerals
Spirits of Wisdom	Group-Souls of the Plants
Spirits of Movement	Group-Souls of the Animals
Spirits of Form	Fire Spirits
Spirits of Personality (Archai)	Gnomes
Archangels	Undines
Angels	Sylphs

These are all beings who are of a lower order than their progenitors, and who have so worked within the divine task that the natural world order and moral world order no longer remain as one but, at least for outer observation, has developed a certain duality. Hence it has come about that we stand before nature and the cosmos as before a maya in which the forces of *nature* appear merely as an impress of the activity of the *nature spirits*. And in the place of an unimpeded inpouring of activity from the hierarchies, we now find the *laws of nature* as an impress of the *spirits of the revolution of time* within the world of maya. Therefore in these offspring we have beings who bring us a step nearer to what is otherwise observed in the domain of external natural science.

While all this is taking place in the orderly and lawful manner that is necessary in order for human beings to arrive at an inner experience of freedom, there are still the comets, which do not fully fit into this orderly scheme. Even though the so-called periodical comets do conform more or less to the general order, the appearance of new comets (and comets are as numerous as the fish in the sea, as Kepler already observed) testifies again and again to a breaking of these laws. The comets constitute an element in which we can surmise something like the direct interposition of spiritual powers, and, indeed, powers of the very highest sort—namely the seraphim and cherubim. That which has to break through any established order is just the very thing that calls for regulation by the highest possible force and insight. The comets constitute a quite remarkable contrivance in the midst of our planetary system and have their polar opposite in the moons of the various planets. As the moons on the one hand are a species of corpse that the planetary system drags about with it, so on the other hand the comets are like incessant cleansers of the astral atmosphere of the solar system. In earlier ages they were regarded with awe as the "scourges" of God, and much superstition has gathered around them. For spiritual sight, too, they are wondrous forms that ever and again sweep the unclean astral forces out of the cosmos, or have the task of bringing fresh impulses into it.

Thus in a certain way we can behold the component parts or "limbs" of the planetary system if—as Rudolf Steiner says in the Helsingfors cycle—we gaze with occult sight at the various heavenly bodies. The moons—and there are also moons belonging to Mars, Jupiter, Saturn, and so on—create the general impression of a corpse. Just as the human corpse is a kind of memory image of what was once living, so the moons of the planetary system are like the memory of an earlier living condition that, however, has now absolutely and completely perished. So the planetary system has, as its lowest member, the moons; and similarly, human beings have, as their lowest member, the physical body. On the other hand, if we observe the totality of the planets in the solar system, we receive an impression that more or less coincides with the occult impression we can obtain when we regard the limit—the boundary—of the human physical body. Therefore the planets represent, so to speak, the *physical body* of the solar system. And, moreover, from the single planets there issue those activities that go to build up the inner organs of human beings.

When we look at the Sun as a fixed star within the planetary system, it awakens an impression that is comparable to that of the etheric body. This is not the etheric body of the human being, but the etheric body of the world of plants in all its purity, free from any penetration by the astral forces.

The astral body of the solar system actually consists of a plethora of beings—including those whom we have described—the hierarchies and the spirits of the revolutions of time. But those beings that stream out from the evil thoughts of human beings also belong to it, as well as those that come from the so-called "laggard" beings in the cosmos. (These are the substances that must be removed by the comets.)

Further, we can also speak of an I-being of the planets. For Earth there is the "spirit of Earth" whose impress upon the outer world may be called the "sense[1] of the Earth." In ancient times this Earth spirit was one of the elohim—Jahweh or Jehovah. Since the Mystery of Golgotha *Christ* is the spirit of Earth—he who has "given Earth her sense." And therefore he has to be found through a much more inward means than any of the other spiritual beings.

The spirits of the revolution of time, who represent the astral body of the Earth, still have a relationship to the astral body of the human being. Both are in a certain sense a multiplicity—a "manifoldness." We can feel this relationship when we allow the seasons of the year to work upon our soul, as is indicated, for instance, in the *Calendar of the Soul* Even the outer expression of these spirits—the laws of nature—is related to the human soul, born out of the human soul. We have a less definite relation to the forces of nature, even when we learn to master them through the medium of our knowledge of nature's laws. These forces of nature are indeed the impress of the nature-spirits, the gnomes, undines, and so on. The etheric body of the Earth is composed of a multiplicity of these beings. But human beings for the most part feel their own etheric body as a unity, and thus do not inwardly feel closely connected with the realm of the nature spirits.

If we take the world perceived by the senses as being the physical body of the Earth as it appears quite simply to our sense-perception, the following scheme emerges:

---

1. "Sinn." Rudolf Steiner did not use this word as "Mind," but as "sense."

Planetary Spirit	Sense of Nature	I
Spirits of the Revolution of Time	Laws of Nature	Astral Body
Realm of the Nature Spirits	Forces of Nature	Etheric Body
World Perceived by the Senses	Perceptions	Physical Body

But there are not only those beings and forces present in the cosmos that have been mentioned. If it were so, the entire cosmos would consist solely of an element of being without any visible substance. The heavenly bodies would not be perceptible to our sight, nor would earthly substance be tangible. In order to understand maya we must also consider that still other beings—called luciferic and ahrimanic in *An Outline of Esoteric Science*—have interpolated themselves into the evolutionary process. These are beings of the higher hierarchies who, however, have not followed the same course of development, but have remained behind while the normal spirits have gone on to ever higher and higher degrees. Thus, for example, there are the laggard spirits of form, who should properly have become spirits of movement, but who have remained behind at the stage of the spirits of form. While the etheric spheres of Saturn and Jupiter were being fashioned by the spirits of form and their inner mobility was being given by the spirits of movement, rebellious spirits of form hurled themselves against the normal spirits instead of taking part in the creation of movement. By remaining in a state of resistance at a certain point within the sphere, they created a form, and this form is actually the planet we now see shining in the heavens! The sphere of the planet remains as an etheric structure in which astral forces are working. The planet itself moves in its orbit on the circumference of this sphere.

At the same time other luciferic beings advanced and hurled themselves against the seraphim and cherubim who were carrying the spiritual light of the Sun out into the whole of cosmic space and robbed them of it, retaining one part of the light in the planet itself and thrusting back another part. This stolen light then changed into external, perceptible light so that the planet became externally visible. At a later stage ahrimanic beings added solid matter to the Earth and fashioned the thick veil of maya that now represents the outer world perceived by the senses. Everything in existence that can be the object of external investigation has in itself, in some form or other, a luciferic element—an outer light—

nature; and an ahrimanic element, which incorporates weight into itself. This, too, belongs to the maya that is spread out over the whole of the spiritual reality.

We can study these things further with regard to yet other forms, the meteors, which are also connected with the comets. The comets appear as spiritual forms that are sent into the universe by the highest spirits, and in the course of their astral "scavenging" they absorb many substances such as gases and so on. But at the same time other creations appear that project themselves against them. These belong to an abnormal class of beings, namely thrones who should actually be seraphim or cherubim. They have remained behind at the stage of the thrones, and now work with that stupendously powerful might that they owe to their having remained in an earlier condition. The thrones are the creators of the group-souls of the minerals, and the laggard thrones therefore produce hard mineral-substantial forms in the cosmos—as meteors and so on, which often either accompany the comets, or appear in more or less regular cycles of time and spatial positions as meteoric showers in the atmosphere of the Earth. Thus these creations, which are to some extent withdrawn from the normal regularity of the laws of the planetary system, represent a lofty spirituality united with the most compacted matter. We will deal in greater detail with the nature of the comets and meteors at a later stage.

It is precisely the behavior of the comets that serves to remind us again and again that it is not possible to explain the occurrences within the planetary system solely by means of the Newtonian theory of gravitation.

Even with respect to the other heavenly bodies, there is always something remaining over that, if it be taken together over immense periods of time, is an expression of the living activity of spiritual beings within the solar system, which has not entirely passed over into the condition of "finished work." But it is only the comets and meteors that actually to some extent introduce the incalculable element—an element of arbitrary self-will. With regard to the other heavenly bodies the incommensurability of their relative periods of movement shows that they demand a different method of observation from the gravitational one that holds good for Earth. *Rhythm* and *periodicity* pertain to the planetary movements and fundamentally constitute their own primeval laws, even as the immediate periphery of the Earth has its laws of gravitation. (Naturally the Earth also partakes of the cosmic regulation of rhythm and period, as it is also a heavenly body.) These laws are the same as those upon which humanity and the other kingdoms of nature are based. By this mode of conception humanity and the universe will once more be united, and after this manner, too, religious feeling will once again be able to find its connection with the starry heavens. Indeed, the stars are for us the traces of divine deeds that lead us up to the beings of the hierarchies, and to the very throne of God himself. Thus Rudolf Steiner could say in the lecture course I referred to in which he pointed the way from anthroposophy to astronomy: "Inasmuch as we behold the world of the stars, we behold the bodies of the gods, and ultimately the form of all that is divine."

October 1927

Concerning Rhythms and Constellations

Spiritual-psychic causes produce in the celestial bodies
positions and motions through which spiritual conditions
are manifested on the physical plane.

—An Outline of Esoteric Science
BY RUDOLF STEINER

THE WORLD OF STARS has shown itself to us as a final revelation
of spiritual beings, who have more and more withdrawn from active
participation, until they demonstrate their astral nature or quality of
being within the etheric only—as Rudolf Steiner says—like a "loving
caress." This process of development—which can be characterized as
"diminishing"—has continued from the Saturn period into our own
time. It concerns chiefly those heavenly bodies that are visible to us
externally, whereas behind the stars, or within the spheres of the stars,
we can still find the active forces and powers of the spiritual beings.
Naturally, though, in those regions too (as is described in *An Outline
of Esoteric Science*) evolution has nevertheless gone forward throughout
the whole of that stupendous period of time. No world of stars was visible around Old Saturn, but instead, there was something like streaks
of flame, out of which eventually the zodiac came into being during the
time of Old Sun. The Old Moon was established in mighty interchanging
activity with the whole of the surrounding universe. When finally Earth
first appeared out of the spiritual state intervening after the end of the
Old Moon, it contained within itself the future planetary system in its
entirety. The separation of the Sun and then of the Moon, out of the
unitary Earth-body during the second and third great epochs (the Hyperborean and the Lemurian), were acts performed by spiritual beings, and
the forces and substances that were thereby drawn out of the Earth were
at first of a purely spiritual kind. We could not have seen them with the
physical eyes of today.

Before the withdrawal of the Sun, the Saturn beings, and then the Jupiter- and Mars-beings had already released their forces from the Earth-body. Mercury and Venus left Earth with the Sun, but did not separate from the Sun until the latter was free of Earth. The reasons for these separations are given in *An Outline of Esoteric Science* and also in the articles on the Akashic records in *Lucifer-Gnosis* (now being reprinted in the German weekly *Anthroposophy*).

As a matter of course, the planets and stars that had then come into existence in the cosmos were not there precisely as they are today, nor did they have the same movements then as those we perceive now. So for a long time after the separation of the Sun from Earth there was not any chronology in the sense that we now understand it, since years and days could not as yet be measured (cf. *An Outline of Esoteric Science*). Also, the movements of the remaining planets were an expression of the beings who dwelt upon them and were regulated by certain spiritual necessities. The way that Mars and Mercury, for instance, have been related to Earth since the beginning of its evolution is described in Rudolf Steiner's *At the Gates of Spiritual Science*; and *The Theosophy of the Rosicrucian*, lecture 7.

In *An Outline of Esoteric Science* is depicted, too, how the majority of human souls were compelled to leave Earth while the conditions of existence there were becoming ever more difficult. Later, when the Moon had also left Earth, and on into Atlantean times, human souls gradually returned. Thus we see an intimate cooperation between the whole planetary system and the Earth, which is still an expression of things that are purely of the soul and spirit.

Spiritual beings descended to Earth from the other planets, clothed themselves in the human forms that were then existent, and instructed the young humanity, teaching them the arts and sciences. Later still they could come down to humankind in the mysteries, but here, too, the conditions surrounding such intercourse became more and more difficult.

These circumstances, which are to be understood throughout as arising out of the state of *revelation* and *effective working* in the sense mentioned earlier, underlay a fundamental change that took place in Atlantean times. The middle point of this period is at the same time the middle point of all Earth evolution. There took place a mighty penetration into the world of the *I*—whose evolution belongs especially to Earth. There came a time when the clouds of mist—the "water-air"—

that lay over ancient Atlantis, parted asunder, and for the first time the Sun became visible. If the hindering influence of the luciferic beings had not been interposed in the beginning of Earth-evolution, this would have been the time—the middle of the Atlantean epoch—when Christ, as bringer of the impulse of the I to Earth, would have been born. The Christ-constellation was there. But humankind would not have been able at that time to receive him in freedom. Therefore his advent had to be postponed and the world had to be so ordered that the I could first unfold itself freely.

It was at that time too that the star beings had so far withdrawn themselves from the heavenly bodies that these were now carrying out their movements within strictly defined orbits and with established periodicity. Those apparently mechanical-mathematical laws, which are still operative, began to work. And it is these orderly laws, which in a certain sense dominated the whole of the middle period of Earth-evolution, whose end is gradually approaching. All this had to happen in order that humanity might attain freedom. Only upon a world not governed by sudden interventions of the will of the gods and by tumultuous spiritual manifestations could the tender germ of the human I, the "I am," develop itself in freedom.

The planetary bodies came to such an exact regularity of movement that it became possible to calculate their orbits and positions. They travel in a sublime restfulness and order along the several paths that their activities appoint for them. For human experience, the universe had then arisen as the "finished work," even though during long periods, indeed, even up to the present time, the human was still in a position to feel the activity of divine powers. And when human beings are in the life between death and rebirth, the "finished work" world vanishes for them, and is then in the actual world of the spiritual beings themselves. On returning with a new birth, the human being experiences with especial clarity the ever deeper and deeper growing twilight of the revelations. At length there remains once more only the effective *working* of the spiritual world. The moment of actual birth is the last expression of the link between the human being and the world of the stars. One is then placed into earthly life, and there remains to perception only the "finished work," whose apparent mechanical behavior can so deceptively entice one from the truth—which is that the destiny of Earth is not merely written upon the face of the great heavenly clock, but is also effected by it.

Now with this effectively established world order certain constellations arise at their proper moment: new Moon, full Moon, planetary aspects, eclipses, and so forth. (We are speaking here of "constellations" in the sense of "aspects," angles of the stars, not of the fixed constellations or starry configurations to which the same word also applies.) That which denotes for humanity the foundation of its freedom is, for the spiritual world, a kind of limitation of the field of its effective action. The constellation that is necessary for any particular event or development must be waited for; it cannot be constrained by any direct interposition of spiritual powers. (A certain exception is, of course, that of the comets, as we have seen.) It is just in such a connection as this that we can see how widely the movements in the cosmos are different from any machine created by human beings! In a truly wonderful way, in living rhythms in which there is nothing whatever of a mechanistic nature, in endless variety that is nevertheless dependent only on a few interrelated numbers, the great cosmic intercourse between stars and planets runs its course in the heavenly expanse. True, every thirty days there appears within the month one full Moon, one new Moon. Yet each time, the Moon appears in the neighborhood of a different star, and even though every nineteen years the full Moon reappears approximately in the neighborhood of the same star, yet all the other connections are each time different. In these rhythms, with their incommensurable numerical relationships, there lies concealed the *life* of the cosmos, which it has preserved for itself even in the midst of its condition as a "finished-work world." Against this, there is the universal law of attraction, of gravity, by which movements may be calculated, and which is an expression of the *death-element* that had to be mingled with the living cosmos in order that human beings could become free. Where we have to do purely with the rhythms of the etheric world, with the frequencies of sound—which has in all ages been connected with the planetary spheres—there we have only simple rational numerical relationships. Rhythmical occurrences and gravitation—these are not incompatible with one another, but they bear the same relation to each other as does the etheric body to the physical body. Thus, the aspects between stars and planets have necessarily to appear out of this regularity of law, and must be awaited at their proper time.

Not only must the active forces follow their foreordained heavenly path, but human beings must also. This they do, to begin with, at birth, when they submit to be born under those aspects that correspond to their karma. But in the ancient mysteries, and up to about the time of the Egypto-Chaldean civilization, human beings followed these paths in a quite special way. One gazed up to the stars in order to know if the gods could come to one. No longer was any continuous intercourse between the gods and human beings possible, as had been the case in earlier times. It was precisely because the correspondence between the heavenly rhythms was not outwardly mechanical that the possibility existed for the gods to descend to humanity in the mysteries. Sun, Moon, and stars all have their own rhythms. The solar day is different from the sidereal day, the solar month from the sidereal month, and so on. And just in these cases when, so to speak, it is not a compulsory aspect that is formed, but where one rhythm, as the result of incommensurability, gains an advance over another rhythm—then there is yet a greater possibility for the spiritual world to intervene. Such were those occasions—perhaps days or only hours—when in the later mysteries the priests were able to foster an intercourse with the divine beings. But even in the ordinary life of today, a very special role is played by what is not an outwardly visible configuration of different stars, but is just such an overstepping of one rhythm beyond another—a difference in speed—that then works as a very real factor into human life. Let us take an example.

Even in the remotest past, in astronomy the difference between the so-called synodical and sidereal revolutions of the Moon was understood. The latter represents the path of the Moon through the world of stars—the time that the Moon takes to travel from one particular star back to it again—for example, from Regulus in the constellation of the Lion, and back. It is quite easy to see with the naked eye how the Moon gets a little further to the east every day. It makes one complete journey around the heavens in about 27 $\frac{1}{3}$ days (more precisely 27 days, 7 hours, 43 minutes, and 11.545 seconds. But even this estimate is only an average one, and varies something like three hours, precisely on account of the inner aliveness of the cosmic system. Therefore accuracy to the minute need not be dealt with here.)

Suppose that at the Moon's first conjunction with Regulus it was full, for instance—then after one revolution through the zodiac (for Moon, Sun, and planets do apparently move through the zodiac to external sight) it would not have returned to its place by Regulus in precisely the same relation to the Sun as before. This is because in the meantime the Sun has been continuing its own yearly path. The Moon will require about two more days before it is once more full—in other words until it is in the same position relative to the Sun as it was when in conjunction with Regulus.

This can be shown by a simple drawing:

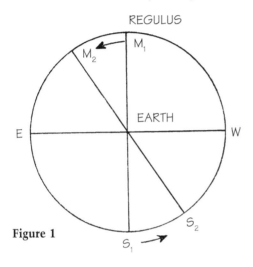

Figure 1

The circle represents the heavenly arc—in particular the zodiac or ecliptic. The Sun and Moon stand opposite one another (M_1S_1) in opposition, as it is called. Therefore it is full Moon. The Moon is next to Regulus, and after making one revolution is back again at Regulus, but must now be at M_2 in order to be in the same position with regard to the Sun, which has in the meantime reached S_2. That is what is called the synodical revolution of the Moon, which takes 29 ½ days (29 days, 12 hours, 44 minutes). In these two and one-fifth days that separate the Moon rhythm in connection with the stars from the Moon rhythm in its connection with the Sun, there is, so to speak, a free space that is reflected in the microcosm, the human being, in the relation between the human astral body and etheric body. While the astral body takes up the experiences of the waking consciousness quickly, the etheric body needs a slightly longer period for these to impress themselves upon it so that they may become recollections, memory. In fact this process needs a period of from one to two or two and a half days. This time interval is the result of the difference between the sidereal and synodical lunar revolutions. In human beings, it is necessary that in this interval they shall have *slept* once or twice. The astral body must have been separated from the etheric body, in order that these impressions can be made upon it. The quicker rhythm of the astral body (the Moon's journey around the stars) is only equaled by the slower rhythm of the etheric body after two or three nights (the Moon's journey related to the Sun). Hence the images of our dream-world are almost always associated with the experiences that lie a day or two behind. (cf. Rudolf Steiner's lecture of May 8, 1920). As I have said, we are speaking here of differences of rhythms and their working as such, not of the constellations or phases themselves as they are actually occurring in the heavens.

Or let us take another example, which again is the expression of a definite time period. This is the greater length of the *solar year* over the *lunar year*. The solar year has, as we know, a length of 365 $\frac{1}{4}$ days (not to speak of minutes and seconds). That is to say, that by the end of this period the Sun is once more apparently in the same spot as before. If we imagine a corresponding twelve (synodical) months for the Moon, we get twelve times 29 $\frac{1}{2}$ days; namely, 354 days (and a few hours) for the so-called lunar year. Therefore we see that the Sun has a somewhat longer period of activity than the Moon, and this is reflected in the space of time lying between Christmas and Twelfth Night—the Feast of Epiphany. It seems as though the Moon had purposely retarded its movement so that pure undisturbed Sun forces could play upon Earth during the twelve or thirteen "holy" nights—the forces of the Sun that sent the Christ to Earth.

It was such time periods as these that were regarded in the ancient mysteries as favorable for obtaining intercourse with the divine beings. One may say that they opened the door between heaven and Earth.

There is still a further stage to be noted in the working of spiritual forces, not only in the differences between the rhythms, but in the *relation* of one cosmic rhythm to another. Always in ancient times, the numerical factors governing the different time rhythms were used as the foundation upon which everything, including human social life, was built up. Even in the Old Testament, which is otherwise unfriendly toward the old astrology, the ancient Chaldean rule is repeated: "I have appointed thee a day for a year" (Ezekiel 4:6). This is the statement most frequently found as representing the old spiritual astrology: one day stands for one year. Let us take, as an example, what we may call the archangelic periods, starting again from the lunar year (mentioned above) or 354 $\frac{1}{3}$ days. If the "day" stands for a "year," we have a period of 354 years and four months. That is precisely the number that the mystic Trithemius of Sponheim indicates as the time when the rulership of one archangel gives place to the rulership of the next in the following order: Michael, Oriphiel, Anael, Zachariel, Raphael, Samael, Gabriel, and Michael.

Thus, reckoning through thousands of years, he arrives at last at September–October 1879, as the date of the commencement of the age of Michael, and June 4, 1525, as the commencement of the preceding age of Gabriel. The rulership of the seven archangels, therefore, covers a time corresponding to seven lunar years, or 2,480 ½ solar years.

A wonderful secret lies hidden in this calculation! We started with the Moon (lunar cycle), then added the Sun and Earth by taking one day as one year, and now with the seven archangels—who follow each other in due course—we have the seven planets represented. Therefore the whole planetary system is secretly involved in these archangel periods, and also the world of the fixed stars, which by reason of its number twelve (twelve synodical revolutions = one lunar year), represents the number of the zodiacal constellations. Primeval wisdom is expressed in these things—a wisdom that lives and weaves in rhythm. But it cannot therefore distinguish between the rhythm and the "chances," or special interventions, of events directly out of the spiritual world that are always to be found in history and work either as a retarding or hastening influence upon the divine ordinances. We know that Rudolf Steiner spoke of the archangel periods as lasting for "from three to four hundred years," and that he also gave certain dates that do not strictly correspond with those given by Trithemius of Sponheim. Thus for the commencement of the Michaelic age he gives November 1879, and also a longer period for the Gabriel rulership. There is no contradiction here; on the one hand actual historical occurrences are taken into account, and on the other hand *only* observation of rhythms. In ancient times these rhythms and time periods were known in many different ways. The more one penetrates into them, the more one learns of the marvelous dance of the starry beings who now only create an external impression of themselves in the movements of the heavenly bodies.

Naturally in every age humankind has also observed the configurations and aspects actually present in the heavens—whether it be the reappearance of the new Moon, its development to full Moon, the path of the Sun through the zodiac, or the conjunctions and oppositions of the planets. In all of this the starry world shows itself in its *activity;* and it is good even now to make oneself familiar with the movements of stars and planets, and to become aware of their positions and their meetings with one another. To notice whether it be a waxing or a waning Moon; whether for many months perhaps Jupiter or Saturn have been shining in the night sky; whether the lady Venus is visiting us as a morning or as an evening star; if perhaps after long absence the warlike Mars stands in the eastern heavens; or how from time to time Mercury becomes visible deep on the western horizon in the evening twilight—to follow all these things brings us gradually nearer to a "living with" these processes by means of which the spiritual speaks to us from the planetary system. And then, too, there is the path of the whole world of the stars—their rising and setting, their regular appearance and disappearance in the course of the year—in which we can take part—so far as the atmosphere of our cities allows it. Everyone can obtain some guidance to this knowledge by studying the ordinary maps of the stars or an annual star calendar.

Here in these Letters, too, we will draw attention to any specially important celestial events for the coming month. But at the same time we must try to awaken a real *understanding* for them, so that it does not become just a question of mere star-gazing or of looking for some astrological "portent." We will continue with this aspect of the subject next time.

For now, however, we will draw attention to the *passage of Mercury across the Sun*, which will take place on November 10. This is an event that does not happen frequently, and only at irregular intervals of thirteen, seven, ten, and three years. The last time was on May 8, 1924.

Unfortunately, very little of this occurrence will be visible from Europe, for the Sun will not yet be above the horizon when Mercury enters its disc. Only the latter half, the exit of Mercury, will be perceptible, and that the more visible the further east one is. No exact indication, therefore, of time can be given; one must catch the right moment as soon as possible after sunrise. [See Notes on the Text.]

The end of the appearance will be at about 9:30 for central Europe; for England the corresponding Greenwich time, an hour earlier, 8:30. Like a little sharply defined black point (thus distinguished from the present numerous sunspots) Mercury will pass across the Sun's disc in 5 $\frac{1}{2}$ hours from east to west. Even though the externally visible body of Mercury will appear so small in comparison with the mighty expanse of the Sun's disc, yet, even so, there will be a diminishing of the Sun-forces through the Mercury-forces. That, too, has to occur again and again at the proper time.

November 1927

On the Diurnal Movement of the Stars

THE REPRESENTATIONS given in the last Letter led us away from the world of beings into the world of their finished work. By the examples that we had before us we were turned in the reverse direction—away from what is externally visible, from what belongs to the "finished work"—toward the inner rhythms of the active forces. The new Moon, the Moon's quarters and so on are outwardly visible in the heavens. They take place in the sphere of "finished work," but are at the same time indicators pointing to conditions obtaining in the elemental world of nature. That this has been proved by experiments is the great service rendered by Lili Kolisko's work (*The Working of the Stars in Earthly Substances*. See also *Das Goetheanum*, September 25, 1927).

On the other hand, where we have to do with surplus—or the difference between two rhythms—there we experience the effective working of *astral* forces. It is the revelation of spiritual beings that is brought to cosmic expression in such conditions as these, as in the successive rulerships of the different archangels. When his period dawns, Michael reveals his activity (which is, of course, also present in the intermediate periods) in such a way that this cannot be pointed to as a momentary celestial configuration, but as the cooperative activity of every rhythm in the planetary system.

The Christ stood in a quite peculiar relationship to the universe at the time when he was walking Earth as a man. We learn about this in the little book by Rudolf Steiner, *The Spiritual Guidance of the Individual and of Humanity*. It was as though the Christ bore the entire starry heavens within himself, unceasingly, with all their aspects and forces as they took place from moment to moment. In other words, that which the finished work shows to humanity was, in him, at the same time both activity and revelation. While in the case of ordinary human beings their moment of birth—speaking in a cosmic sense—remains for them a single event, for the Christ it was as though he were continually "being born" at every moment. During the time that Christ was on Earth, humanity lived for three years once more in the immediate company of a being belonging to the spiritual world.

We are now obliged to learn about the world of finished work, insofar as it reveals itself to our senses, and more especially about the world of stars as it is revealed to our organs of sight. The starry heavens are distinct from the rest of our surroundings on Earth, because they cannot be heard or tasted and certainly not touched. Only when we can get through to the *work-world* do we discover that Earth is the mirror of the heavens, and, that as the old hermetic saying affirms: "As above, so below."

In order that we may once again be able to realize this, there is one conception that must unconditionally vanish from our consciousness. It is that conception which has arisen as a result of the Copernican system and that, through the general popularizing of science, haunts everybody's brain with more or less distinctness. It is the idea that the stars are so far away from Earth that the distance must be computed in thousands and tens of thousands of "light years," one light year being the distance light travels in one year. Such a concept turns the universe into an infinitely vast and empty space, wherein—despite their immense numbers—comparatively few and isolated stars are scattered and wandering. One of them is our own Sun, a star of moderate magnitude and no longer in its first youth, and Earth meanwhile is a little speck of dust, dark in itself, and without any significance at all. (The more recent representations fortunately tend again toward the idea that the universe is enclosed and measurable, and in fact measurements are suggested. But here we must concern ourselves with the concepts that—mostly subconsciously—occupy human souls today.)

We cannot begin to explain here how this conception of the world has arisen. As has been said it was a result of the Copernican system, and in the deeper sense was a historical necessity for the age of the consciousness soul. Previously, humanity had no other idea than that the realm of the stars, which is also the sphere of the dead, is in direct juxtaposition to the planetary sphere, that the world of the stars is immediately behind the Saturn sphere, as one can see depicted in the old charts. In those days people thought of the star-world less as spatial than as temporal—as rhythmic and cyclical—as we have seen. When Ptolemy repeats the old saying: "The Earth stands to the heavenly bodies (that is, to the distance to the sphere of the fixed stars) in the relationship of a point," that is not meant in the sense of an *infinite* universe. As Ptolemy says, "the firmament is spherical and turns like a sphere." Rather it is the equivalent scientific expression of his age for the ancient opposition of Heaven and Earth in Genesis.

It was only when Copernicus removed Earth from its central position in the universe—which, since primeval ages, had been felt to be its position—that the question of the dimensions of the universe really arose. The spheres were conclusively broken through. For those people who first accepted the Copernican system, this breaking through of the "crystal heaven"—which for the feelings of the people of the Middle Ages had been growing ever more and more substantial—gave a sense of liberation. This liberation of the universe from its cosmic bonds was for Giordano Bruno as if a city had been freed from its enclosing walls and become capable of unlimited expansion. He sang the praises of this immeasurability, of this, for him, joyful conception of the endless multiplicity of inhabited worlds. This was fateful for him and [was one factor which] led to his death by burning at the stake.

It was only when the attempt was begun to find proofs for the Copernican theories—which, as is well known, did not take place until centuries after the promulgation of the teaching—that the stars were driven ever further and further away. The universe vanished into dust, became emptier and emptier, and the stars were engulfed in an ocean of darkness and cold. And so humankind, in the age of the consciousness-soul, was thrust more and more into dependence upon itself, directing its reasoned thinking upon the appearances derived from the senses, while at the same time wishing to interpose its own corrections upon these appearances.

If we go back into the age of the sentient soul, the Egypto-Chaldean age, we find that it is not the sense-perceptible cosmos that then worked upon humankind, but the imaginative cosmos—that which is revealed behind the world of the senses. Indeed, the sense-world, the world of the stars as it is visible to us today, was for the ancient peoples—to whom we also once belonged in our souls—not there at all. In its place they had the experience of pictures—imaginations—that showed them the world of stars "from the other side," as Rudolf Steiner expressed it. A spatial conception would have been quite out of place. For those people who experienced these things—the ancient Chaldeans for example—the starry and planetary worlds are really nearer and more comprehensible (in the sense of being "able to be grasped") than a mountain close at hand whose peak is enveloped in clouds. Even the Greek Gods lived upon Olympus in a world far removed from the world of human beings.

It was precisely in the Grecian age, when the Egypto-Chaldean culture had sunk into decadence, that humanity's consciousness of an outer world of stars began to be awakened. The ancient images faded away. The image evoked by visual appearance was the one that was revealed especially to the intellectual or mind-soul. It was an image of the rounded vault of heaven, with the stars attached to it, and the planets making manifold interlacing movements in between. The intellectual soul directed its thinking attention upon this picture. What resulted from it was laid down many centuries later in the Ptolemaic system. Rational thought, from which all imaginative conception gradually vanished, but which had for its foundation the images of sense-perception, was applied to what appeared to the senses.

It was Copernicus who, at the beginning of the fifth post-Atlantean cultural epoch broke through the sense appearances. The thinking of the consciousness soul (or spiritual soul), still bound to the nerves and sense system of the human being, desires to correct what is put before it by one part of the "head-man"—namely by the senses. Thus arises a world-picture that is barren and comfortless. It leads eventually to such extravagances of thought as the theory of relativity. The experience of the senses no longer has any value. Yet that thinking—which has been set free by sense-experience and which depends upon it—can offer us nothing but an impossible world-conception.

All this goes to show with greatest clarity that we must approach the problem from quite another side. We shall be able to understand what Rudolf Steiner said in respect to rational concepts. "Astronomy is something that actually does not enter into our head; it will not fit in there." It is not by theorizing that we shall get any nearer to astronomical reality. Let us permit the sense appearances to speak to us, even while we think of Goethe's profound saying: "The senses do not deceive, but the judgment deceives." For what the visual sense reveals to us, for example, is indeed a part of reality. It is that part which belongs to the "head-man," and it is what will be able to be our guide to the spiritual, which lies hidden behind all visible things.

In the first place there is the interchange of day and night, which is mirrored for us in the east to west movement of the Sun and stars. This is undoubtedly something that concerns our whole being—it influences body, soul, and spirit. We need only observe a little child to see how it is really the effect of the daylight that gradually rouses it to consciousness. On the other hand, though the twenty-four-hour period is impressed into our metabolism and assimilation, we have already set ourselves free from it to a great extent in our sleeping and waking— especially where spiritual activities are concerned.

If we regard day and night in this sense, we find we are concerned with all-embracing facts, which again are themselves the expression of lofty beings. To our sense of sight—to the "astronomical eye"—these facts are inscribed in a certain way upon the heavens—inscribed as a revolution, as a rotation of the entire starry firmament upon an axis. The rising and setting of the stars, of the Sun, and of the Moon, and the nightly wanderings of the stars and planets, all these reveal to us the first of the great rhythms that, roughly speaking, completes itself in twenty-four hours.

Suppose we think first of all only of the stars—obliterating for the moment the Sun, Moon, and planets from our consciousness, then we shall have a picture of something eternally the same, which no longer differentiates itself into "day" and "night." It represents far more an everlasting night, in which the stars alone, in their rising and setting, suggest a certain measure of time. Some in fact never appear either to rise or set (the so-called circumpolar stars). One of them seems to remain quite stationary, and that is the pole star toward which Earth's axis points—or, in the ancient phraseology, "through which the heavenly axis passes."

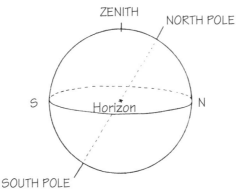

Figure 2

Let us take quite a simple diagram [Figure 2] which, though abstract, can nevertheless explain many things we can discover again in the heavens. Only we must imagine ourselves *inside* the drawing, right in the center. Let the circle that is shown in the plane of the drawing represent the meridian of the place from which the drawing is made, that is, the circle that passes through the zenith, being the highest point immediately overhead—and through the pole star—or more correctly, the pole of the heavens.

This circle intersects the horizon exactly at the southern and northern points. The horizon is represented by the curve so named in the drawing. The central point of this curve marks the spot at which we stand—for everyone is at every moment standing in the central point of his or her universe and in a sense has their own heaven, their own zenith, their own polar elevation and cardinal points about them.

If one asks where exactly Earth is in this drawing, we come to the remarkable conclusion that fundamentally speaking, Earth is only represented by the horizontal plane, or also solely by the point in the middle, when we recollect that of course the section of the circle whereon we stand cannot reach to the starry vault although heaven and Earth appear to be touching each other on the horizon. Otherwise how could the Sun and Moon and stars rise and set? A representation of this kind makes us realize something of what the old astronomers expressed in their idea that the Earth stands toward the heavens in the relation of a point to a circle.

The stars too, in our imagined sunless firmament, describe great or small orbits around the polar star [Figure 3]. Among them are some that rise and set at two diametrically opposite points—describing what is called a "great circle." These points are the western and eastern points of the horizon. We have hypothetically eliminated the Sun from our picture of the universe, so that we will not be led to the concept of "east" and "west" by the rising of the Sun. If the world were really so constituted, we should be compelled to measure time solely by the passage of the stars. We might perhaps do so just in the same way as we do as "sun-people," by dividing the star-day into twenty-four hours. Only they would be somewhat different hours from those we know!

The world without Sun, Moon, and planets is of course a miserable abstraction. We feel at once that in such a world the human being would have to be quite different from what it is. Yes, one can say that

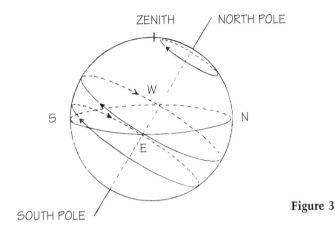

Figure 3

the human being could consist of a physical body, but would have no etheric body, no astral body, and no I. We could be something like a mineral with a cosmic consciousness. In an eternal sameness the world would revolve in everlasting night, with the same stars forever rising and setting.

Into this hypothetical world, which we have set up for the sake of clarity, we introduce the solar, lunar, and planetary realities! There enter into it at once life, growth, diversity. But time also undergoes a change. It becomes a little slower, as though a slight retardation, a slight restraint had entered into it. For the Sun, which has now become the ruler of the day, separating it from the night, now arrives always a little later at some point (let us say at the "meridian," when it "culminates"—or at the eastern horizon where it rises) than any star by which it was previously accompanied. The star, we might say, has hurried on a little ahead. At first perhaps it was obscured by the rays of the Sun, but after a little while it once more becomes visible before sunrise, because it has hastened ahead. The entire starry heavens seem to be moving forward (from east to west) in relation to the Sun's course.

We can also describe this fact in another way: The twenty-four hours of the sunless "star-day" that we spoke of just now are somewhat shorter, because they pass more rapidly than the twenty-four hours of the "sun-day" by which we are accustomed to regulate our life. Even though the Sun rises at different times during the year in different places that do not lie exactly at the equator, it always arrives at the meridian in the middle of its day's course. It culminates at the highest point for the day. The time lying between two such mid-days we calculate as twenty-four hours.[1] But the time between two consecutive culminations of any particular star, measured by the same unit as that by which we measure the Sun, is not twenty-four hours but only 23 hours, 56 minutes, and 4 seconds. So the stars move somewhat more quickly than the Sun and the Sun stays more or less behind.

Now, since we are not like minerals ensouled with that automatic consciousness we have spoken of, we regulate our daily lives not in accordance with star-time but with sun-time. In our reckoning of time we somehow accompany the Sun and not the stars. It is only the astronomer who makes use of the changeless star-time in his calculations and observations.

Later, we shall show how, since our reckoning is connected with the Sun and not the stars—although the daily revolution of the stars around the axis of the Earth is actually the signal phenomenon of the course of the day, the exact mirrored image of the turning of Earth upon its axis—we shall show how on the other hand the stars clearly reveal this difference between their own rate of speed and that of the Sun during the course of the year, by the fact that they continue to rise at an ever earlier moment on the eastern horizon. If, for example, we observe the zodiacal constellations at this autumn season at about nine or ten o'clock in the evening we shall see the Twins (Gemini) rise; a few weeks later, it will be Cancer, and in midwinter the mighty Leo, while by that time Gemini will be rising at about eight o'clock.

These differences, which only make themselves noticeable after days and weeks of observation, are summed up in those three minutes and fifty-six seconds that make the sidereal day different from the solar day. Thereby we see how the stars move forward with a more rapid movement compared with the slower progress of the Sun by which we have to regulate our days—and for the reason that we do not consist merely of a physical body, but also of etheric body, astral body, and I.

Rudolf Steiner has shown how this difference between the solar system and that of the stars is connected with the opposition between the essence of Lucifer and that of Yahweh. It is to be noted that after

---

1. Owing to the marvelous mobility and life of the whole cosmos, even such correct estimates cannot be wholly accurate in reality. One can only give approximations. The Sun passes the meridian sometimes a little earlier, sometimes a little later, but in fractions of time that are only a question of minutes.

the withdrawal of the Sun from the Earth, the influence of Lucifer made itself felt upon humanity. The movement of the Sun had then to be so ordered that it acted as a counterpoise to the accelerated and premature efforts of the luciferic beings. Lucifer wishes to unfold certain capacities in humanity too quickly, and especially to develop the thinking power—the intellect—which is torn away from the cosmos. This tempo is expressed in the rapidity of the revolution of the stars—or expressed in a Copernican way, in the rapidity of Earth's revolutions around its axis. The good gods were compelled to check the tempo of the Sun somewhat—which is after all a star among the other stars—and not allow it to share the same rate of movement as the rest.

Thus humanity, in order to have knowledge of the world, does not merely require the quickness of intellect but needs also the rather slower process of *experience*. We reach conclusions more speedily with our reason than we do by means of inner experience.

In a certain sense we have here the same thing as was described in Letter two about the relation of the Moon to the Sun and stars. The repeated overtaking of a star by the Moon takes less time than the overtaking of the Sun. If we had introduced the *Moon* into our hypothetical sunless picture of the universe, we should have come to know only the sidereal period of the Moon, and not the completion of the sidereal month with the synodical month, which takes $2\text{-}^{1}/_{5}$ days.

What we have described above is, when seen from the standpoint of human life, the same as if we should say: Yahweh had to call a halt to the too rapid progress of the luciferic beings. And it is again the same as when, in respect of the externally visible heavens, we experience how the Sun remains behind the stars, as, moving onward during days and weeks and months, they come to their rising ever earlier in the eastern sky and to their setting ever later in the west.

For this coming month (December) we would draw attention to the *total eclipse of the Moon* on December 8, which will be visible in Europe soon after sunset. In eastern and central Germany the rising full Moon will commence to enter the shadow of Earth in about one and a quarter to one hour; in western Germany and Holland after half an hour; and in Paris and in London at the moment of its rising. (This is not including its passage through the penumbra of the Earth, which takes place an hour before and an hour after the actual eclipse.) The time of the commencement of the obscuration is 16:51 European time

(15:51 Greenwich time) for all places concerned. The end of obscuration is 20:17 E.T. (19:17 Greenwich time). To this must be added one hour of obscuration by the penumbra of the Earth—which, however, it is often hardly possible to distinguish. Totality will last from 17:54 to 19:14 (16:54–18:14 Greenwich time). The eclipse will not be visible in America, except the latter part of it, and that only in the far north.

On December 24 there will be a partial eclipse of the Sun, which, however, will not be visible either in Europe or America.

Rudolf Steiner explained the significance of solar and lunar eclipses from the spiritual point of view on June 25, 1922, in a lecture that was printed this year in the *Goetheanum* (13–15), and we therefore refer you to this. In these Letters we will speak later of the circumstances through which eclipses are brought about.

December 1927

The Annual Movement of the Sun

Introduction

THE APPROACHING season of Christmas directs our thoughts toward the yearly course of the Sun. Having arrived at the lowest point of its path, it begins gradually to ascend once more from December 24 onward. This is that "apparent" course of the Sun which is called the ecliptic (the term has been derived from the word *eclipse*) and passes through the middle line of the zodiac. This is the path along which the Sun moves during the *course of the year,* though in the opposite direction from that along which it moves in the course of the day. Whereas every day we see the Sun travel from east to west across the whole space of the vault of heaven—or at least across half of it—yet it moves in its *yearly* course a little bit every day from *west to east,* on the average about one degree, (in 365 $\frac{1}{4}$ days, actually 360 degrees) and thus journeys through the zodiac,[1] unobserved because the light of day prevents any comparison with the stars that are behind it.

That is the movement spoken of last time as the diurnal movement of the Sun, which is slightly retarded. This retardation—regarded from another point of view—is caused by the *annual* movement of the Sun, which is in opposition to, and takes place in a different circle, from the former—namely, in the ecliptic; whereas the diurnal movement runs parallel with the equator.

A luciferic advance pushing ahead during the day, and a Jehovistic, divine-spiritual holding back during the year—thus the forces play into one another. During the year arises everything connected with growth, coming into being, and passing away, everything that "takes time" to ripen, and is also bound up with human feelings. Etheric and astral forces are added to the physical element that is in the mere revolution of the Earth.

---

1. In the direction: Aries, Taurus, Gemini, etc.

In order to learn to understand these fundamental conditions better, we shall need still further explanations. But this season of the year lays it upon us not only to open a chapter out of astronomy, but also out of astrosophy, which is concerned precisely with those active beings whom we must observe in connection with the Sun. Therefore we will continue the rather more theoretical explanations next time, and this time introduce some observations on the "threefold Sun," similar to what I have been able to give in some of my lectures.

The Threefold Sun

In approaching the mystery of the threefold Sun we are approaching the greatest mystery of the whole of world evolution. Naturally it would be impossible for us to speak of this mystery had it not been for Rudolf Steiner, whom we may regard as the renewer of the mysteries for our present age. It was he who directed us on different occasions to this mystery, and who showed us its connection on the one hand with the threefold human being, and on the other hand elevated it to its connection with the highest and holiest of all mysteries, one the human spirit can scarcely grasp, the mystery of the threefold unity.

This knowledge of the threefold Sun, said Rudolf Steiner, was taught in the ancient mysteries. And in the different ages of humanity's evolution, different things were taught about it. These were different— not in the sense of being contradictions naturally, but in the sense that in the advancing evolution of humanity, human beings themselves must also be inwardly connected in a different manner with this mystery and with the beings with whom they come into contact in relation to the threefold Sun.

Concerning the first Sun, which is known to us all as it appears and disappears from day to day in the sky, and which to our eyes is radiant, even dazzling, we are taught—to put it more generally at the moment—that it is a physical-material Sun and makes all the objects of the world visible to our eyes. But in the ancient mysteries it was taught: the Sun only shines and radiates for us because Lucifer has made it visible. He has opened our eyes—which themselves were created from out of the Sun—and made us able to behold it. A luciferic Sun, which in its external constitution—as it is today described from the scientific standpoint—contains what is luciferic, that is, what they called the first, the outer, visible Sun.

But concealed within it is another Sun. This is the one to which as human beings, we owe our life of soul, our memory, our ego. Because of it the human being is an ego-being who can string its experiences upon the thread of memory and can thereby always know itself again and possess in this way its own enclosed soul-life, an ego-being who unites thinking, feeling, and willing. And the beings to whom humanity looked up in ancient times as the donors of this human soul-life were called—according to the old Hebrew nomenclature—the elohim. It was said of them that they were to be found in the Sun, that they represented a soul and spirit Sun rather than the outer, material Sun. We know regarding one of these elohim, Yahweh or Jehovah, that he united himself with the Moon. But the elohim who belong to the spirits of form, to the second hierarchy, are those who live within the Sun, hidden from our external gaze. Thus there is a second Sun within the first visible one. And the first Sun, kindled by Lucifer, concealed this second one in which not only the elohim but also spirits of motion, spirits of wisdom—the whole of the second hierarchy—are to be understood as dwelling (in a certain sense), although it is also correct to regard the spirits of form as the actual representatives of the second Sun.

But—as it was taught in the ancient mysteries—behind this second Sun is hidden yet another one, the real spiritual Sun. There dwells that Sun-Being who above all others first united his being with the Sun, and by so doing first made it what it is—the most radiant star in the whole cosmos. It is this being who has been called by many different names, but who, for the humanity of this present age, can be known only by the name of Christ. For it is this third Sun that has united itself to the Earth through the Mystery of Golgotha. In pre-Christian times people could not point to this uniting of the third Sun with the Earth. But they could point to the fact that this being, who could be known as the essential Spirit of the Sun, had given the ego to humanity. This ego does not only depend upon the thread of memory, vanishing when memory ceased, for example, in sleep, but is an ego that passes from incarnation to incarnation, and reveals the human as a permanent and divine being. In speaking of this third Sun, people spoke of the progress of the Sun-Being down to Earth throughout the course of a long evolution of humanity, and had to say: This being has descended through the infinitudes of universal space to the Sun and has come from the Sun to Earth.

If we consider the different post-Atlantean epochs of civilization we shall find there are different stages in humankind's relation to the Sun in its various aspects. These stages are connected with the fact that humanity's capacities for evolution were always changing from age to age—that humanity's relationship to the spiritual world was always changing.

In the ancient Indian epoch we find humanity pointing to a being, Vishvakarman—the one who had "created all things"—of whom it was said that he was beyond the human sphere. The name expresses for the Indian what Christ means for us, but the Christ could have no relation with the ancient Indian culture because the time for it was not yet ripe. But in the second epoch of civilization, the ancient Persian, we see in what manner Zarathustra is aware of the Sun, and how he sees it surrounded with an aura—the "Great Aura," *Ahura Mazdao*. It speaks to humanity as the Sun-Being, revealing itself as the being we have described as the true spiritual Sun, the first Sun (which I enumerated above as the third).

In the third post-Atlantean epoch, human beings became conscious of the *activity* of the spiritual beings, as described previously. Then the Egyptian spoke of Ra Osiris, the Sun god. Ra was Osiris's representative on Earth, but as Ra, he is the being who conducts the Sun around the starry heavens, causing it to circumnavigate the waters of heaven in the "boat of the sun." For the Egyptians felt the sky to be related to the watery element. That is the second Sun, the active Sun, that radiates warmth and light upon Earth; but it is not primarily external light that is meant, but the inner light that also illumines human thoughts. Such is the Sun of which the human was first conscious in this Egyptian epoch.

But when we come to the later Egyptian periods, when the essential Egyptian culture was about to be replaced by another, then we can see that the *external* Sun comes to be more and more observed. Indeed we find attention first drawn to the activity of the external, physically-perceptible Sun by the great Pharaoh Akhenaton, Amenhotep IV, who lived in the fourteenth century before Christ, and whose "Hymn to the Sun" has come down to us. In it one finds strongly emphasized all that streams out from the Sun and comes to Earth as physical Sun rays that give warmth and light to humankind.

Glorious is Thy rising on the horizon of Heaven,
O creator Aton, Who was alive at the beginning of all things!
When Thou risest in the eastern sky
Every land lies beneath you shining in beauty.
Thou art great and resplendent and sparklest high above the Earth;
With Thy radiant hands of love
Thou embracest all lands and everything Thou has made.
Thou art Ra, Who guideth and guardeth all things
And bindeth them with bonds of Love.
Though thou art far, yet are Thy rays upon the Earth,
And Thy countenance is ever toward it on Thy journeyings.

Here, then, it is the *working* of the Sun streaming down to Earth that is worshipped.

This is even more the case when we come to the fourth post-Atlantean epoch—the epoch in which the Mystery of Golgotha took place. It is true that among the Greeks there were still indications pointing to a threefold Sun. Out of their own spirituality, out of their connection with the spiritual in their mysteries and the mysteries of neighboring peoples, they had a conception, or at any rate a slight idea of the threefold Sun. They felt that the first, the spiritual Sun, was the source of all morality. The *good* was bound up with it. And it is in this sense that Plato speaks of the good as a fundamental principle, and connects it with the Sun. So the spiritual Sun was conceived as the source of the moral.

The Greeks called the second Sun *Helios*. Of course the Greeks had many Sun gods, but Helios is the God who leads the Sun around the firmament and causes it to shine upon humankind. He is really the same for the Greeks as Ra Osiris was for the Egyptians. The Greeks did not feel the third Sun, the one we experience today in the outer world, to be simply a brilliant and dazzling orb, but we may say they really felt it as the whole sun-filled Earth ether—as the whole etheric periphery of the Earth that is irradiated through and through with sunlight. In this there lived the spiritual beings of their gods. Zeus reigned there supreme; and Zeus is in a certain sense a luciferic being, as indeed are all the Greek gods. Zeus was for the Greeks the representative of the third Sun—the physical, external one, not quite in the same sharply defined sense as we feel it today. For we must still include the ether as it was spread out over the whole land of the Greeks, before we can realize what the Sun was to them as it shone upon Earth below and upon Olympus above. Thus a threefold Sun was still part of the teaching of the Greek mysteries.

It is different when we come to the Romans. In contrast to the Greeks, the Romans were a far less spiritual, more abstract people. At first the Romans maintained a connection between their own spiritual life and that of the Greeks, and permitted a great deal to be imparted to them by the Greeks. Therefore, for instance, we find the Romans calling upon Helios to guide them to one whom they now worshipped as the Sun god, *Mithras*. In the Mithras cult we have a Sun-being, a god of the Sun who is represented riding upon the bull, that is, upon the cosmic-planetary totality.

But especially in those times when Roman culture was spreading over the whole world and with it the worship of Mithras as the religion even of the simple Roman soldiery, we find that only a twofold Sun is recognized: an external Sun, as we know it, and a spiritual Sun that was adored in the Mithras cult. The threefold Sun had been "melted down" into a twofold one, with the disappearance of the knowledge concerning the real spiritual Sun.

We know, indeed, that in the meantime the Mystery of Golgotha had taken place, when the spiritual Sun had united itself with Earth. We know too that many of the mystery schools only penetrated to this knowledge with great difficulty, and for a long time knew nothing of the Mystery of Golgotha or of its having taken place—thereby showing that they were not really valid mysteries. So in later Roman times we perceive this deeply moving fact, that the Romans knew of only two Suns and that the knowledge of the third, which is the original spiritual Sun, had vanished. In this we behold something that is profoundly connected with the whole later spiritual evolution of humankind.

We know how often Rudolf Steiner said that human beings consist of body, soul, and spirit—that we are a trinity. He also said that this trichotomy of the human being was abolished by the decree of the eighth ecumenical council held in Constantinople in 869 A.D.—that the human being was thereafter considered as consisting of body and soul only. But this decree, which thus laid down a dry and barren dogma, would never have been possible had evolution not progressed in such a way that knowledge of the original Sun was lost from human consciousness, and humanity forgot the spiritual Sun they once honored and worshipped. The duality, the twofold rather than threefold division of the human being, had to be preceded by a duality in the cosmos.

The spirit—discarded by the Council of 869—is the true human ego that goes from incarnation to incarnation and can also only endure when it unites itself with the Christ-being, the spiritual Sun. Thus humanity passed from a threefold to a twofold Sun; the secret of the Christ as the Sun-Being was lost, and we have gradually acquired that noncosmic Christianity under which our culture is suffering today.

But when we go further, we perceive the natural consequences of this course of events in that even that Sun which the Romans knew and honored is being forgotten. We see how today there remains but one Sun—the outer solar phenomenon—the ball of the Sun that is perceived in the sky and that science investigates and describes and explains in its own way, and holds to be the only one that really exists. To speak of anything spiritual in the Sun today is not possible in the sense either of science or of religion, if we hold to what is customarily accepted. The human being of today regards the Sun as a mere glowing ball of gas—a globe of incandescent gases that sends heat down from the sky like a stove. This Sun, the last that is left, is the luciferic Sun where beings—from the highest to the lowest—who have remained behind, are living and ruling and working.

Rudolf Steiner, who from one standpoint had the greatest respect for natural science, as indeed all must have who know anything about it, once described it in a single terse phrase: "What actually is taking place in natural science? This: *Ahriman is describing Lucifer.*" These words express to the fact that the faculties Ahriman has unfolded in humanity—the means of knowledge, as well as the instruments and accessories of knowledge that have been discovered through the ahrimanic forces—are being used to depict everything in nature that is fixed, that has remained behind. "Ahriman describes Lucifer." And so this Sun that is the Sun of the laggard beings, is the only one now known to humankind. For beautiful as it is—Lucifer is a radiant being—it is nevertheless a being that is composed of unprogressed beings. The Sun is investigated with the spectroscope and the telescope and all the other inspired discoveries that emanate from Ahriman. This kind of investigation leads to the following result. People say, "Yes, the Sun must have an inner nucleus, but of this we can know nothing, we cannot know what is taking place there. For this nucleus is hidden by what is superimposed upon it."

Now it is just this central point of the Sun, this "nucleus," of which we say that it is a space that is not a space in the ordinary sense of the word (Rudolf Steiner always said that it was "emptier than emptiness"), that it is not merely empty but is a negative, "sucking" space. It is there that the spiritual beings—the beings of the second hierarchy—have their habitation (one is obliged to use a "spatial" term). Natural science quite rightly says that nothing can be known of this solar kernel because the surface of the Sun covers it, and we observe only the surface. On the surface there is first the photosphere. That is what we see when we observe the Sun through a dark glass [verified as optically safe] or when the Sun is setting. What is this photosphere? (We include the chromosphere and atmosphere.) It is what actually gives us the impression of a real solar disk or globe, hence something spatial. But that which is spatial, which is not a negation of space, is precisely the product of the laggard spirits of form. It is the normal spirits of form who in reality dwell in the center of the Sun. It is their being that constitutes the inner being of the Sun. But the laggard spirits of form place themselves in front of the others; they are beings who should really have been spirits of wisdom, but have remained behind in their evolution and so produce the illusory picture of a spatial Sun that travels spatially across the sky. Space is actually rayed out with the light. It is the product of the *abnormal spirits of form*. Simple people suppose that space must have a certain shape, but it has not. That is really an imaginary conception called forth by the laggard spirits of form. They ought to be spirits of wisdom, but have stayed behind at the stage of the spirits of form, and conjure up before us the idea of space that we would like to sense as having a certain shape, but that nevertheless has none. (There is of course far more than this concealed within the mystery of space; but we can begin by feeling this much.) And the symbol for such a space that is yet no space, is the disk of the Sun, which seems to be composed of glowing gases, and is manifest to us as the photosphere.

Dark spots may be discerned within the photosphere—sunspots. In comparison with the light that streams out from the photosphere they appear as darker places. Within them are those beings who have not taken part in the transition from the Old Saturn evolution to the Old Sun evolution, who remained stationary during the Saturn evolution and so have not absorbed the quality of light that came into existence with the Sun. These are *laggard spirits of personality*, archai, who completed their human stage on ancient Saturn.

It is always possible to see the photosphere if we dim down the sunlight sufficiently. It is only very seldom that sunspots can be seen with the [protected] naked eye. As a rule they are only to be seen with the [light-filtered] telescope. Still more difficult to see are the so-called protuberances or solar flares. They are visible during a total eclipse, but also at other times by means of special instruments that darken the light. Then the solar flares appear.

At first they make the impression that they are leaping out from the circumference of the Sun like flames, not unlike incandescent streams of lava shooting out of a volcano on Earth. But even in these appearances there is something that is contradictory as regards the being of the Sun. For on the Sun everything tends to draw toward the center—toward that etheric space which annihilates all that strives toward it. Let us turn to Rudolf Steiner's description of the Old Sun condition (as it is given, for instance, in lecture four of *Genesis: Secrets of the Bible Story of Creation*) of the wonderful shining light-forms that stream through the Sun, liberate themselves from it, and fall into it again, continually appearing and disappearing. That is what is living today in the solar flares—the laggard quality of beings belonging to the ancient Sun. In the same way the sunspots are an expression of the laws governing ancient Saturn when there was no light but only heat. In the solar flares are those angelic beings (presumably archangelic beings) of the Old Sun condition who have remained behind. They are in fact ahrimanic beings.

The last phenomenon that natural science studies with regard to the Sun is that remarkable manifestation known as the corona, which surrounds the darkened disk of the Sun at a total eclipse. In this faintest objective form, this manifestation that is widely extended but only faintly luminous, we have those angelic beings who have remained behind from the Old Moon condition. *Laggard angels* are what we behold in the corona. These beings of the visible Sun must all be regarded as having "remained behind."

Let us turn once more to the threefold nature of the Sun as it may be considered today. But we can only just touch upon this subject of which there is so much that might be said.

We know that the human being has also been described to us as threefold, as consisting of head-being, chest-being, and metabolic-and-limb-being. The head-being contains principally the most solidified matter. It is primarily associated with matter; the spirit is most withdrawn from it and scarcely enters the material substance at all. It is here that the spirit comes to consciousness in us. The spirit finds, so to speak, an element of resistance in the rigid brain in which it can reflect itself. This is our most material portion. Our head for the most part contains destructive forces, disintegrating forces. These must of necessity always be there so that consciousness may arise in us. But the consciousness we develop only upon a foundation of disintegrating forces is that consciousness which was first of all kindled by Lucifer. It is not without cause that we speak of the "light" of our thinking, the light of our intellect. We have in this case to do with a light in our own thought life that really represents a luciferic thought-life—a luciferic light—that shines in us as the Sun of knowledge, it is true, but primarily as the luciferic Sun.

This clear day-waking consciousness is also connected with the daily revolution of the starry heavens. The Sun shares in this over-rapid revolution insofar as it takes part in the diurnal movement from east to west. But the Sun in its annual course acts in a retarding way—as we have seen—upon the luciferically-conducted diurnal revolution. The Sun in its annual movement acts not upon the head, but upon the heart—upon the life of feeling.

In the chest-being spirit and matter are interwoven. There is a continual oscillation from one to the other. The breathing process is in the chest-being, and from here proceeds the whole circulation of the blood, rhythmically organized. This is the region where those spirits are at work who breathed breath into the human being—the spirits of Yahweh-Elohim, who have united themselves with humankind in love through the medium of the chest-being at the beginning of Earth evolution. Here then is the second Sun, the Sun of the second hierarchy, with whom the Christ united himself in a quite special manner before he united himself with Earth. In the blood, in rhythm, in pulsebeat the second Sun dwells within us.

In the metabolic-and-limb-aspect of the human being spirit and matter are the most closely interwoven. Naturally we cannot hold fast to those ordinary ideas that represent the metabolic life as something inferior. People do not particularly value the spirit where it is so intimately bound to matter, but this nevertheless brings about the marvelous building up and preservation of the whole human being, recreating what the head destroys. While we are incessantly pouring destructive and annihilating

forces into the body through the luciferic intellect, the processes of life
are as incessantly replenished through the metabolic-and-limb being. In
the metabolic-and-limb being we can see on the one hand the working
of the Father principle, which indeed penetrates and brings into order
all material substance. We can at the same time understand the words
of Christ: "I and the Father are one." Here spirit and matter are indeed
united. We must not of course try to carry these words too far. They
are words of the mysteries; they must, if I may say so, be taken with
their whole aura. But it is an integral part of the Holy Sacrament that
the substance of God should be conveyed to the metabolic human being
so that people may experience the divine.

In this way we can try to understand the spiritual Sun, which is
bound to the metabolic being, and also to the will-being. *Light* dwells
in the head-being. *Love* undulates and weaves in the chest-being. *Life*
streams in the metabolic-and-will-being. And in these three words,
light, love, and life, we have a purely Christian nomenclature for the
threefold Sun. The knowledge of the threefold Sun has never been lost
in esoteric Christianity. Indeed these words have been bound up with
the Christ. He who spoke them knew that the three Suns are fundamentally one.

The first and highest Sun is the Sun of Christ. It was there in the
primeval beginning, and created all things. The second Sun came into
existence as the beings of the higher hierarchies, under the leadership
of the Christ, liberated spiritual forces upon Earth that were too strong,
and thus had to establish another solar body in the universe. This one
would not have been visible to our physical eyes. It was only through
the activity of the luciferic beings that the Sun became surrounded by
more visible, more luminous, and indeed more dazzling substance.

The Christ Sun has united itself with Earth. It is this event that
we commemorate at the Easter festival. At the holy Christmas time
we celebrate the birth of that child who was to become the bearer of
the Christ. The Christ child is born year after year, for the Sun comes
year after year once more to the same point, which is the lowest one
for its annual course. At that point it develops least the high powers
that lead it astray, and at the same hour it is visible without perceptible
light to the spiritual gaze as the midnight Sun. In the Christ events that
commence thirty years after the birth—with the baptism in the Jordan

River on January 6—and last for three and a half years, lies the germ of
the fact that the second Sun will be able to unite itself with the finally
spiritualized Earth at the end of Earth evolution. There too is the germ
for the redemption of the luciferic Sun that, unredeemed, must consume
the Earth. So at the Christmas festival let us remember that from now
humanity must make it possible for the Earth to realize its destiny, which
is to become a Sun.

January 1928

On the Annual Movement of the Sun and Stars

WE ARE LIVING NOW in a season when the days are growing longer and the Sun is mounting higher. A glance at figure 4 will show us the Sun on this same ascending path although at a later period of the year, namely, when it is just about to enter the zodiacal sign of the Ram.[1]

In order to obtain a clear view of these conditions we must at first regard them independently of the diurnal movement of the Sun—or, if preferred, of Earth. As in the third Letter, we hypothetically removed the Sun, so now we must turn our attention quite away from the revolutions of Earth, and thus from the rising and setting of the Sun and stars in the east, and so on, so that we can be clear as to what movements still remain in progress in the firmament.

If we look at it in this way, it becomes evident that in the course of the year the Sun appears in a certain way in the west and strides over the horizon—going through the meridian (that is, reaching its highest point) so that in the autumn it sets, so to speak, in the east. Then at Christmas it will have reached the lowest point of its course. Thus it proceeds through the ecliptic—which, as I have said, is the circle that passes through the middle of the zodiacal constellations—and this takes a whole year. This movement is not in itself perceptible to the eye, since the sunlight hides the stars, and we have moreover so established our

---

1. [Here are given the zodiacal constellation names and their signs, or symbols. See Notes on the Text.]

Ram (Aries) ♈	Lion (Leo) ♌	Archer (Sagittarius) ♐
Bull (Taurus) ♉	Virgin (Virgo) ♍	Goat (Capricornus) ♑
Twins (Gemini) ♊	Scales (Libra) ♎	Waterman (Aquarius) ♒
Crab (Cancer) ♋	Scorpion (Scorpius) ♏	Fishes (Pisces) ♓

time that this movement is included in it. (Please see Letter 3 concerning the difference between solar day and stellar day.)

Therefore this movement reflects itself, as has been described, in the stars, which now carry out a contrary movement (all these are only "apparent movements" from the point of view of modern science), that is to say in the direction contrary to that indicated by the arrows in the drawing. Thus in the course of the year we first see the setting of the Ram, then the Bull, then the Twins and so on, every month another constellation of the zodiac. Similarly every month a new sign rises in the east. This east-west movement (which must not be confused with the diurnal or daily movement), is actually a double maya. It is the inversion of the Sun's movement from west to east, which is concealed by "Sun-time," and in the Copernican sense must be regarded as an apparent movement only. But the last fact need not concern us at present.

The wider heaven of stars, of course, shares in this movement. It is not only the new zodiacal constellations that appear in the course of the year above the horizon. Other constellations too mark the seasons by their earlier or later appearance, provided they are not circumpolar—that is, they are not among constellations so near to the Pole that they never set. The most characteristic ones in the winter sky are Orion—threatening the Bull with his club; sparkling Sirius in the Greater Dog—the most brilliant of all the stars in the heavens; Procyon in the Lesser Dog, and so on. In the summer months in our part of the world there is Vega, in Lyra, and Arcturus, Hercules, and Cygnus high over head. But the course of the seasons may be best observed by watching the zodiacal constellations.

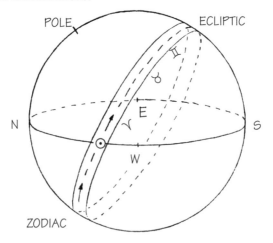

Figure 4   ZODIAC

This movement takes place upon an axis that can also be indicated by a certain point, just in the same way as the prolongation of Earth's axis leads us to the pole star. The polar point of the zodiac (the animal circle) is very characteristically placed in the constellation of the Dragon. The ancient dream-like clairvoyant wisdom regarded the Dragon as being in a sense the guardian of this point in the heavens. The Dragon is comparatively easy to find as it winds its way between the Greater and Lesser Bears, and with its last coil near to the head—which is represented by a little square of stars—it winds around the pole of the ecliptic. This pole thus lies at an equal distance from every point on the ecliptic.

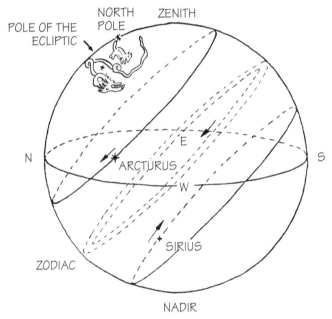

Figure 5

The place on the diagram in Figure 4 marked "Pole" is the equator or north pole of the heavens, which is situated near the end of the "tail" of the Lesser Bear. It is around this point that the whole diurnal movement from east to west takes place; and around the former, which is situated in the Dragon, takes place the annual movement, considered from the standpoint of the Sun.

In this diagram [Figure 5] we have a picture exclusively of the annual movement, as in the third Letter we had exclusively one of the diurnal movement. In the latter the pole was shown in the opposite direction, though it could just as well be shown otherwise. There, the middle circle was what we call the *heavenly* equator. All diurnal movements proceed parallel to it. But here the central girdle represents the zodiac, and the smaller circles show the annual movements, for example, of Arcturus or of Sirius. [See also Notes on the Text.]

But now let us examine both movements together. That is, let us look neither at the merely annual nor the merely diurnal movements, but ask ourselves what actually takes place in the course of a day.

Then it will be quite obvious that the diurnal movement really is that which is carried out on the equator, and parallel with the equator, from east to west. But by the equator we do not mean the *earthly* equator that passes around the Earth halfway between the poles, but a continuation in a certain sense—of the plane of a circle *into* the vault of heaven, where this vault extends between the two heavenly poles north and south). Thus it is seen to be a circle that cuts the horizon, from any place, in the center of east and west, and over the south is raised to a height that is directly dependent upon the geographical latitude. The nearer we are to the North Pole, the flatter lies the equator, while the more elevated is the pole star.

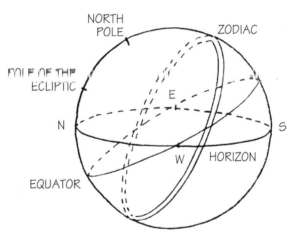

Figure 6

In contrast to this movement that is carried out in twenty-four hours, the other—the annual course of the stars parallel with the zodiac—is a much slower one, for it takes 365 days for its completion. Thus, for instance, the constellation of Taurus will have risen in about two hours, but in accordance with this annual movement it will take about a month before the constellation of Gemini will rise at that same hour in the evening. The entire zodiac is naturally carried along in the daily revolution in the same way as all the other stars, and since the zodiac is not parallel with the equator, this revolution gives rise every day to a most remarkable serpentine movement of the zodiac in relation to the equator, and hence in relation also to the horizon and meridian. (See Figure 6.)

Anyone who has a good opportunity for observing the starry heavens—that is, anyone who does not live in a city—can notice how even in a few hours the zodiac (that part of it which is either in the east or west) intersects a different, that is, a fresh point of the horizon, slightly further toward the north or south, or else that it is then elevated above the horizon either higher or lower, more steeply or more level. In this diagram, for example (Figure 6), the zodiac is represented (for the Northern Hemisphere) higher than the equator. Its intersection with the horizon lies somewhat northeast and southwest. After perhaps an interval of two hours it would be intersecting the horizon exactly at the east and west points; and would then appear on the other side of these cardinal points. Meanwhile the half-circle that is above the horizon would at the same time be growing flatter and flatter. The whole process is repeated in the contrary direction after several hours have passed.

What the zodiac thus carries out during the course of a day may be seen to be the same as what is carried out during the year, if we always make our observations at the same hour—say at midnight. In the winter nights, bejeweled with the Bull and the Twins, the zodiac will stretch high into the heavens, and in the summer nights drop to the horizon with a flatter curve. Its rising and setting points on the horizon also shift.

The same appearances may be observed in respect of the points of sunset and sunrise, and the higher or lower paths of the Sun in the course of the seasons—for the Sun is always to be found within the zodiac. On March 21 [this year], the Sun rises [closest to due] east and sets [closest to due] west. Then its rising moves day by day a little to the north, and its setting too. (By the time the Sun arrives in the west, the zodiac has also shifted this far north.) Further, the point of midday—of culmination—also rises higher, so that the "diurnal arc" grows longer and longer. And so it goes on until June 22, when the Sun in our latitude is about thirty-six degrees removed from the western point at its setting.

Further south, the difference is less. Then comes the retrogression, and on September 24, the east and west points are arrived at once more. From that time onward the rising and the setting of the Sun occurs daily more to the south, the point of culmination is daily lower, and the diurnal arc shorter and shorter. [Above dates are for 1927.]

Anyone who can see the western or the eastern sky from the window of their room can follow the changing positions of sunrise and sunset clearly, for, if one has some object against which to measure it (a house, tree, or mountain), the difference is quite noticeable from day to day. Also, the pole of the ecliptic or the zodiac—the point in the Dragon— must revolve daily around the pole of the equator—the point in the Lesser Bear. As against this, we shall see later that in respect of the great Platonic year of 25,920 years, the point in the Dragon is then an immovable one, and that the point of the Pole must itself revolve around it. For this reason, humanity in different ages has a different pole star by which it must find its orientation.

Even in the Greek age, seafarers looked during their voyages in mid-ocean to a bright star in the Dragon (the most brilliant of all the stars in this constellation, one near the end of the Dragon's "tail") as their pole, or guiding star, while in the same epoch the point described as the pole of the ecliptic was still the pole of the ecliptic. So, one can surely feel, thinking of the thousands of years' duration of the movement of the celestial pole, that it was proper that the Dragon was set as watcher from aeon to aeon to guard the "unmoving pole amidst the constantly changing flux of appearances." But we will speak more of these things at a later date.

We will now return to the annual movement of the Sun that is from west to east, and causes it to traverse all the signs of the zodiac in the course of the year. When, for example, the Sun is in one degree of Aries, it will, so to speak, remain the whole day in this degree, even though its progress is of course continuous, and it must make its diurnal revolution in company with this particular part of the zodiac parallel with the equator from east to west. Thus it not only rises at this point in the first degree, but also traverses the meridian, and sets, within it. By the time it rises again it will have entered the second degree—and so on. The ecliptic, or circle of the Sun's path, is like every other circle divided into 360 degrees, and is subdivided into twelve times thirty degrees reckoning from one of the two points where the zodiac and the equator intersect—namely from that point where the Sun is on [about] March 21, the so-called vernal equinox.

It is interesting to compare these movements with those of the Moon. The Moon has always been the great instructor of astronomers, as its principal movements can easily be observed. For this reason the Moon has also at times misled them. Since it has no rotation upon its own axis, but always turns the same side to Earth, the ancient astronomers were led away from the idea that such rotation was possible, and they thought that as the Moon did not do it, neither could Earth. When Newton, in the seventeenth century, tested his law of gravitation by this peculiarity of the movement of the Moon and found it corroborated thereby, he came to the conclusion that there must be a universal application of this law to the entire universe from "Earth" to the most distant star. Thus, he was ultimately responsible for the introduction of materialism into astronomy.

The Moon takes part in the diurnal movement in company with the Sun and all the stars and planets. That it does not *appear* to rise every day definitely and clearly in the east (actually, of course, it does do so!) is due to the fact that the movement from west to east that corresponds to the annual movement of the Sun, comes into question very strongly where the Moon is concerned, whereas, in the case of the Sun, as we have seen, it only results in quite a small difference every day. The Moon traverses the whole heavens in 27 $\frac{1}{3}$ days, instead of in a year, and in the establishment of the duration of a day the Moon is not taken into consideration. Thus it does not transfer its movement upon the stars as the Sun does in its annual movement, but carries out its movement clearly before our eyes. Every day or every night it stands about thirteen degrees more to the east—the Sun only one degree. When the Moon happens to be close to a particular star or planet one can easily observe, even in the space of an hour, that it moves past the star from west to east, while at the same time it is moving with the star or planet in the whole general revolution from east to west. If we imagine this movement retarded twelve times, we have the movement of the Sun in its yearly course.

The orbit of the Moon lies also within the zodiac, even though it does not strictly correspond to the ecliptic path of the Sun. The zodiac is really a belt of about the width of its constellations, and therefore it can contain more or less inclined orbital paths. The Moon as well as the planets have such orbits that are slightly inclined in relation to the ecliptic.

We spoke of the relationship between the Moon and the Sun in our second Letter. When the Moon has been near the Sun—that is, when it is new moon and it reappears for the first time as a thin crescent, it has, in the course of its monthly movement, delayed [eastward] behind the Sun to the extent of two or three days, so that the Sun no longer hides it by its light. We must also picture to ourselves that, on that particular day when the Moon first becomes visible again in the western evening twilight, it has also risen that morning shortly after the Sun has risen in the east, and has, so to speak, followed it all day—though with a constant retardation of several degrees. While the morning sunlight still outshines it, it can nevertheless, quite soon after the Sun has set in the evening, be seen shining as a young and brilliant sickle, which following the diurnal movement soon afterward disappears on the western horizon.

Until full Moon is reached it will have traveled right away from the Sun in the opposite direction toward the east, until it finally rises when the Sun sets. From that time on we can observe how it rises later every day, just as at the beginning of its monthly course it sets later every day. This retarding of its daily rising and setting covers at the most something over an hour, but can also cover distinctly less than this. These interesting differences again have to do with the oblique position of the zodiac in respect to the equator, and introduce a wonderful diversity into the world picture

We have gone so thoroughly into the fundamental concepts of the diurnal and annual courses from the standpoint of their outer visible appearance because only when these are completely grasped is it possible to understand and become familiar with the heavenly events. Everything else can be easily grasped when built upon these movements, once they are fully comprehended.

February 1928

Concerning Our Planetary System

IN SUN, MOON, AND EARTH, we behold that trinity of heavenly bodies that is the great characteristic sign of the evolution of the cosmos. They draw the gaze of the spirit back to the ancient Sun-time, to the Moon-time, and thus to the beginning of our Earth evolution, when the Sun and Moon one after the other withdrew from the composite Earth body. Only ancient Saturn remains over from a yet earlier condition of existence.

In this whole process are expressed mighty facts of evolution. We are reminded of the temptation from Lucifer, who then in company with all his hosts received a leading part to play upon Earth; of the self-sacrifice of Yahweh who united himself with the Moon, while the spirits of equal rank, the elohim, remained with the Sun; and of the deed of the Christ who as their highest representative also forsook Earth with the spirits of the Sun. (See *An Outline of Esoteric Science*.) Behind the solar system as it is today, there lie spiritual facts and conflicts as well as the progressive stages of evolution. The planets, too, must be regarded in this way—if they are to be for us something more than mere wandering points of light.

During the ancient Moon-evolution there were already, besides the Sun and Moon, a great number of other heavenly bodies. (See *An Outline of Esoteric Science*.) These were the result of certain beings having remained behind at various stages of progress during the Saturn, Sun, and Moon stages of evolution. These beings united themselves with certain substances that had also "remained behind"—because unless they did this there would never have been matter but only a quality of "being" in the world. Taking these substances with them, they left the Old Moon and created colonies in the universe for themselves so that they could continue their activities in accordance with their nature. That these separations did not take place without conflicts we learn in Steiner's lecture cycle *The Spiritual Hierarchies and the Physical World* (given at Dusseldorf in 1909).

There it is described how our present planetoids that are situated between Jupiter and Mars are in a sense the ruins of a titanic battle that was fought from the time of the ancient Sun to that of the Moon, which was an attempt to contract the old Sun-body, which then extended as far as the present orbit of Jupiter, down to the orbit of Mars. At that time the Sun itself extended beyond the other heavenly bodies owing to its more advanced spirituality, which it owed to the presence of that being whom we know in the later Earth-evolution as the Christ.

Around this Sun that had been compacted by the spirits of motion, circled the ancient Moon, and this revolution is, in a certain sense, the first rotary movement to appear in the solar system. In the wonderful lecture cycle *Inner Experiences of Evolution* [given by Steiner in Berlin, 1911] it is shown how this creation of movement was originated by the spirits of motion out of an inward dissatisfaction—an inward longing—that must arise in those beings who cannot share in the progressive advance of evolution. Something like an inner unrest took possession of these beings and brought the heavenly bodies into movement, and thus, in this luciferic, retarded element of the cosmos, we have the origin of every planetary movement—the origin of the "erring stars" as, with a delicate sense of feeling, they once were called; notwithstanding that their wanderings have long since come under laws of regularity.

During the Earth-evolution first the Saturn beings, then those of Jupiter and of Mars, separated themselves off from the general Earth-planet and founded their habitations in the cosmos. Not only superhuman beings who could not continue in the Earth-evolution even in its earliest stages withdrew in this way from Earth to the newer planets, but human souls also. Then at the close of the so-called Hyperborean age, the Sun itself left the Earth, taking with it those beings who soon after formed the planets Mercury and Venus between Earth and the Sun. These were beings who had been smitten by the luciferic influence—that is, they had not been able fully to attain the goal of the Moon-evolution. They stand nevertheless far above humankind, whose teachers and guides they had been in primeval times. We must observe the difference between the regularly advanced beings such as the archangels or the archai in the Mercury or Venus spheres—(the planets Mercury and Venus in their orbits only mark a certain limit to these spheres)—and the more or less laggard beings that are connected with the individual planetary *bodies*. But there are naturally also normal spirits of the higher hierarchies connected with the planets. We have spoken already in the first letter of the activity of the luciferic types of beings at the time of the creation of the planets.

When the Sun withdrew from Earth it took with it more particularly the various ethers—the life-ether, sound-ether, and so on, but also a more material substance, namely the *air*. Already during the ancient Sun-time the Christ had united himself with this element of air, even though this—at that time—comparatively substantial element was not adapted to his lofty nature. Thereby he laid the foundation for that sacrifice which was fulfilled on Earth in Palestine—the descent into a human body and in it, the passing through death. Therefore when the Sun left the Earth, he had to clothe himself with what was then the densest substance—the air—in order to incorporate it into the Sun, so that later, on Golgotha, the sacrifice that once more drew the Sun and Earth together really could take place. (Cf. *Wonders of the World, Trials of the Soul, and Revelations of the Spirit,* lectures 8 and 9—given by Rudolf Steiner in Munich, 1911.) Thus on the Sun of today we find the different beings and substances that have already been described. We find also a certain relationship between the Christ-filled gaseous and airy constituents of the Sun and the present air of the Earth. And we can understand how a second coming of the Christ "in the clouds," in the element of air, is spoken of. It is not the ordinary external air that is meant, but that kind of etheric air that was present at the beginning of Earth-evolution.

In these primeval ages things were different as regards Earth and Moon. The Moon was obliged to leave Earth when the luciferic influence had brought about such life conditions there that human souls with but few exceptions could no longer inhabit human bodies. This Moon, which then left Earth, was really an "imaginative" form; it consisted of substances that the human eye of today would not have been able to perceive. It contained primarily the activities of the Old Moon, which would have stimulated in human beings a powerful "atavistic" clairvoyance that would have prevented them from attaining freedom. The further attacks of Lucifer and of Ahriman compelled the good gods, and especially the Yahweh god, to transform the Moon in a certain way, to make it harder and permeate it with matter drawn from the Earth so that the Moon assumed a dense mineral form that was then able to withstand the onslaughts of Lucifer and Ahriman. The power of imagination that issues from the Moon and even today manifests in our life of fantasy, became so weakened in the course of evolution that instead of the old clairvoyance, it can create for us no more than the shadowy images of our life of thought. Thus the freedom of the human being was made secure.

We see from all this how the history of the origination of the heavenly bodies must start from the consideration of the evolution of the higher and also of the laggard beings. Then gradually the human being becomes the principal factor in the whole process. It is for the sake of humanity that the cosmic bodies must be founded in the universe, and that beings forsake their dwelling places and descend upon the Earth.

This description brings us only as far as the first stage of the evolution of the solar system, of which we spoke in the first Letter. The "world of finished work"—the measurable world—strictly regulated according to law also in respect to the various members of the solar system—did not arise until the middle of the Atlantean epoch. And after human beings—in the manner indicated before—had experienced a recapitulation of the preceding stages in the post-Atlantean cultural epochs, they then, in the Greek civilization, gradually began to concern themselves in a theoretical manner with the solar system. The earlier peoples, the Egyptians and the Babylonians, did not as a matter of fact *think out* the things concerning the world of stars, but they directly experienced the laws of the cosmos, and felt themselves instructed by the stars with respect to earthly happenings. The earliest Greeks were still occupied in this non-theoretical way with the starry worlds.

As Rudolf Steiner stated in his book *The Riddles of Philosophy:* "We should, for example, entirely misinterpret the concepts of Thales if we supposed that he thought out, or pondered over, the processes of nature as a merchant, or as a mathematician, or as an astronomer might do; and that he then in an imperfect way gathered his knowledge together as a modern investigator might into the sentence: 'Everything originates from water.' In those ancient times, to be a mathematician or an astronomer and so on meant having a *practical* relationship to things—as much indeed as any craftsman whose handiwork rests upon artistic ideas, and not upon any intellectual-scientific system."

With the "birth of thought" it was inevitable that human beings should create thoughts for themselves about the universe. While the planetary system, dominated as it is by its regulated laws, remains, even in its movements, in a state of comparative repose and tranquillity, there has come into existence upon the Earth during the course of time the often agitated and ever-varying picture that humanity has made for itself of the solar system. The Greeks who traveled to Egypt and Babylon in order to undergo initiation there came to know of the age-old records made by these peoples of the movements of the planets and the rhythms of solar and lunar eclipses and so on. This knowledge affected the Greeks of Plato's time with almost shattering intensity. That the planets could travel back and forth, that they could show times of immobility or irregularities of movement, was repellent to the Greek sense of beauty and divine activities. They felt the heavenly bodies to be divine beings—or at any rate the bodies of divine beings. Aristotle, for example, does not speak of Venus or Mercury, but of the star Aphrodite, or the star Hermes. The luciferic element that belongs to them was not felt to be ungodlike, since all the Greek gods were more or less luciferic in their nature. "But is it conceivable that a god should be staggering like a drunken man?" asks one of those old astronomers. Plato left a certain task behind for his pupils—to explain the movements of the planets in such a way that they should appear as uniform motions, that their courses should be circular. For it seemed to Plato that nothing but uniform movements formed after the divinely conceived pattern of a circle were appropriate for the gods.

At this point we can see the important transition from the instructions given in the mysteries about the planetary spheres, to that knowledge of the planetary movements that are in a certain way circumscribed by the spheres. Nevertheless the planets were still felt to be entirely connected with the spheres. The whole sphere must move in such a way that the harmony of the movements results in the planetary orbits with their retrogressions and stationary pauses. Eudoxus, who was initiated in Egypt and was connected with the Platonic school, was the first to solve the problem set by Plato. Aristotle carried it further, right into the physical domain one might say, where for the time being it had to stay. The fifty-five spheres he makes use of in order to explain the movements of the five planets and the Sun and Moon already represent something mechanistic, and are far removed from the teaching about the spheres given in the ancient mysteries, which was the result of research into the life after death. The problem was next dealt with from a more

mathematical and geometrical standpoint by the astronomers of the
Alexandrian school. Gradually the spheres lost their substantiality and
became merely circles that rotated upon and within one another.

It is necessary to give this historical account so that we may gain an
understanding of the Ptolemaic system, which was a summation of all
that had gone before. Ptolemy, who worked in Alexandria in the second
century after Christ, also regarded the spheres only as the background
of his system, but he felt himself to be absolutely the one who fulfilled
the Platonic task. Thus, in his famous *Textbook of Astronomy,* [the
Almagest] he says:

> When we set ourselves the task of proving for the five planets, as
> well as for the Sun and Moon that their apparent anomalies are
> all capable of being attained by a uniform circular revolution—
> because only these movements are appropriate to godly beings,
> while irregularity is unknown to them—then we may regard the
> bringing of such an attempt to a successful issue as a great achieve-
> ment, indeed as the ultimate goal of a mathematical science that
> rests upon a philosophical basis.[1]

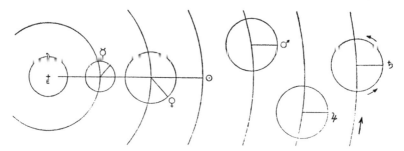

Figure 7

Therefore he places circle upon circle, epicycles upon deferents (or
eccentrics), until the orbits of the planets with all their peculiar loops
and curves are shown. Thus he makes all the planets revolve around
Earth, and—with the exception of the Sun and Moon—not directly,

---

1. Original translation into German by K. Manitius.

but so that the planets describe small circles (epicycles) whose centers revolve on large circles (deferents) that embrace Earth. The deferents of Mercury (☿) and Venus (♀) are described like that of the Sun (☉) in *one year,* and the epicycles of Mercury and Venus during a period corresponding to their synodical revolution—that is, the time between one conjunction with the Sun and the next. With the outer planets on the other hand, the small circle is described in one year, and the large one in the time the planets take to travel through the whole zodiac, in other words, one sidereal revolution. For Jupiter (♃) this is twelve years, for Saturn (♄) nearly thirty years. A remarkable peculiarity of this system is that the centers of the epicycles of Mercury and Venus are always in line (shown in the drawing) with the middle point of the Sun.

Meanwhile, the planets themselves are each guided with a certain regularity around the center of their epicycles on their own line or "stem." On the other hand, the outer planets must always have, within their epicycles, their own line (or "stem") parallel with the first mentioned [Sun-Earth line], while the epicycle can at the same time be at any point of the corresponding deferent or large circle.

In the drawing, in order to save space, the planets ♂, ♃, and ♄ are all drawn close together and near the Sun. Indeed, they might just as well be shown on the other side of the Earth and Sun, that is, they might be in opposition, as the Moon is when it is full. But with regard to the inner planets, one sees that they have a much closer relationship to the Sun out of whose womb they have directly come. They can never be very far from it—and are as though bound to it by an immense "stem" that passes through the centers of their epicycles. Thus, in the Ptolemaic representation, many different and intimate laws of the solar system come to expression in a beautiful manner, so that one recognizes in them their far-off origin in the wisdom of the mysteries. Also, the profound nature of the difference between the outer and inner planets—the supra-solar and sub-solar—which is so unclear in the Copernican system (through the exchange of the parts played by the epicycles and deferents and so on), is here very much in evidence.

This quite schematic and somewhat modern presentation of the Ptolemaic system gives only one epicycle (with the exceptions of the Sun and Moon, which have none), and one deferent, on whose circumference the center of the epicycle travels. In its full form the Ptolemaic system is much more complicated, but here its main characteristics are very clear.

It has been said the revolutions of the inner planets in epicycles corresponds to the synodical period of revolution, for Mercury 116 days, for Venus 584 days. Ptolemy himself presented it in this way. The little stems, however, revolve in relation to the plane of the zodiac and the plane of the diagram, and their sidereal periods are 88 days for Mercury and 225 days for Venus. The reason for this difference between sidereal and synodic periods is the same as in the case of the Moon. With the outer planets the stems revolve once in one year, as the Sun and the inner planets move in a year on their deferents. Ptolemy himself did not know the sidereal periods of revolution of Mercury and Venus. That is purely the result of calculations. The synodical period of revolution, though, is known by directly observing successive conjunctions of the planets with the Sun.

The system is a purely kinematic and geometrical one. In other words, the problem set by Plato is solved entirely according to the knowledge of that time (for the uniformity of the different movements has been retained in it), but without taking into consideration the driving forces that exist behind the movements.

But for the thought of today, influenced as it is by Newton, a planet that revolves in a circle about a given point, in which nothing is present; where there is neither body nor matter; that is a purely mathematical point or a "fictitious planet" (that is, actually the central point of the epicycle that revolves upon the deferent), is a mechanical impossibility. The ancients, however, did not trouble themselves about mechanisms. The guiding of the planets and of their cycles was performed by the gods, and there was no thought of "attraction" or "gravitation."

Even Copernicus (1473–1543) still retained the soul-attitude of the ancients. His system is also geometric. But it is simpler than the Ptolemaic. Geometrically, it is equally possible for the Sun to be in the center, and for the planets to revolve around it and for Earth to turn on its axis. This system was also known in ancient times by the Greeks, but did not gain adherence. Another geometrically possible system is the old so-called Egyptian system in which Mercury and Venus are given as revolving around the Sun, and to which the interesting system of Tycho Brahe (1546–1601) bears a certain resemblance. Kepler (1571–1630) evolved his three laws out of the Copernican system by a mechanistic method still permeated with spirituality, but which for the first time set aside the Platonic demand for a universal uniformity of circular movements.

Newton (1642–1727) applied the mechanical terrestrial and lunar laws to the whole universe. He did away with the last remaining celestial sphere and substituted for it radial forces, earthly force components. By this means a further necessary stage in the evolutionary history of the human spirit was accomplished. The question of the movements in the planetary system became, for the entire middle period of Earth-evolution (i.e., from the Atlantean epoch to our own time) a question that has no longer to do with the gods, but is mainly an affair of human consciousness and its attitude toward the universe.

March 1928

Concerning the Movements of Venus and Mercury

The Easter Festival

WE HAVE SEEN HOW PEOPLE have regarded the planetary system from many different standpoints throughout the course of time. Each of these views has a certain justification and is even necessary, as we can see by considering the spiritual history of humankind, which is also an "education of the human race." Thus we can also understand that with the renewed awakening of consciousness in respect to the spirit at the present time and also in the near future, a new conception of the universe must arise. This new picture of the world must be born out of very different soul powers than those that led to the Ptolemaic or Copernican systems. It would be a mythical belief to suppose that Copernicus with his idea of solitary spheres rolling through space had found the right idea for all time.

But it would also be a mistake to suppose that a new conception of the planetary movements such as that given by Rudolf Steiner could be accepted in the same way as was that of Copernicus. It is precisely because a new consciousness must be evoked that the lemniscate form of the movements Rudolf Steiner described cannot be represented by any abstract scheme. It is absolutely necessary that out of the whole range of spiritual scientific endeavor, the conditions be created for the discovery of a new system. For it is not an intellectual explanation of the universe that we need but a new connection of the feeling and the will of humanity with the cosmos.

This, however, can only bear fruit through knowledge, that is, through coming to recognize the phenomena themselves or humankind's knowledge of the phenomena, now and in the future. Every representation of the appearance of these things, whether in words or in diagrams, can only be one-sided. In particular, two-dimensional drawings can only give one aspect, that which one then wants to illuminate. Therefore we have to try to conjure up a more or less complete picture by means of a representation of a variety of viewpoints. The reader must be able to alter his or her point of view every moment. Since we now wish to come to a description of the different planetary movements we must especially bear this in mind.

We will first consider merely what the eye can see taking place in the heavens, and its corroboration, which we have already stated in the third Letter. Now we find the two lower planets, Mercury and Venus, appearing alternately as morning and evening stars. We may compare them with the Moon, which during the last days before new Moon is in a sense a morning star, and after conjunction with the Sun, when it appears as a young and waxing Moon, is in a sense an evening star. However, the Moon can always withdraw further and further from the Sun—it revolves of course around Earth and is so to say bound to it and not to the Sun as though by a "stem." Venus and Mercury can only withdraw a very little way from the Sun and during the day are overpowered by its brilliant light. Given favorable conditions Venus can indeed be seen with the naked eye even in the middle of the day, and is always visible through the telescope.

Now we can easily picture the relation of Venus or Mercury to the Sun in that they are both revolving around the Sun. In Figure 7 of the previous Letter the deferents of Mercury, Venus and the Sun, all of which rotate in the same period of time, *one year*, can be regarded as coinciding with one another. In that way we pass over from the Ptolemaic system into the so-called Egyptian. Copernicus also proceeded in such a way that he left out the deferents of the lower planets and transplanted the center-points of their epicycles into the Sun, and had Earth also revolve around the Sun. We can here incidentally make the remarkable discovery that in figure 8 the Copernican sequence of

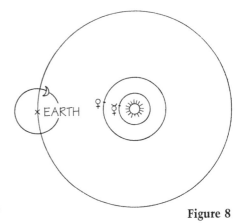

Figure 8

the lower planets: Earth, Moon, *Venus, Mercury,* Sun, occurs of itself; while in Figure 7 the old esoteric sequence of Earth, Moon, *Mercury, Venus,* Sun, is adhered to.

Without going in detail now into the very complicated question of the "transposition of Venus and Mercury," it can be shown here how it is that both Ptolemy and Copernicus call the same heavenly body "Venus" though giving it a different place in the sequence. We must also remember that the Ptolemaic system did not actually take the spatial relationships into consideration, but rather the temporal relationships and the similar rhythms that must arise from them. And thus Mercury is found to revolve on its epicycle in less time than Venus does, and is therefore—from this aspect—the nearest to the stationary Earth. Ptolemy was far from considering the relative distance of the planets from Earth or from the Sun. Instead he merely established the order of the *spheres.* And thus it was clear to him that the spheres of Saturn, Jupiter, and Mars are farther away from Earth than the sphere of the Sun (they are supra-solar), and that Venus and Mercury are nearer than the Sun. He says, though, that other and more ancient astronomers were even doubtful about this, and that from the observations of that time, it could not be decisively known:

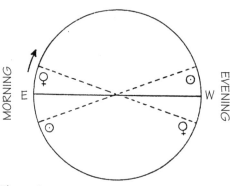

Figure 9

> Thus a greater amount of belief seems to be due to the older astronomers' methods of arrangement, which separates the planets that are in opposition from those that do not come into opposition, but which always remain near the Sun.[1]

The idea that Mercury must be the planet nearest the Earth, and that Venus is next, is actually borrowed from a tradition, and this tradition is one that originated in the mysteries. For in the mysteries it was known that human beings in the life after death pass first through the Moon-

---

1. Ptolemy's *Handbook of Astronomy,* [the *Almagest*] vol. 2, book 9, chapter 1.

sphere, then through that of Mercury, and then through the sphere of Venus. But so far as external observation is concerned, and the observations and calculations that become possible later (those concerning, for example, the passages of Mercury and Venus in front of the Sun) it has become equally clear that the little reddish-colored and scarcely visible Mercury stands nearest the Sun, while the brilliantly shining Venus, being further from the Sun, stands nearer to Earth. Therefore what is presented to us is a non-agreement—a confusion of the *spheres* with their corresponding *planets*. That is as far as we can deal with the subject at present.

Let us now take the case—one that lies before us in this present month of March—where Venus is morning star. In Figure 9 let the circle represent the zodiac wherein the Sun and Venus are moving, and the line EW the horizon at any given place. (In making representations of the heavens the east and west points are reversed as compared with maps of Earth—east to the left, west to the right, so that the highest point of the path occurs in the south.) The arrow gives the direction of the diurnal movement. The upper half is therefore the visible arc of the sky. Let us imagine that the time is immediately before sunrise. Venus is ahead of the Sun, visible in the east as morning star. She is now actually to the west of the Sun, and thus when she is most distant from the Sun in the *eastern* sky, one calls it the "western elongation." As soon as the Sun rises, or even a little before, the light of Venus is extinguished. She becomes invisible to us by day. Since she is wandering ahead of the Sun she sinks first in the west, and is therefore below the horizon before she can show herself in the evening twilight. (We can picture this situation as shown in Figure 9 as being on the same evening in the west at sunset.)

This is repeated for a considerable time—in the case of Venus, for several months. Only, as a morning star she is always getting further from the Sun; that is, she rises at an increasing

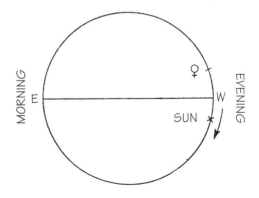

Figure 10

length of time before the Sun, until the greatest elongation is attained. She then begins to draw nearer to the Sun again, until she approaches conjunction, when she rises simultaneously with the Sun and is therefore invisible. After a time, she reappears on the other side of the Sun. And now we can picture to ourselves how the Sun in its diurnal course sets in the west while Venus only reaches the horizon in its wake, and so has become the evening star [Figure 10].

We can represent this process in many different ways. One more is given here and shows how Venus—and also Mercury—must show phases similar to those of the Moon. While in the last diagram the zodiac was shown in the flat plane of the drawings, this time it must be represented more or less in perspective. Here we have the path of Venus around the Sun and the Earth as though seen by distant spectators looking at their play of movement, but without regard to the horizon, that is, without regard to any particular point on the surface of the Earth. So we get the accompanying diagram [Figure 11].

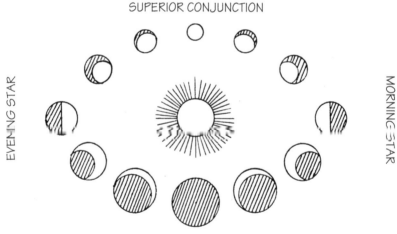

SUPERIOR CONJUNCTION

EVENING STAR

MORNING STAR

Figure 11   INFERIOR CONJUNCTION

We observe that we have something like a "new Venus"—the inferior conjunction—when Venus is between Earth and the Sun. Her nearness to Earth makes her appear as a very large disk, and only for a few days during the conjunction is she scarcely, or not at all, visible. Immediately after this she appears as a morning star in the eastern sky. And she is then, notwithstanding the size of the disk, still somewhat feeble in her light, for she shows only a weak phase like the Moon's thin crescent.

Her form is therefore similar to that of the waning Moon, which is also visible in the east. After about thirty-five days she reaches her greatest brilliancy in this still-small phase but with a relatively large disk; and she looks not unlike a five-day-old Moon—but a waning one.

Then, after another thirty-five days she reaches the "greatest elongation," or distance from the Sun. She mounts to a greater height in the eastern heavens, and rises at her longest time *before sunrise* (more than four hours)—in order after seven months gradually to return again to the neighborhood of the Sun. She is then "full Venus" and in her "superior conjunction," and is on the other side of the Sun, as may be seen by the smallness of her disk.

Thus with both Mercury and Venus there are two kinds of conjunction and no opposition. We can certainly compare the superior conjunction to full Moon, although Venus can never, viewed from the Sun, be on the far side of Earth.

When, after the superior conjunction, Venus has passed the Sun, she appears on the other side of the sky in the west as the evening star. Then she again passes through her phases but in reverse order, comes to the greatest elongation, greatest brilliancy, and returns to the Sun. When she reaches the neighborhood of inferior conjunction, she describes a loop. She apparently stands still for a short time [in relation to the stars] and then retrogrades for about six weeks, traveling from east to west against the Sun, which in its annual movement goes from west to east. The inferior conjunction takes place about the middle of this retrograde movement. Now she becomes the morning star again—the star of Lucifer—which was once his dwelling place and for which he now longs. To the ancients, Venus as the morning star was "Lucifer-Phosphorus." But as the evening star she was "Hesperus" because something quite different rayed out from her. Mercury or Hermes, as the morning star—as a being—also differed from Mercury as the evening star. For the planet as morning star was the radiant messenger of the gods who comes on winged feet bringing divine knowledge to Earth, while as evening star he was the guide who led souls into the underworld—or, in the modern sense, the guide to the true imaginations, and the world to which they belong. (Cf. Rudolf Steiner's *True and False Paths in Spiritual Investigation,* lecture 10.)

The actual phases were altogether unknown to the ancients. They are, in fact, invisible to the naked eye. Even the clear sickle shape of

Venus appears to the eye unaided by any instrument only as a brilliantly radiant star. Galileo was the first to discover the phases, when in the year 1610 he directed the newly invented telescope upon Venus.

We must now turn to the Sun, which we have represented as though standing still, and once more bring it so to speak into movement—as it travels in the course of the year through the zodiac, while Venus and Mercury are turning round it—so that we may observe the so-called synodical revolution. Venus requires 584 days, or 19 $\frac{1}{5}$ months—more than 1 $\frac{1}{2}$ years—to proceed from one inferior conjunction to the next. During half of this period—about 290 to 294 days—she is either a morning or an evening star. Around every conjunction there is a certain time during which she is invisible to the naked eye. The conditions are similar for Mercury, although his time periods on account of his greater proximity to the Sun are all much shorter—altogether only 116 days. He can only attain a distance from the Sun of twenty-nine degrees versus Venus's forty-eight degrees and is therefore much more difficult to see. He can achieve in one year as many as seven conjunctions and four not-quite-complete loops. Venus under certain conditions is content with only one conjunction in a year, and if this happens to be a superior conjunction, then she makes no loop in that year. In order to get an idea of the liveliness of Mercury's movements, we will give here a drawing of his path (again from a particular standpoint) as it may be shown for a given year. The whole mobility of Mercury is expressed in this drawing:

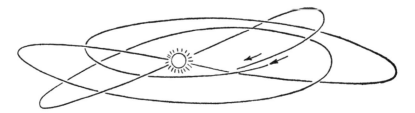

Figure 12

At the present moment Mercury is a morning star. In favorable circumstances he can be seen about March 22 in the east, as then he has reached his greatest elongation. After May, he is once more an evening star, and there is again a possibility of seeing him about the beginning of June, and so on a few times during the rest of the year. At present Venus is a morning star, and reaches superior conjunction with the Sun on July 1, and so as the summer advances, and on into the autumn, she will be shining once more in fullest splendor in the evening sky.

The superior planets, whose movements are somewhat easier to follow, shall be described some other time. But we will here add something concerning the approaching festival of Easter.

*   *   *

The Easter festival is known, in respect to astronomy, to be remarkable for its variability, and the method of prescribing its date. In the assignment of the date of Easter, which is the memorial festival of the greatest event in the history of the world, we have a last reminiscence of the ancient wisdom of the mysteries and the experiences of initiation. For the Council of Nicaea, which introduced the movable date for the Easter festival in the year 325 and established the rules whereby it could be calculated, took place immediately before the dawn of that period of world history when it ceased to be possible for humankind to have cosmic thoughts. The council itself did not proceed in such a way that—regarded from our modern standpoint—any particularly divine inspiration could have been expected of it. Nevertheless, we may find a very profound wisdom manifesting itself in the establishing of the Easter festival. It must always take place on the Sunday following the first full Moon after the commencement of spring.

The commencement of spring is marked astronomically by the Sun's crossing of the equator. We see the Sun and Earth in a certain relation to one another in that the Sun has triumphed over the dark regions of Earth. Next, the Moon also enters into this relationship—it must be a full Moon. Then we await the coming of the Sunday in its order in the succession of the seven days of the planets. As Rudolf Steiner explained in his last course of Easter lectures, we have here a cosmic manifestation of an earlier initiation experience.

In the ancient mysteries one learned to enter with one's etheric body into the light of the full Moon, to pass out into the cosmos. With one's higher members—the astral body and ego—one shared the forces of the Sun. The human being became a Sun bearer even though with the etheric body only the reflected Sun rays that come from the full Moon might be taken up. The ancient mysteries had died out, and the souls of human beings could no longer be led out into the cosmos. But the human being looked out upon the external full Moon just at the time when Earth begins to send her soul out into the cosmos to meet the Sun, and saw Sunday as the "day of the Lord"—and united Sun, Moon, and Earth, just as Sun and Moon had once been spiritually united with the human being.

Let us now regard this from another angle. How much is expressed by these respective relationships of Sun, Moon, and Earth for the establishment of the Easter festival, the festival of resurrection! Christ, Yahweh, Lucifer—the whole evolution of humanity is displayed as in a cross-section! Yes—there is in this relationship something like a memory of the third stage of cosmic existence—the stage of the "activity" of the starry powers. For the Moon may be at the full a longer or shorter time after March 21 [in 1582 the beginning of spring was ("once and for all" –E.V.) fixed at the twenty-first of March in the Church calendar—see Notes on the Text], for it may occur either at the beginning or end of the week. That is to say the three events—the Sun's crossing of the equator, the full Moon, and Sunday, can be either quite close together or quite far apart, and in each and every case the activity of the cosmos is different. Exactly how they occur must either be discerned in the heavens or can be calculated according to the old rules that were established by the council. These rules are again a beautiful example of the old rhythmical astronomy. They are calculated according to definite rhythms that do not concern themselves with the irregularities—which are by the way "regular irregularities"—of the lunar revolution. Thus, occasionally we may have an Easter day when the full Moon has not quite arrived! Indeed, the whole manner in which the memorial celebration of a once definite historic event has been associated with a *movable* date, reveals the profound depths of the ancient mood of the human soul. We might perhaps regard this as somewhat antiquated today. But we must also ask ourselves whether the reasons given for fixing the date of Easter, as is proposed—whether this sweeping away of an ancient treasure of wisdom—is justifiable; and whether the fact that up to the present these efforts have failed does not point to a prevailing of the old spirituality over modern materialism? Might it not be that in this also, Michael—as is his special task—will carry over something of the past into the present in a way that is *justified?*

The old starry wisdom has faded away—or has fallen under the dominion of Lucifer. But here, in this one point, in the establishment of a movable Easter festival, it still lives on in our modern culture. It lives on in a justifiable way because it is brought into direct contact with the Mystery of Golgotha. Therefore it is also possible to speak of the ancient wisdom in modern words. And what is happening here is that something like a mutual relation of powers between the Sun, Moon, and Earth is being expressed.

Rudolf Steiner once pointed out that the beginning of spring is so joyful an experience for humanity because the up-springing forces of Earth tell us that she is still ready to continue to bear us until we have fulfilled our mission upon her. She will only be able to do so, however, so long as the Sun does not merely outwardly cross the equator, but still preserves in reality and truth the forces that can overcome the chaotic forces of Earth's winter. The Sun forces are not at the present stage of Earth evolution in a state of increase, for the Sun has already given Earth of its best; they are decreasing. It is the Moon that, as full Moon, robs the Sun of its forces. So with the coming of every spring the Sun has grown weaker in its effective working; and we may well ask: will the Sun be able to keep Earth alive long enough for humanity to complete its evolution? Then the full Moon looks down upon us—earlier or later in the beginning of spring according to the constitution of the year—as the wrathful Jehovah looked down upon a humanity that had fallen to the temptation of Lucifer in the paradisial dawn of Earth. But on the Sunday that follows the full Moon, Christ rises from his earthly tomb, and humanity knows that if it unites itself with the power of Christ it will help the Sun to carry the Earth.

April 1928

More About the Planetary World

WE NOW COME to the consideration of the outer planets, Saturn, Jupiter, and Mars, which from the spiritual point of view are quite different from the inner planets. Once more we shall find that our observation can gain more when we regard these planets in accordance with the Ptolemaic conception of the universe, because in this system, the inner planets are separated from the others by the Sun. In the Copernican system it is Earth that stands in the place of the Sun and the planets are accorded their positions in a more or less uniform succession from their common center: Sun, Mercury, Venus, Earth, Mars, Jupiter, Saturn. According to this method the Moon is not regarded as a planet but as a satellite of the Earth, just as the outer planets also have their moons that revolve around them. The order of succession as it is given in respect of the *spheres* of the planets is: Earth, (Moon) Mercury, Venus, Sun, Mars, Jupiter, and Saturn. Here the Sun appears as the link between the inner and outer planets and also as their separator.

The outer planets are characterized first by the greater freedom of their movements in respect to the Sun. From the point of view of the Sun they can be on the far side of the Earth. Then we see them shining in the night sky while the Sun is below us on the other side of Earth. Hence there is a preference among astronomers for the opposition of the outer planets (which for quite other reasons is not shared by the so-called astrologers) because such times are favorable for observing them. When, for example, Saturn is in opposition, it is at midnight, roughly speaking, that he passes through the meridian, or in other words, he culminates, reaching the highest southerly position in his nightly path. Thus he is visible the entire night. Especially when Mars is in opposition (this is always to be understood as in opposition to the Sun), he receives a great deal of attention from astronomers. This is particularly so when the time of his opposition brings him very near to Earth, which due to his eccentric orbit varies greatly according to the circumstances. It may perhaps be remembered how a somewhat unscientific excitement was aroused over the Mars opposition that took place in the summer of 1924. Since then Mars has again visited us in a similar way, only this time was rather farther from Earth. This year, too, he will again be in opposition to the Sun.

Jupiter and Saturn, who do not have such eccentric orbits, geometrically speaking, as Mars has, are much more regular in their appearances. Also, the times of their return to opposition and conjunction are shorter than those of Mars. There again we must note the difference between the sidereal and synodical revolutions, as we did in the case of the Moon, Mercury, and Venus.

The former represents the planets in their relation to the world of stars—their "astral relationship," so to speak, and the latter, their relation to the Sun, which is more of an etheric nature. The sidereal revolution is the time the planet takes to journey through the zodiac—that is, to return to the same star. Meanwhile, the Sun too has been journeying through the zodiac and—if we start from a conjunction with the Sun—a little more time is required before the Sun is reached again. Thus we get the synodical revolution.

For *Saturn,* the actual time of revolution, the sidereal, is as you know, almost thirty years, or more precisely twenty-nine years and 167 days. If in one year the Sun has returned to its former position in the zodiac, then Saturn has accomplished only one-thirtieth of its journey, that is to say, as much as the Sun has traversed in one-thirtieth of a year or twelve days. Therefore the Sun requires somewhat more than twelve days to overtake Saturn again. (It is all rather like the problem of Achilles and the tortoise.) Thus the time period of Saturn's synodical revolution amounts to only 378 days, or one year and thirteen days. So it follows that Saturn arrives in the eastern night sky, comes into opposition, and so on, only about twelve or thirteen days later every year. Thus, for instance, if it had been in opposition in the previous year on May 26, it would be on June 6 in the present year, on the June 18 the following year, and so on. Saturn's conjunction with the Sun, when he becomes invisible for more or less protracted periods, always occurs six months and six days after opposition. In between lie the so-called quadratures, that is, when Saturn forms a ninety-degree angle with the Sun, so that the planet is culminating around the time the Sun sets. In contrast to this synodical revolution of Saturn, which is in the main determined by the Sun, there is his own slow and ponderous movement through the zodiac, the thirty-year sidereal revolution. During his course, Saturn remains two and one-half years in each sign of the zodiac, and meets the Sun two or three times in succession in every sign during the Sun's yearly course through the twelve constellations.

The sidereal revolution of *Jupiter* takes almost exactly twelve years. Thus the Sun requires one-twelfth of a year, or one month, to overtake Jupiter on his return, after his yearly course, to the original starting point. Thus, each time the opposition takes place about a month later. This year, the opposition is on October 29, and the conjunction on April 6, when Jupiter will be invisible for the time being. A year ago, the dates were September 22 and March 1.

In the case of *Mars,* the time lying between two oppositions is considerably longer, just because he travels so much more swiftly across the heavens that it takes the Sun longer to overtake him. His sidereal revolution takes between 687 days, not quite two years, and his synodical revolution 780 days, two years and about fifty days. This year he comes into opposition to the Sun on December 21, and is just now beginning to rise in the early hours of the morning. After July he will rise before midnight, and then earlier and earlier until the end of the year.

Bear in mind the important fact that all these movements do not take place uniformly, but with retrogressions and pauses. The planets describe loops or zigzag lines during every synodical period; indeed— and this is again a remarkable difference—this occurs in the case of the outer planets during opposition, and in the case of the inferior planets during the inferior conjunction. The loops are of very considerable extent. Their length extends over many degrees in the heavens and can therefore be observed easily by the unaided eye if one has one or two bright stars in the neighborhood as points of comparison. During last spring the stars in Scorpius were very distinct indicators for observing the loop made by Saturn. This year Saturn is to be found in the extreme easterly portion of the Scorpion, so that less convenient points of comparison are present. However, the retrogression of Saturn that began on March 30 and will continue until August 18 can still be observed with the naked eye.

With regard to Mars, we shall have very good indicator stars during the second half of the year and on into next spring, in the Twins and the Bull. The annual movement of the planets is, like that of the Sun and Moon, in the direction from west to east, in contradistinction to the diurnal movement. Thus we see Saturn, when he is not retrograding, traveling from Scorpius in the direction of Sagittarius. Then his movement slows down until it comes to a stop for a few days (this year it took place about March 29), and then he travels the opposite way toward the west, in the direction of Antares, which however he does not actually reach. (In this description we have left out of account the daily revolution of the entire starry heavens.) Toward August 18, there is again a slowing down of the movement followed by a stop, and then again a further progress from west or east. At the end of eight months the whole process is repeated. The actual opposition comes in the middle, between the two pauses, in respect to both time and space. Saturn will not enter Sagittarius until next year, and will remain there until 1931. The more slowly a planet travels, the longer is the time of retrograde motion. While Mars accomplishes its retrograde movement comparatively quickly (80 days during one synodical revolution of 26 months), Jupiter takes 120 and Saturn 140 days respectively for their retrograde movements in each synodical period. *Uranus,* who is outside the orbit of Saturn, makes one journey in 84 years, and thus requires only 369.6 days for his synodic revolution, and spends 5 months of the year in retrograde motion. With *Neptune* the number is 165 years and 367 $\frac{1}{2}$ days respectively.

Against this, if we observe the whole period that a planet requires to describe its loop—and therefore not merely the retrograde part of the movement but the two moments when it passes approximately the same place on its path—we shall find that Mars takes about four and one-half months to describe the loop, Jupiter six months, and Saturn eight months. We can see by this what an important part the loop movement plays, even from an external standpoint, in the whole manifestation of planetary life.

It is best to regard this loop-formation purely as a phenomenon, that is to say, not to attempt any perspective explanation either in terms of the Ptolemaic or of the Copernican systems. For it is an actual manifestation visible to outward view and can also in the lemniscate form of the planetary movements only be conceived in the sense of a real happening. Indeed, Rudolf Steiner has drawn our attention precisely to this fact that the outer planets are most effective in their

working when they are forming loops. In the case of the inner planets, their greatest effectiveness is in the remaining parts of their orbits
when they are at greatest elongation, or greatest brilliancy, or when
they are in superior conjunction. The Venus loops, of which there are
five in eight years, are, as regards their size, the most considerable of
all the planetary loops. But in spite of this they are accomplished more
rapidly than those of the outer planets, and in the orbit of Venus they
represent something quite different from what is represented by those
of Jupiter and the others.

The naked eye can see very little of the retrogression of Venus, and
of that of Mercury scarcely anything, since they take place at about the
time of conjunction. It is a peculiar fact that Venus and also Mercury
accomplish a reversal of their movement every time they return to the
Sun again after greatest elongation—though here it is not a question of
a backward movement in the ordinary sense, even though in the case of
the evening star the direction is from east to west. Venus, for example,
is not then moving *against* the direction of the zodiac, through Gemini,
Taurus, Aries, and so on, as she does when retrograding in the loop.
Rather, the phenomenon is caused by a slowing down of the direct
movement in comparison with the Sun, a gradual retardation that leads
to the short pause that precedes the actual retrogression. The conditions are somewhat different in respect to the morning star. In trying to
understand these conditions we are led, even by purely external indications, to the fact that Venus as morning star and evening star reveals
two different beings. The same holds true for Mercury.

The forms in which the loops can be represented in a drawing in
their relation to the ecliptic are given here for Mars and Saturn as they
are presented by their path for the year 1928. As Venus does not make
a loop this year, the representation is given for 1927. (See Figure 13.)

Figure 13

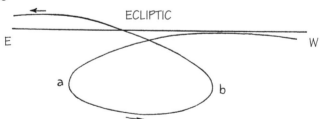

*Path of Venus from July to November, 1927. Retrograding from August 21
(a) until October 3 (b).*

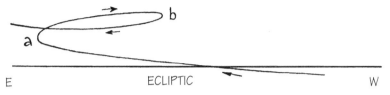

Path of Mars from September 1928 to April 1929. Retrograding from November 13 (a) until January 28 (b).

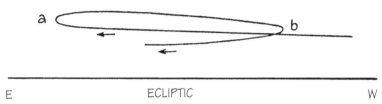

Path of Saturn from the end of 1927 until November 1928. Retrograde from March 30 (a) until August 18 (b). The scale in comparison to that of the paths of Mars and Venus is three times larger. [See Notes on the Text.]

Mars does not come into opposition until December 21. The planet is then in Gemini, having been easily observable during the late summer in Taurus.

Jupiter will be moving retrograde through Aries from the beginning of September until the end of December, and his movement will be easy to perceive. We have already spoken of *Saturn. Uranus* is in Pisces, *Neptune* in Leo near the star Regulus. Both planets are invisible to the naked eye, and even a small telescope will not reveal them—otherwise they would not have remained undiscovered up to the eighteenth and nineteenth centuries!

If we look at the planets more from the spiritual aspect we shall find, as has already been indicated, that the inner planets present in many respects the reverse of the outer planets. What the latter perform as more spiritual functions, the former carry more into physical and organic activities. In Rudolf Steiner's *Man and the World of Stars* (lecture 1, Dornach, November 26, 1922), it is explained how the human soul, which is passing through the life between death and rebirth, comes in the Mars sphere to the world Logos or world Word, and in the Jupiter sphere to the world thoughts, and in the Saturn sphere to world orientation. That is to say, the human being experiences the cosmic archetypal images of those forces which during the first years of childhood one must again master as Earth forces. This occurs in the time when one is passing through the true realm of spirits (as understood in Steiner's books *Theosophy* and *An Outline of Esoteric Science*). At this point, having traversed the Sun sphere and having laid aside the astral body—the "third corpse"—the human being enters the spheres of the outer planets as a true cosmic-spiritual being. Then, on the return path to a new birth, one comes by degrees under the influences of the planets according to their various "gravities." Rudolf Steiner spoke of these forces of weight or gravity that human beings appropriate to themselves when they once more awaken to a feeling of longing for rebirth. Saturn gives them the joyful longing as its gravity; Jupiter the joyful acceptance of earthly tasks; and so on.

Next the Sun transforms the qualities that at first have been spiritually attained into something of a more physical and etheric nature. From Venus we obtain the capacity to speak, later on, the language of Earth that resounds through our larynx. Mercury bestows thoughts that we are able to think with an earthly brain—in contrast to the cosmic wisdom of Jupiter—thoughts of logic and the associative power of reason. Finally, the Moon guides us into the region of earthly gravity and plants in the soul those forces that enable us later to develop the capacity to walk upon Earth. Thus in a certain sense Saturn corresponds to the Moon, Jupiter to Mercury, and Mars to Venus. During the whole of this descent to Earth the positions of each planet in the zodiac, its orbit, (whether or not it is forming a loop), and its role as an evening or morning star all play an important role.

When a person has reached Earth he or she begins, in a certain sense, once more with the Moon. In the first seven years development lies under the influence of the Moon forces, the second seven under those of Mercury, and so on. The first capacity the child attains is the ability to walk and stand upright and move about within the domain of earthly gravitation. Then follows speaking, and finally, thinking. That there seems here to be an apparent inversion of the sequence of forces need not surprise us—it is that inversion already briefly mentioned which must again and again occur between Venus and Mercury.

Both the inner and outer planets stand differently with regard to the present-day human being. The inner planets, whose spheres are only traversed when human beings, on their path of return to Earth, have once more become clothed in the astral body (the etheric body is added in the Moon sphere), have much to do with the determination of human karma. Even though the "parcel of destiny," as Rudolf Steiner called it, is only taken up on reaching the Moon sphere, both Venus and Mercury already work strongly upon the aspect of karma that expresses itself in the bodily nature. The nation, family, and language of the coming Earth life are decided within these spheres, while character and temperament are also formed by the Sun and the inner planets. During Earth life the organs of execretion, the lymphatic glandular functions, and so on are under these influences.

On the other hand, the outer planets give the human being more freedom. They have at least partly withdrawn their activity from human beings in such a way that they can no longer work directly upon them through the moral effect of nature. In earlier ages—which began to come to an end, although not completely, at the time of the Mystery of Golgotha—the workings of Saturn, Jupiter, and Mars in the outer realms of nature were indeed such as to come to expression in human beings as forces of moral upbuilding. It was with the senses, especially with the eyes, that earlier humanity was aware of the workings of Saturn. For example, as the light was thrown back by objects as color, people experienced it quite naturally as a spiritual force, as something moral. World thoughts streamed in with the sense-perceptions; the world Word resounded from the objects and beings of the sense world. They became for human beings not merely knowledge, but an ethical force. But by this means it was not possible to become wholly free. Therefore these forces had to gradually withdraw from nature in order that humanity should attain freedom.

External nature lost its cosmic moral element; it offered human beings merely dead sense perceptions upon which they could direct their abstract power of thinking and knowing. It was a long process, which we can observe right into the Middle Ages, during which the ancient conception of nature permeated with spirit came to an end, and modern natural science began.

But whereas these forces withdrew from the outer world they did not become ineffective. The human has now to grasp them anew in free spiritual activity. Instead of "breathing in" the moral forces of Saturn in the colored light of natural objects with our eyes, now through an inner effort, through the given exercises in concentration, we must create in ourselves the faculty for developing spiritual sight. By sinking deeply into the world-thoughts one must unite oneself with the liberated Jupiter force. And one must learn so to control the forces of speech that they are not only conditioned by our organism, but can become a manifestation of the world Logos.

One can see that the whole path of development leading into the higher worlds—what Rudolf Steiner called modern esotericism, which has been built up since the Middle Ages—is contained in this short description. Instead of a last despairing search for moral forces within natural processes, as was carried out by the alchemists; instead of an adherence to old astrological rules, which had value for a certain time during the period when human beings were still unfree in relation to the cosmos; it is necessary for modern human beings (who are modern in the sense of the Michael impulse) to make use of the planetary forces that have for their sake withdrawn themselves from our earthly environment, and must be grasped by human beings in freedom.

In the light of these things we should consider Rudolf Steiner's works—*The Philosophy of Freedom, How to Know Higher Worlds,* and so on—and also what he has given our movement concerning speech formation. Then we shall once more realize from another aspect the vast scope and the cosmic lawfulness of his life's work.

While the outer planets have withdrawn themselves from the domain of external nature in respect to their moral workings, they still work on within the human being. But here their activity is more delicate, more spiritual than that of the inner planets. The latter are more concerned with creating the conditions of destiny, the former are those that tend toward giving humanity freedom. Indeed, Rudolf Steiner has also said that inattentiveness to these liberated forces of Saturn, Jupiter, and Mars, which is so prevalent in our external civilization, must lead in the future to evil consequences. Neurasthenia as a characteristic symptom of civilization, increased susceptibility to illusions, and a growing tendency to untruthfulness result if one allows these forces to play freely in one's life without creating in oneself fresh spiritual organs that will be able to absorb them. In this knowledge of the workings of the planets upon the human being lies concealed a stern warning not to take up the teachings of spiritual science as mere doctrines only, but as a summons to real individual activity.

May 1928

Eclipses of the Sun and Moon
Whitsuntide

THIS YEAR THE MONTH OF MAY brings the beginning of the first period of the eclipses, which continues into June. A second period follows six months later, in November and December. These periods, each of which includes from one to three eclipses, occur every year, but each year their beginning occurs earlier—on an average twenty days earlier, although it can be either a mere eight days or an entire Moon period of four weeks. In order to present a picture of the constantly recurring and ever earlier appearance of the eclipses, we will give the corresponding dates for the past several years:

1924	*Sun*	March 5	July 31, August 30	—
	Moon	February 20	August 14	—
1925	*Sun*	January 24	July 20/21	—
	Moon	February 8	August 4	—
1926	*Sun*	January 14	July 9/10	—
	Moon	—	—	—
1927	*Sun*	January 3	June 29	December 24
	Moon	—	June 15	December 8
1928	*Sun*	—	May 19, June 17	November 12
	Moon	—	June 3	November 27

From this table one sees the two periods distinctly denoted. That there were apparently three eclipse periods in 1927, in January, June, and December, arises only from the fact that the third period has come over, as it were, around the turn of the year, from January 1928. One also sees that—as already stated—the number of eclipses in each period can vary from one to three; that within a period there is always an alternation of an eclipse of the Sun with an eclipse of the Moon and vice versa; and on the other hand that each new period can begin either with an eclipse of the Sun or an eclipse of the Moon. If only two eclipses take place (as in 1926), which represents the minimum, the two eclipses are always both of the Sun. Naturally, the proof for all these rules cannot be given here in a short space.

What has here been described as "eclipse-periods" is not only connected with the movement of the Sun and Moon (or of Earth), but also with the movement of the points of intersection of the orbits of the Sun and Moon that are called nodes, of which the ancients spoke as the dragon's head (ascending node) and dragon's tail (descending node). For the Moon's path these nodes represent something similar to the points of spring and autumn on the path of Earth and Sun, in that they depict an ascent and descent of the Moon on its orbit and also are in retrograde motion. This retrograde movement of the nodes, which make a full revolution once in eighteen years seven months, brings about the earlier entry of the eclipses in each year since these are connected with the places of the nodes.

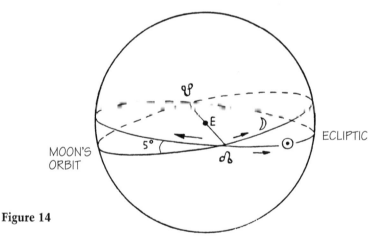

Figure 14

The orbit of the Moon makes an angle of five degrees with the ecliptic or orbit of the Sun, which is somewhat exaggerated in the drawing. The other planets also appear to have orbits in the heavens that are more or less slanting in relation to the Sun's path, the ecliptic. These orbits, however, all lie within the zodiac, which is a fairly wide belt. Some of the smaller planets or planetoids between Mars and Jupiter are exceptions, often having orbits that are so much inclined that they can wander far outside the zodiac. In fact, they do not belong to the "normal" formation of our solar-system, but are the result of a war in the universe. (See Rudolf Steiner's *The Spiritual Hierarchies and the Physical World,* lecture 5.)

It is a good thing to sometimes look up the node points in the sky—they also play an important part in our soul-life—and from their position to picture to oneself the Moon's orbit for the month in question. At the present time the ascending node lies in Taurus in the neighborhood of the star Aldebaran (see next drawing); the descending node at the opposite point of the zodiac, in Scorpius, above the red star Antares. The Moon's orbit therefore is highest above the Sun's orbit in the region of Gemini, Cancer, Leo, and so on, though to be sure all these relationships in connection with the Moon alter fairly quickly. Already in April of next year one node will be in Aries, the other in Libra. (It is the actual constellations that are always meant.)

Before we go further into the matter of the nodes themselves we must bear in mind the principle of the eclipses as they present themselves in a purely external manner. And as a matter of fact something very different underlies the eclipses of the Moon and those of the Sun.

Since the orbits of the Sun and Moon differ by five degrees, an occultation of the Sun by the Moon—in other words, an eclipse of the Sun—can only take place either when it is new Moon, or when both are in the neighborhood of one of the nodes. If the Sun in its yearly path has already separated itself from the node or if it is still too far away from it (the limits amount to eighteen degrees for an eclipse of the Sun and twelve degrees for an eclipse of the Moon) then the Moon's orbit and the Moon itself upon it ascends either above or below the Sun. Thus no occultations can take place. That is what happens at every new Moon. A conjunction takes place but not an occultation. Only in the neighborhood of the nodes can the disks of the Sun and Moon lie one over the other. One can observe this from Figure 14.

That portion of the ecliptic is depicted (See Figure 15.) in which the eclipses of the first period of this year take place. The ascending node is given for four consecutive points of time, a, b, c, d, in its retrograde movement, corresponding to the [a, b, c, d] positions of the Sun on June 3, June 17, July 17, and August 15.

On May 19 there is a total eclipse of the Sun (the node would then lie somewhat to the left of [the Sun]. The orbit of the Moon at this point

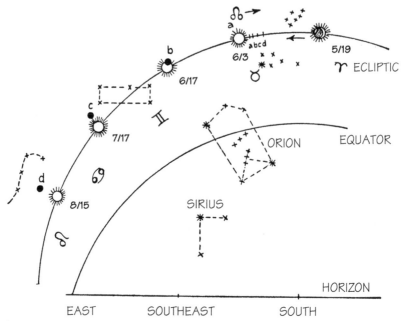

Figure 15

already passes rather sharply below the orbit of the Sun, for the Moon is still ahead [west] of the ascending node. That an obscuration, and even a total one, can nevertheless come about is due only to the fact that the Moon in these days is nearest to Earth (in "perigee") and its disk is at its greatest so that this, at least for a short time, can cover the Sun. On Earth the eclipse takes place in the neighborhood of the South Pole and is—even as a partial eclipse—scarcely visible in inhabited regions.

Fourteen days later, on June 3, is full Moon. The Sun then lies directly at the ascending node (a), the Moon opposite to it at the descending node in Scorpius, and there is a *total eclipse of the Moon.* (The Moon in this case could naturally not be represented in the Figure).

Again fourteen days later, on June 17, there is a new Moon. Now, however, only quite a slight partial eclipse of the Sun takes place. The Moon's orbit rises, and the Moon moves in a sloping direction across the outermost edge of the Sun's disk.

At the next position on July 17, the Sun is already too far from the node, and the Moon no longer comes in contact with it. By the time of the next new Moon, August 15, the difference is still greater. Not until the Sun has arrived at the other node, in November, does an eclipse occur again. The Sun crosses this node on November 23, the new and full

Moon of that month (November 12 and 27) are so placed that only two, not three, eclipses can arise. Of these five eclipses only the partial eclipse of the Sun on November 12 will be visible in central Europe, and the total eclipse of November 27, also in northern and western Europe.

The eclipses of the Sun and Moon of a given year are always repeated in the same order, and with only a difference of ten days, on the same dates, eighteen years later. The five eclipses of this year correspond therefore to those of the year 1910, but instead of May 19, on May 9, instead of June 3, on May 21, and so on. Only this present year's new Moon of June 17 did not on July 7 in that year bring about an occultation.

We will go into this extremely interesting fact of the arising and passing away of eclipses next time. There we have the noted Saros period already known to the Chaldeans, which is closely connected with the retrograde movement of the nodes. Very much of extraordinary importance is bound up with the Saros period, of which, however we will also speak next time.

In order to describe the eclipses and explain them in an external sense we must bring into consideration an element of spatial perspective, which we otherwise do not need to use. In the case of an eclipse it is a question of the Sun, Moon, and Earth standing before one another in space and even of the casting of a shadow by one body upon another. If before we were able to sketch the orbits of the Moon and the Sun on the vault of heaven and to show their points of intersection, the nodes, now, in thinking about the eclipse itself we must keep in mind that the path of the Moon lies *within* the path of the Sun. The Moon is nearer to Earth than the Sun. This is a radial instead of a spherical point of view. These two points of view the eclipses demand already manifest to us something of their twofold nature.

In external reality an eclipse of the Moon actually comes about through the Moon's entry into that cone of shadow which the Earth casts into space from the side turned away from the Sun. The old Greek astronomers already knew this explanation of eclipses, indeed they inferred the spherical shape of the Earth from the outline of the shadow on the Moon. One finds this shadow cone in the ordinary astronomical works depicted for the most part purely diagrammatically, without considering the relative sizes, because these cannot be reproduced on an ordinary printed page. The cone that the Earth must cast into space as shadow is indeed extraordinarily long and narrow in relation to the diameter of the Earth, if one works with the calculations usually given for the distances of Moon and Sun. If one takes the diameter of the Earth as one-half inch the shadow would be about four and one-half feet long, while the Sun on the opposite side would have to be thought of as 500 feet distant. At about one-third of its length, the shadow is intersected by the Moon's orbit. The middle points of the Sun, Earth, and Moon lie in a straight line that must meet the heavenly vault in the neighborhood of the Moon's node. Then the eclipse of the Moon comes about—otherwise the Moon's orbit at full Moon passes just over or just under the shadow. At the spot where the Moon at the eclipse comes in contact with the shadow, the shadow has only a breadth of two to three full Moon disks. In figure 16 the Earth's shadow is diagrammatically represented but approximately in the right proportion, at any rate as far as the Moon's orbit, and the last two-thirds of it are indicated by the dotted line.

It is certainly justifiable to question whether this shadow really exists, a shadow that, when there is no eclipse of the Moon, actually falls within "empty space." Is a shadow conceivable that would fall into nothingness? In the environment nearest of all to the Earth, in the air encircling the Earth, it causes the phenomenon that for us is night inasmuch as it manifests itself in the atmosphere. The Earth revolves in about twenty-four hours under the cone of the shadow and the cone itself would completely revolve once in a year. Beyond the Earth the shadow can actually only be present as an elemental creation, as a place of abode for spiritual beings of darkness. Only when the Moon enters into its sphere does the shadow become in a way embodied, because it can then fall upon a material body. So then, in these considerations we find already indicated those things that will later be said about the spiritual beings of the eclipse.

In eclipses of the Sun, the Moon places itself before the Sun's disk and now itself produces a shadow that can touch Earth with its furthermost point. In the case of a total eclipse one may see this shadow, which can have a breadth of over 140 miles, pass across the surface of Earth with great swiftness from west to east, covering everything in the darkness of night. (In a drawing [Figure 17], this Moon shadow would be only a thin line. Here

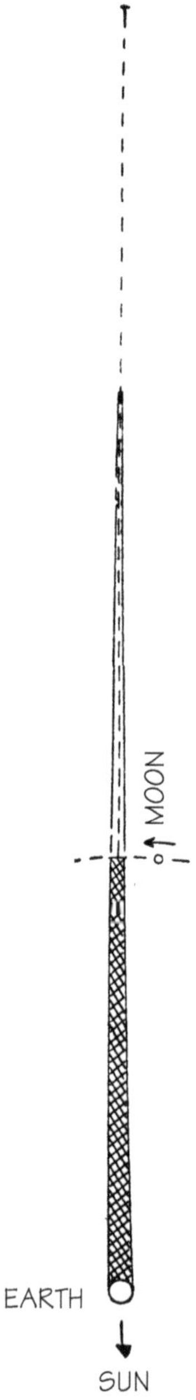

Figure 16

MOON

EARTH

SUN

also it would be possible to attribute reality to it only within Earth's atmosphere.) If the Moon does not pass over the middle of the Sun's disk, but somewhat higher or lower, then only an incomplete obscuration occurs—a partial eclipse.

Each total eclipse of the Sun is moreover only a partial eclipse in those countries that do not lie in the central zone, but lie to the left and right of the shadow belt. At times, if the Moon stands somewhat farther from Earth (that is, in apogee), the cone of the shadow is unable to reach the Earth with its apex, but floats as it were over the Earth. This is a so-called annular eclipse instead of a total eclipse.

Here perspective or parallax play a significant role. It is different in the case of eclipses of the Moon. If the Moon comes completely in contact with Earth's shadow the eclipse is a total one, and is so for all parts of Earth that have the Moon above their horizon—a considerable part of the whole surface of the Earth. Eclipses of the Sun are a much more localized phenomenon.

Thus do eclipses appear to external observation. That something other than the merely external phenomenon comes to pass through them has already been indicated by Rudolf Steiner in 1910 in *The Mission of Folk Souls* (lecture 9):

> When the ancient man of the north wanted to make comprehensible what he saw during an eclipse of the Sun (in the time of the ancient clairvoyance man naturally saw differently from the way he sees today with the use of the telescope) he chose the image of the wolf pursuing the Sun, and in the moment when the wolf reaches it, the eclipse is produced. This stands in innermost harmony with facts. . . . The materialistic man of today will say: But this is superstition; there is no wolf pursuing the Sun. . . . But, there is something which seems to the occultist much more of a superstition—that is, the belief that an eclipse of the Sun arises because the Moon places itself in front of the Sun. For the external vision it is quite correct, just as much as the wolf is correct for the astral vision. Indeed the astral outlook is even more correct than that which you can find in books, for that is still more subject to error.

Figure 17

This passage does not speak merely of what occurs among the heavenly bodies moving in space, but of what goes on in the *spheres* when an eclipse approaches.[1]

For the eclipses are indeed "such transitional phenomena that stand midway between the purely physical-cosmic and the cosmic-spiritual" (lecture, June 25, 1922, *Goetheanum* 6:14). They deny the spiritual in favor of the external spatial. Space—as we on Earth (where it is a legitimate phenomenon of earthly existence) believe ourselves to know it, is to a degree drawn into the cosmos by the eclipses. The shadow, be it from Moon or Earth, and otherwise only present in the elementary conditions, condenses to a visible form.

We know indeed from the lecture just been quoted that all this has its good basis and its necessity in the universe. There must also be safety valves for the evil that lies in will and thought, and these are the eclipses—the absence for a longer or shorter period of the light of Sun or Moon. Since evil has been admitted into the world through divine decree, the eclipses are also something laid down in the divine plan. One might almost say: as the "world of finished work" was set in place the divine wisdom could just as easily have arranged things so that there should be no eclipses. If the Moon were a little farther from Earth than it is, and its disk could never entirely cover the disk of the Sun, there could never be a total eclipse of the Sun. (At the same time, however, humanity would then have had to be quite differently constituted.) Inasmuch as the eclipses occur, a way is left open into the cosmos for the spirits of darkness and evil in such degree and place as may be needful. But the good, that spirit whom we call the Holy Spirit, lives neither in space nor in time. And in the Whitsuntide festival we have the remembrance of that experience which lifted the disciples of Christ for a little while out of space and time.

Let us then consider the three festivals that early Christianity has placed at the beginning of the year—counting from the winter solstice when the Sun is in its lowest position. The Jesus-child was born into earthly space in the depths of winter. The Earth lay there as a star in the cosmos, and upon it, as it were, the whole cosmos directed its gaze. The Christmas festival reveals to us all that is spatial permeated by the

---

1. See also the comments in L. Kolisko's "The Sun-eclipse of June 29th, 1927," in the *Goetheanum* No. 5, January 29th, 1928.

cosmic forces of the Father streamed through by the Sun, but only as midnight Sun.

In the Easter event space is already overcome. The Christ is risen, he has conquered death, the Earth, space. Even the remains of a spatial nature, the holy corpse, has vanished from the tomb. But the Risen One appeared to the disciples here and there in a body that is like the physical-space body and yet not like it. Then begins his working in time. For the further evolution of the Christ impulse it is not space that has meaning, not even space of the Earth within which Christ Jesus has lived. Christ has died for human beings of every race and can only be followed in time, as his impulse spreads itself over Earth. The establishment of the Easter festival is also arranged according to the principles of time, as we have already described.

But the Whitsuntide festival is the remembrance and continuous renewal of that event which in the deepest sense is neither a space nor yet a time event. Here the human being is actually on the other side of space, and here shines the Holy Spirit from beyond space and time into the human spirit. As tongues of fire, as lightning—and lightning has no time and rends space asunder—there streamed from the souls of the Apostles that which the Holy Ghost poured out over them. The Holy Ghost is that spirit which does not live in the material and is therefore holy, that is to say healing, and works in human beings in a health-giving way. He is that spirit of whom Christ said that he could only come when the Christ himself had passed through the Mystery of Golgotha, and through having overcome death and space, had again united himself with the Father. And those who were present when the Holy Ghost could for the first time manifest himself in the world heard the Apostles speak "to every person in their own tongue." Space was overcome, for each was at the same time in his or her own country, at home. Time was overcome, for the Mystery of Golgotha stood as a directly experienced event before the souls of the Apostles. From beyond time and space there came shining in what, for that time and for all future time, the Holy Ghost had to say to humankind.

It is fitting to think these thoughts in a time that began with an eclipse of the Sun on December 24 of last year and also has the Whitsuntide festival falling in a period of eclipses.

June 1928

More About Eclipses

The Saros Period

IT WAS STATED LAST TIME how the Moon's nodes, those points of intersection of the orbits of Sun and Moon, which at the present time are in Taurus and Scorpius, pass once around the entire zodiac in eighteen years, seven months, and a few days. These periods play a part in each human life. For the nodes are not to be conceived as merely mathematical points, as points where the extended plane of the Moon's orbit intersects with the apparent path of the Sun, as the astronomy of today would have to express it. Rather they are a kind of gateway for the astral—astrally sensitive points in the natal chart of every human being. Steiner has pointed out that each time the nodes return to the place where they had been at someone's birth: when a person is eighteen years, seven months old; thirty-seven years, two months old, and so on, that person is then especially susceptible in their subconscious to the astral world, which can manifest itself through remarkable dreams, and so on. The nights we live through in these times are the most important of our lives. Only, for the most part, people "sleep away" these important periods because they are not made aware of them. (See lecture of April 16, 1920, in Steiner's *Mystery of the Universe*.) In the case of Goethe, who experienced such a period fully four times, the influence of the transition of the nodes can be shown in a most interesting manner from his biography, from the diaries, letters, and conversations. It is a good thing for anthroposophists to endeavor to find such points of time in their own life. One may perhaps be able to find them for the half-periods too—after every nine years, three and one-half months, when the ascending and descending nodes have exchanged places in the zodiac. These periods moreover, have their reflection in the so-called nutation of the Earth axis, which we shall speak of next time.

A certain shorten-
ing of the revolution
of the nodes gives the
Saros period, which
has to do with the
recurrence of the
eclipses. Let us sup-
pose that there has
been a total eclipse.
Sun, Moon, and node
(S, M, N) have stood
very closely together
in a certain place in
the zodiac.

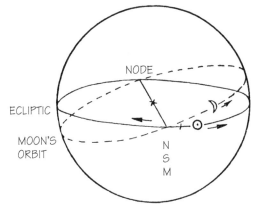

Figure 18

Now each of the three continues its respective movement. The Sun
passes around once in about a year, the Moon in a month, and the node
in the opposite direction in eighteen years, seven months. It happens
that shortly before the node has traveled back to its former place, after
eighteen years and ten days, it meets with the Sun again, and the Moon
too is again on that spot (meanwhile the Moon has gone round 223
times, the sun 18 times), so that the former eclipse repeats itself, under
practically the same conditions at point N. There have, of course, been
eclipses of the Sun and Moon as often as they come together with the
nodes at some point or another of the zodiac. At the Saros period, however, the distance of the Sun from the node, the position of the Moon,
the magnitude of the phase of the eclipse correspond to the relationship
of eighteen years ten days before—almost exactly correspond. On this
account also the further eclipses that have gone before or followed after
the first one repeat themselves in the same order. It was already pointed
out in the last Letter how the series of eclipses from 1924 to 1928 correspond, with very minor exceptions, to the series of eclipses in the years
from 1906 to 1910, and also to the eclipses between 1942 and 1946, with
a difference of only ten or eleven days. There is therefore a succession of
Sun and Moon eclipses that takes place over a period of eighteen years,
ten days, and then, after a long interval, repeats itself.

It is precisely in this rule that one can experience once more the
wonderful living quality of the cosmic "mechanism." For all these relationships "almost" hold good, and the slight difference that occurs in

every case brings about variety in what otherwise would be uniformity. A certain eclipse returns under almost the same conditions after eighteen years, ten days (it may also be eleven days depending on whether there are four or five leap years). Through these ten days being added to the eighteen years the Sun has traveled about ten degrees further, and therefore the eclipse does not take place exactly in the same place in the heavens but ten degrees to the east. Moreover, it is not exactly ten or eleven days, but ten days, seven hours, forty-two minutes. The new eclipse will take place on the given day plus seven hours, forty-two minutes—in other words almost a third of a day later. That means, since Earth has completed another third of a rotation around its axis, the eclipse (especially if it is a typically localized eclipse of the Sun) does not take place on its return in the same region of Earth as the first time, but in another region that lies a third of the Earth's circumference to the west. The next one will take place about two-thirds of the Earth's circumference further west. The third recapitulation, the fourth eclipse occurring after fifty-four years, thirty-three days, is the first to fall almost in the same region as the first, moved, though, somewhat to north or south. Hence arises a series of three eclipses and the Saros period of fifty-four years, thirty-three days. However, the new eclipse after one Saros period does not fall at exactly the same distance from the node as the former one, but moves gradually—quite slowly—from east to west toward the node and passes it. Indeed because of this it comes about that in course of time a new Moon falls so near a node that a quite slight obscuration of the Sun's disk is possible. The eclipse makes its appearance on the first occasion as a quite small partial eclipse, taking its place then further in the Saros succession. The next time, after eighteen years, ten days, it will likewise be partial, but already slightly larger. After six to ten Saros periods it will have moved so near to the node that it appears as a total eclipse. Then for the length of many centuries it shows itself as a total (possibly annular) eclipse. Every eighteen years it comes somewhat nearer to the node, then passes over it, until it becomes again merely partial and finally ceases to be an eclipse at all. Then it is merely a new Moon without occultation. A similar thing occurs with regard to the eclipses of the Moon except that the full Moon always has its position by the node opposite to the Sun.

These relationships can be followed easily if one looks at figure 15 in the last Letter. The eclipse of June 17 is one that is occurring for the very first time. It was not included in the series of 1910 (as has already been indicated) and was "born," so to speak, as an eclipse on that date. In eighteen years, ten days the distance of the Sun and Moon to the node will be a little less than at present, and the node, as stated before, will lie ten degrees further toward Gemini. Because of this the disks of the Sun and Moon will be able to cover each other somewhat more fully. Not until the twenty-second century will this eclipse take place near enough to the node to be total.

Or let us trace the eclipse of May 19. It lies quite to the right of the node, which means that it is moving away out of the eclipse range. As a matter of fact it was total *for the last time* on May 19. Next time, on May 30, 1946, it will be partial and then diminish continuously until August 3, 2054, when it will cease to exist altogether as an eclipse. If we trace this eclipse back, in 936 A.D. it was an annular eclipse (a kind of total eclipse, but with the Moon's disk being too small) and has therefore been in existence for 1,000 years. It was "born" quite to the left of the ascending node on June 24, 792 A.D., and will "die," as has been stated, on August 3, 2054.

We therefore have in the eclipse period of this year the rare event of a Sun eclipse that is newly arising and of another that is ceasing to be total. The life span of a total eclipse of the Sun is about 1,200 years, while that of an eclipse of the Moon is somewhat shorter.

The coming eclipse of the Sun on November 12 is again a partial one because of its having passed beyond its period of totality (which lasted from 1171 to 1874 but was actually annular), and it now appears afresh as a partial eclipse. The first time it was partial was in 1892.

One can picture to oneself all this life and movement of the eclipses yet more distinctly if one follows them not in the heavens, but on the Earth, especially in the case of the eclipses of the Sun, which have a very defined path. These come about because the Moon's shadow draws a belt [or line] over the Earth, describing a path on the surface of the Earth, during a period of almost four hours, with the speed [greater than that] of an express train. The totality itself at a given place on Earth can last at most for eight minutes. After eighteen years this path comes back, lying a third of the Earth's circumference further on, and after fifty-four years it is almost parallel to the first path.

Now it is a fact that a newly arising eclipse of the Sun—as for example that of June 17—always strikes Earth first at one of the poles:

at the North Pole in the case of an eclipse that occurs by the ascending node—the Dragon's head; at the South Pole when it occurs by the descending node—the Dragon's tail. It also always reaches its first totality in the polar regions. It then gradually descends, comes in course of centuries nearer to the equator (it takes place then by the node) and travels over the other half of the Earth in order to end its life by the opposite pole. Applied to the solar eclipses of the present year we can have a quite concrete representation.

> *May 19*. Originated June 24, 792 A.D. at the North Pole. Total now for the last time and therefore in its total phase taking place entirely in the region of the South Pole.

> *June 17*. For the first time, therefore occurring entirely in the Arctic ocean.

> *November 12*. Originated April 17, 991 A.D. at the South Pole (having taken place at the descending node) and already in the phase of partiality, and therefore in its greatest phase taking place in northern regions. In the slighter phases of its partiality it still stretches far over Asia and is also to be seen in our regions at sunrise as a very slight eclipse.

The eclipse of the Moon on June 3 lies near the node and is therefore more or less in the middle of its life, in the center of its period of totality. It was not visible in our regions simply because the Moon at the time of passing through Earth's shadow had not yet risen: its visibility lay west of North and South America.

> *November 27*. This eclipse of the Moon rather resembles the one just mentioned only in that the Sun lies by the descending node. Also total, it is at the middle of its life period, already lying more to the north. There is only a short period of visibility—at least for western and northern Europe, just before the Moon sets. It is not visible at all in central Europe.

The paths of the eclipses of the Sun on Earth—as they are drawn by the point of the Moon's shadow cone grazing Earth—are most wonderful. The threefold Saros period [of 54 years] will be sketched here three times [solid lines in Figure 19] for the eclipse of the Sun that took place last year on June 29, which many will still remember. It was total in northern England and Scandinavia, and followed a path through the North Polar

Sea and the northeastern part of Siberia. It is still comparatively young, having arisen first as a partial eclipse in 1639 and as a total eclipse in 1891. Thus it still always takes place in northern regions.

In the diagram the North Pole is the center of the circle, and the circle itself represents Earth's equator. The line from the North Pole to zero degrees is the Greenwich meridian.

The three eclipses [54 years apart] of each the three Saros periods between 1891 and 2035 are depicted. The eclipses of each period are denoted by a different kind of line.

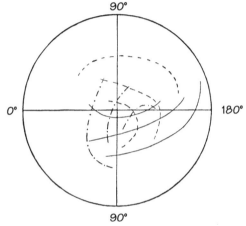

Figure 19

One sees the gradual descent from the North Pole to the equator, from which in later centuries a further descent to the South Pole will follow.

We see the Earth to a certain extent spread over in space and time with a marvelous network of paths of eclipses, so that everywhere at some time evil may have the opportunity to work out its effects.

Every year a succession of eclipses moves from the North Pole to the South Pole, and another succession (that of the descending nodes) mounts up in the opposite direction. These paths in the course of the centuries are written into the Earth in manifold lines. Indeed, one gets the impression by following these drawings that one has to do with the imprint or footprints of definite beings of the eclipse, which live out their birth, their life, and death in quite a definite way from pole to pole. A single eclipse in its Saros recapitulations covers Earth with a succession of beautiful lines, as shown above in the case of the eclipse that appeared in 1927. Another, such as the eclipse of May 19, which has just passed away, left really scratchy brush marks on Earth's surface. Again, others have their Saros periods lying in such a way that every two eclipse paths intersect in the form of a crescent moon. (See figure 20. The numbers denote the year of the eclipse.)

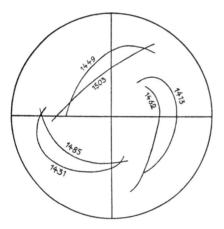

Figure 20

In the scientific literature of the nineteenth century, which is so rich in admirable research material, is the outstanding work of Oppolzer, *Canon of Eclipses,* in which all these relationships are represented both in calculation and diagram. Compare also F. K. Gunzel, *Special Canon of the Eclipses of the Sun and the Moon.*

Altogether there are about seventy eclipses, thirty of the Moon, and forty of the Sun. [See Notes on the Text.] The eclipses of the Moon generally give a less individualized impression than the eclipses of the Sun. Nor do they describe such definite paths, but rather cast a shadow over a whole portion of the Earth. We can understand this if we look upon the eclipses as "safety-valves": The eclipses of the Sun for the evil *will* that streams out from Earth into the cosmos, while the eclipses of the Moon allow the evil *thoughts* from the universe to flow into Earth.

In the lecture on sunlight and moonlight already referred to *(Goetheanum* 6.13–15), it is said that the ancient initiates gave their questions over to the cosmos at sunrise when it was new Moon. An eclipse of the Sun likewise happens at new Moon and indeed always at a part of the Earth where the Sun is actually rising. The priests of the mysteries awaited the answer at full Moon. There we are reminded of the eclipses of the Moon, that can only take place at full Moon. In this sense we see how eclipses betokened to the old initiates an interruption in the course of their duties. The act of will that is contained in the question could not take place at the time of a solar eclipse and the illumination of thought that should bring the answer could not take place at an eclipse of the Moon. Thus we understand why people in earlier times, before the advent of "abstract science," used to trace the entry of the eclipses so earnestly. Here perhaps also lies the real foundation of the tragic story that was always related in popular works of the two Chinese astronomers Hi and Ho, who had neglected to correctly announce an eclipse of the Sun of 2154 B.C. to the emperor of the celestial empire. According to one account this was because they had drunk too much, according to another because they had miscalculated; in any case they were both beheaded. If they were executed because of a miscalculation the sentence was certainly unjust if one considers that right up to the last century it was not possible to calculate to the minute the entry of the eclipses, and that even today there is still always an uncertainty of several seconds. The extraordinary mobility and changeableness of the Moon's path never allows it to be confined in fixed formulae.

During an eclipse of the Sun the evil in the will impulse of human beings leaves Earth without being consumed by sunlight and passes out into the universe in this condition, where it then does further harm. But much that belongs to the kingdom of evil takes place on Earth in the strange livid light that precedes the darkness of the total eclipse. Out of the creations of human technology—as Rudolf Steiner has related—fearful demons arise during the eclipse, thus showing the true nature of what is magically confined and bewitched in our present-day machinery. And during an eclipse of the Moon, evil persons are given the opportunity to let themselves be inspired by the "thoughts of devils."

We see from all this how it is possible through spiritual science to realize the importance of the sentence that we have already quoted: "But one learns then also how rightly to value such transition-phenomena which, one might say, stand midway between the purely physical-cosmic and the cosmic-spiritual."

July 1928

The Precession of the Equinoxes

IN ADDITION TO ALL THE MOVEMENTS in our solar system that we have already considered, we must turn our attention to yet another, which from the anthroposophical point of view has very great significance. It is the retrogression of the vernal point on the ecliptic, which is called a "precession," although this movement, like the movement of the Moon's nodes, is a backward one.

This motion can be described in many ways from a purely astronomical standpoint. It belongs to the great rhythms of the universe since it completes itself in a time period that according to occult tradition is 25,920 years. Present-day astronomy, on the basis of its calculations, gives a somewhat different number. This is because it was regarded as a cosmic rhythm (in the sense that was given in Letter 2) and also because of a somewhat different reckoning of the year from that of today.

As the Sun passes annually through the zodiac it crosses the celestial equator twice—at the beginning of spring and at the beginning of autumn. It is on the intersection points of the ecliptic and the equator that this comes about. The vernal and autumnal equinoxes, when day and night are equal, correspond in a certain way to the nodes on the Moon's orbit. (For the other planets the corresponding points are also called nodes.) The Sun reaches a point of intersection on March 21 (according to the [Church] division of the year that has been in effect since 1582). The beginning of the zodiac is reckoned from this point, so that the statement "a star or planet has a longitude of 300 degrees" means that measured on the ecliptic it is 300 degrees (five-sixths of the circumference of the circle) distant from the point of intersection of the Sun; from the vernal equinox. [See Notes on the Text for Letters 5 and 7.]

Now this beginning point does not remain the same; here again there is movement, variability. When the Sun has passed through the zodiac, or the ecliptic, in the course of a year, it no longer finds the vernal point on the same spot, but rather slightly advanced, so that the year is actually shortened. The astronomical beginning of spring, or the crossing of the equator, occurs about twenty minutes earlier each year, or, expressed in spatial measurement, the first point of spring lies 50" (fifty seconds of arc) to the west on the ecliptic. In 72 years this point moves through a whole degree (1°)—and in the course of 2,160 years through

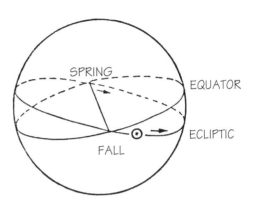

Figure 21

a whole sign of the zodiac. Our entire cultural life depends on this slight shortening of the year by twenty minutes.

It is not just this mathematical point, or the mathematical line that joins the two points of intersection, that moves its position, but it is the equator, Earth's equator, that extended as a plane becomes the celestial equator—that causes the revolution and thus lets the line of the equinoxes revolve through the ecliptic. We can therefore equally well trace what goes on by observing Earth as by observing the heavens.

The Earth can be said to have the motion of a top. Its axis (the axis of the equator) describes a cone around the ecliptic axis in the space of 25,920 years. One can easily make this movement comprehensible on an ordinary globe of the Earth. The axis of the ecliptic, which has its north pole in the constellation of the Dragon (see letter 5), cuts the Earth at the highest and lowest points (according to the position in which the globe is habitually mounted). In other words, it is to be thought of as a vertical line, and the plane of the ecliptic projected on to the Earth is thought of as a horizontal plane. (That is, naturally, a kind of convention, "vertical" and "horizontal" always having only a relative meaning.)

One lets the axis of the equator, which is easily distinguishable on the globe, describe a revolution, a cone, around this vertical direction, without the Earth rotating around the axis at the same time. One therefore disregards the daily rotation, but lets the whole Earth carry

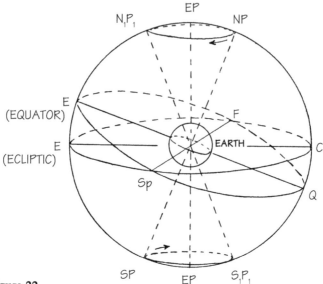

Figure 22

out from east to west the top-like movement that has been described. In reality, the Earth needs 25,920 years for a single revolution of this kind. At the same time it is clear that the Earth's equator also shows this movement; it rises and sinks to a certain extent while the horizontal plane that passes through the center of the Earth and corresponds to the plane of the ecliptic remains unchanged. Thus we only have to transfer these terrestrial relationships to the visible heavens in order to arrive at the motion of the celestial equator (EQ) in regard to the ecliptic (EC), or likewise of the equator-poles (NP–SP) in order to obtain the ecliptic-pole (EP). This means for the star-world that the axis NP-SP will describe a circle in the heavens in 25,920 years around the Dragon point, the ecliptic-pole. After half this period of time it will have reached N_1P_1-S_1P_1 and both the North Pole and the South Pole will point to quite a different star. Our present pole star has not always had this function, as we have indicated already in Letter 5. If one looks for both the poles in the sky, in the Little Bear and in the Dragon, one will be able to picture to oneself the circle that will be described by the pole of the equator in the course of thousands of years. If NP in the above diagram points to the present Pole Star, then N_1P_1 lies not far from Vega. This is because in 10,000 years this will be the pole star. At the same time the vernal equinox will then lie in Virgo.

From Rudolf Steiner's many lectures and explanations we know that the duration of the ancient culture periods was measured by means of this progression of the vernal point. If the zodiac is divided into twelve equal parts, each "sign" is passed through in 2,160 years. For this space of time the "Taurus age" of the Egypto-Chaldean civilization lasted, and for the same length of time the "Aries age" of the Greco-Roman civilization; and today we live in the age of Pisces. In the first edition of Steiner's *Calendar of the Soul,* these relationships are indicated in simple but momentous words:

> During one month the position of the Sun can be viewed within one constellation of the zodiac. After the passage of a year the same positions more or less repeat themselves. This expression "more or less" is justified because in the course of progressing time an alteration of positions takes place. If we gazed upon the rising sun in March in former centuries, we also were gazing at the constellation of Aries; today, we would be gazing at Pisces.

Just as we connect a letter to its sound we can connect the position of the Sun in a constellation of the zodiac to our experience of the changing process of the universe. In the ordinary course of the year the impressions that the different months can bring us change relatively quickly. It is because they may also be experienced in their inner nature that Rudolf Steiner's *Calendar of the Soul* has been given to us.

In quite another and more powerful way the experiences of the human being are different in the various periods of civilization. They come to expression only through the different incarnations through which one passes in the different periods. Whereas the Sun passes in its yearly course through the zodiac—Aries, Taurus, Gemini, and so on—the human being at each incarnation finds the Sun at the beginning of spring in a different constellation, or at any rate at another point in the same constellation, figuring backward, Taurus, Aries, Pisces, and so on. While this remains in deep unconsciousness for the vast majority of humankind, wise people have always recognized the signs in the heavens. It can be proved that in the old periods of civilization they were led through a kind of mystery act. This could not happen in our age (which began in the fifteenth century, according to this method of calculation) because the previous 1,500 years were a time in which the mysteries were absent.

From the "letter" that is inscribed in the heavens at the vernal equinox, we may come closer to the reality, to that actual occurrence of which the ancients were really aware, and to which they gave witness in their myths. Without the movement of the vernal point there could be no real historical progress for humanity. An age *must* be different when at the moment of spring it is the Pisces forces, or the Aries forces, or the Taurus forces that mingle with those of the Sun. (It is in the end an actual movement of Earth itself that brings all this about.) For the human being the precessional movement is something like the constantly changing view from the window of a train. Without precession we would always remain in the same place historically, and the successive incarnations would offer nothing new to us. To the continual sameness of the daily rotation, to the yearly revolution with its but slight variation, is added this remarkable movement of the precession, which again in a way represents the retarding of the Sun in relation to the stars, just as the yearly motion interposes with a retarding effect upon the daily motion. The Sun that rises on March 21 with a star in Pisces will after a long time—several centuries—rise together with a star in Aquarius. Only some days later does it appear on the horizon together with its former fellow traveler, the star in Pisces.

In ancient times the spiritual significance of precession was undoubtedly known as well as its numerical aspect. For the number 25,920 was named the Platonic number. One remembers the secret teachings of Plato, who brought the original Egypto-Babylonian cosmology to Greece. Precession was then discovered from quite an external astronomical source in about 150 B.C., with no apparent connection between this discovery and the mystery tradition. The Alexandrian astronomer Hipparchus found, simply from the comparison of his observation of the longitudes of stars (their distance from the vernal point measured on the ecliptic) with that of older astronomers, that all the distances had increased in the course of centuries and all to the same amount. He inferred from this a backward motion of the beginning of the ecliptic, the vernal point, by which the distance of the star from the original point of calculation must gradually increase.

Because of the precession's slow movement it was possible only many centuries later to discover how great—or rather how small—it actually was. From the Platonic number (which was not directly mentioned by Plato, but can only be inferred from a very obscure passage in the eighth

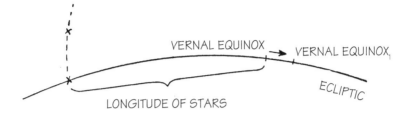

Figure 23

book of his *Republic*) it certainly follows that the alteration must be one degree in seventy-two years (25,920 ÷ 360 = 72). Hipparchus appraised the motion at one degree in one hundred years. Ptolemy also (120 A.D.) made his calculations with this figure. The Arabian astronomers of the early Middle Ages were the first to arrive at better numbers. Copernicus brought forward a whole series of calculations for precession that he regarded as altering in the course of time, and that he placed at one degree in eighty-five and one-half years for his own time. It is only very gradually that the extent of precession has been more accurately known, and then scientific observation has returned almost exactly to the number known to antiquity.

This scientific astronomical discovery of precession had a peculiar fate. It was very strongly opposed and denied especially by all those who were engaged not merely in exoteric astronomy but in the astrology that flourished vigorously at the close of the Greek age. That the beginning of the zodiac—the starting point for all calculations—should not always lie at the same place, that the *signs* Aries, Taurus, and so on could be severed from the *constellations*—these were not thoughts that people wanted to accept. They looked back to the Babylonian observations, thousands of years old, which had never shown any variation. Then finally, when a retrogressive movement of the vernal point was no longer to be doubted or denied, people clung to the hope that perhaps it was a matter of the vernal point merely moving back and forth within definite limits in a kind of pendulum movement.

Gradually scientific astronomy and traditional astrology parted company on this question of the precessional movement. Ptolemy himself was a noticeable example. As an astronomer he quite accepts the precession, is proud to increase in his star catalogue the star longitudes taken over from Hipparchus by the sum of the precessions from 150 B.C. to 125 A.D. (although still on the assumption of one degree in one hundred years). But at the same time he was also an astrologer, and wrote his *Tetrabiblos* quite in the spirit of the astrology of older times. There is no trace there of the precession. That is to say, Ptolemy takes the first degree of Aries as the beginning of the zodiac, although in his time the vernal equinox had already moved a few degrees into Pisces—a fact that comes out quite plainly in the star catalogue in his *Almagest*. So in his works we see him using "sign" on the one hand and "constellation" on the other—an error that has become far greater today since we have experienced a further 1,800 years of retrogression.

Just let us think for a moment what it means! The zodiac had long before been divided into twelve equal parts, each of thirty degrees, and these had been called Aries, Taurus, Gemini, and so on, and calculations had been made starting from Aries. The constellations themselves first received more or less defined outlines when people began to make the star catalogues. They were not equally divided in the zodiac, not always being thirty degrees, but ranging from twenty-one degrees to forty-three degrees. The equal division of the zodiac into twelve parts corresponds in a certain sense to the course of the year, if one considers this from the beginning of spring. The first month after the Sun has crossed the equator and is ascending is the Aries month (March 21–April 21), the second, the Taurus month (April 21–May 21), and so on. The beginning of summer is in Cancer, of autumn in Libra, and of winter in Capricornus. This held good more or less for the whole period of the height of Greek culture. At a certain point, however, when the vernal point passed from Aries to Pisces, this law ceased to have full validity—and we can place this point at the time of the Mystery of Golgotha. At that time the vernal point, retrogressing, passed over into Pisces. Yet, as already mentioned, the people persisted in denoting one degree of Aries as the beginning of the zodiac. (Indeed, even present-day astronomy does this, using Aries one degree as base point for calculating the coordinates of the ecliptic and the equator.) Today, however, the vernal point is already situated fairly near the end—or rather the beginning—of Pisces.

In this way a discrepancy has arisen that indeed points to something deeper. It was not by accident that Christ had to appear at the turning point of time, when the entry of spring left the "light" signs of the zodiac and entered the "dark" signs. (See my lecture in *Anthroposophical Movement,* 1925, nos. 19, 23, 27.) Whoever continues to describe Aries as the beginning of the zodiac really denies the Christ impulse and at the same time the spirituality of the starry heavens, the real spirituality that, for instance, emanates from Pisces and which is of quite a different nature from that which formerly emanated from Aries and still earlier from Taurus. When one denotes the first month of spring as the Aries month, one is considering only the annual course of the Sun and is continuing to give its twelve divisions the old names.

It is certainly undeniable in this regard that the old designations also have an ever-enduring justification, as for instance the name of the "Scales" for that month in which the Sun, now descending, crosses the equator at the autumnal equinox; or the "Crab" as the turning-point of summer, the summer solstice, and so on. We also find the old names used in this way by Rudolf Steiner, for instance in the poem "Twelve Moods" that many know from its presentation in eurythmy performances, or in the expression, "Since Mercury stood as evening star in the Scales," used at the laying of the foundation stone of the first Goetheanum. Mercury had crossed the equator on that day (September 20, 1913), shortly before the festive ceremony, and thus had a position of "equilibrium" between the upper and lower zodiac. This point, to be sure, is now lying in Virgo. But if it had been said, "Since Mercury stood in Virgo," then the whole idea of a standing at the point of balance would not have been expressed. [See also Letter 1, Year Two.]

One can perceive the distinct division that has actually entered our civilization through cosmic necessity. For in a quite definite sense Aries *is* actually the beginning of the zodiac, just as the head is the beginning of the human being. Therefore, too, came the wonderful balance of Greek culture, when the first point of spring was actually in Aries and the harmony between cosmic and earthly life was also depicted in the heavens. With the passing over into Pisces this harmony was destroyed. It *had* to be destroyed through the Christ impulse that had bound the cosmic forces to the Earth in a substantial spiritual way. No longer are Yahweh and the elohim the spiritual rulers of the human race; with the progressive backward motion of the vernal point, new forces were released. A short time after his earthly life Christ appeared under the symbol of a fish, while formerly he was venerated as the good shepherd bearing the lamb, indeed, as himself the Lamb of God.

Truly today the time has come, almost 2,000 years after the Mystery of Golgotha, for us to approach the question of the precession in earnest, and to consider the relation of the real *constellations* to the Sun, Moon, and planets, whereby we can observe the true workings of the constellations—which must no longer always be concealed under the obsolete designations. The anthroposophical *Calendar of the Soul* in its first edition confines itself entirely to the constellations as is clearly shown in the introduction and the accompanying illustrations. The little calendar issued this year by the Mathematical-Astronomical Section is based on the same principle. The difference is still more striking where it is actually visible in the sky, which cannot be with the Sun since its brightness obliterates the other stars. In farmers' calendars and also in the so-called astrological ephemerides one finds the position of the Moon and the planets completely given according to the old "signs." So one would find, for instance for Saturn, that since December 1926, he is in Sagittarius, whereas, as already noted in Letter 8, and as just a glance at the evening sky now can show, he is still actually in Scorpius. The same holds good for the Moon in the calendars with "astronomical" instructions; it's placement is wrong by almost a whole sign. This is because the retrogression of the first point of spring has brought this point and with it the whole circle of the year already more than twenty-six degrees away from the beginning of the constellation of Aries. In this way the human being is actually diverted from the contemplation of the starry heavens if the statements one reads in the calendar are never found to be in keeping with what one can actually observe. We ought indeed to have two expressions, one for the twelvefold division of the year's cycle, the signs, and one for the configurations of stars visible in the sky, the real constellations of the zodiac. The traditional names, Ram, Bull, and so on, have actually something of both in them. It is therefore so extraordinarily difficult to make a correct distinction between sign and constellation. On some night when the stars are clear one merely needs to recognize the Ram quite plainly outlined in the sky, its head turned to the rear, in order to see again the old imaginative pictures from which the constellations receive their names. The same is true for Leo the Lion, Sagittarius the Archer, and so on. On the other hand, the equinox always remains "the Scales" even if this point, as already stated, now lies in Virgo. We must really be clear that the names arise entirely from the old dream-like clairvoyance, and *all of them* are basically out of date for

our time. Modern humanity must experience the starry heavens differently—whether it is sign or constellation. Therefore the *Calendar of the
Soul* with its picture of the zodiac points in such a grand way to a new
spiritual sight. But in a certain sense the names for these pictures, the
new names for the starry heavens, are lacking! Perhaps if such names did
exist, the older names could be preserved for the "signs." But they would
have to be totally severed from the visible constellations and be only
the divisions of the ecliptic-equator. Thus, for instance, the designation
"Saturn in Sagittarius" would mean the following: Saturn stands two
signs (from sixty to ninety degrees) distant from the intersection with
the equator, and it is thus in the lower part of the zodiac, just before
the zodiac's lowest point. At the same time it must be mentioned that
Saturn is at that moment actually located in the *constellation* formerly
called Scorpius, which in the heavens has the appearance of a Scorpion
and is represented in the *Calendar of the Soul* as a kind of Janus head
with a double countenance of a man and a woman.

These things are spoken of here only in order to point, perhaps, to
a distant future perspective. To give new names would have meaning
only if they were universally accepted by civilized humankind. Otherwise one would merely pursue a cosmological sectarianism. There is no
doubt, however, that only what anthroposophy has to bring by way of
science—and particularly also of art and of inner spiritual experience
of the starry heavens—will allow the conditions to ripen that can some
day lead to appropriate naming, be it of the constellations, of the signs,
or of both.

With the next number the Astronomical Letters will have completed
the first year. It has not been possible to bring to a full conclusion the
course of study intended in these Letters, as may readily be seen. There
is still much to be said about important realms of astronomy, as, for
instance, the actual world of the stars. A second year will therefore follow, which at the same time can form a new beginning, inasmuch as
cosmological and astrological problems will be dealt with more com-
prehensively in a spiritual-scientific sense. Further details will be given
in the next number and then also in the *Newssheet.*

August 1928

More About the Precession of the Equinoxes
Nutation

WE HAVE SEEN that the movement of the vernal point, which is called precession, may be described from three perspectives:

1. The vernal point goes around the entire zodiac once in 25,920 years, the Sun passing from time to time into a different constellation of the zodiac at the entry of spring. This is an "apparent movement" from the standpoint of present-day astronomy.

2. During this same period, Earth's equator moves in such a way that its axis completes a revolution around the ecliptic axis. This is the top-like movement of the Earth looked on as an "actual" movement.

3. Also during this same period, the north pole of the Earth's axis describes a circle around the North Pole of the ecliptic, so that in the course of time different stars become the pole star. This too is an "apparent movement."

It is good to look for the corresponding points in the sky, too. The vernal point is found most easily from the great square in the constellation Pegasus, which lies in the east every night at this time of year—late summer. The vernal point is to be found to the right of the line that connects the two stars situated one above the other on the left of the square. It lies in a region where there are few stars and cannot be located by any nearby bright star.

To get an idea of the majestic slowness of the precessional movement, we can realize that the length of the side of the Pegasus star square (it is, of course, not a mathematical "regular square") is fifteen degrees, so that the vernal point would need over 1,000 years to travel a similar distance.

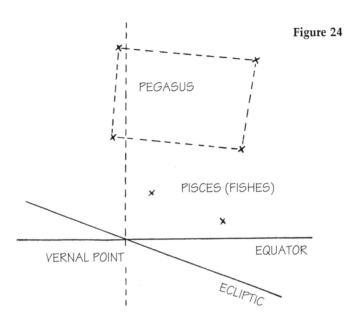

Figure 24

The autumnal point lies in Virgo, in the upper part of the constellation toward Leo, in one of the two wings with which she is often
represented. Roughly speaking, the point lies between Regulus and
Spica, nearer the latter. At the time of the Mystery of Golgotha it lay
quite near to Spica. This was, as already described, the star by which
Hipparchus discovered quite externally—from visible phenomena—the
precession of the vernal point. Since we are now approaching autumn,
the autumnal point—the autumnal equinox—is no longer easily found
in the evening twilight. Soon the Sun will be in conjunction with it.

The summer point, the high point of the Sun's path, from which the
Sun begins its descent [a few days before] St. John's Day (June 24), lies
right at the end of Gemini not far from the lower horn of the Bull. It comes
up in the early morning shortly before dawn, since the solstice is already
two months behind us. The winter point, the winter solstice, is to be found
in Sagittarius, in the constellation that in the short summer nights rises
above the southern horizon in its characteristic centaur form. It already
lies toward the edge of the constellation where Ophiuchus, the serpent
bearer, breaks into the zodiac and separates Sagittarius from Scorpius.

In connection with the significance of the vernal point to human
history, reference must here be made to something that otherwise can
easily lead to misunderstanding. The different culture-periods com-

mence, speaking astronomically, not at the beginning, but in the middle of the constellation with which they are then identified. (Refer to the following drawing, which gives, more or less sketchily, the outlines of the constellations.) In former times, the signs were also reckoned from the middle of the constellation—later from eight degrees onward. Hence the Sun somewhere around 4300 B.C. entered the constellation of Taurus from the Gemini side, and left it in 1800 B.C., whereas the Taurus age is reckoned from 2907 B.C. to 747 B.C. The vernal point from about the year 1800 B.C. to the Mystery of Golgotha was in the constellation of Aries, but the Aries age—the fourth post-Atlantean period lasted from 747 B.C. to 1413 A.D. There is then each time a period of transition, during which the Sun at the beginning of spring is already in the new constellation but cannot as yet fully draw its forces from that constellation.

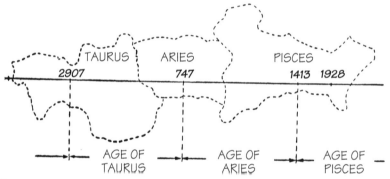

Figure 25

One may consider from this viewpoint the declining civilization of Rome. The Roman age actually reached its culmination with the event of Golgotha. Things on the Earth, however, still went along on the same old tracks for a long time because of the law of inertia (which, however, does not apply to the cosmic All) even when inwardly the old ways had already broken down. The whole of the Middle Ages up to the beginning of the fifteenth century must be considered as part of Greco-Latin culture, for Roman spiritual life still held sway in those years in spite of the spread of Christianity.

The knowledge of precession is linked in a remarkable way with the history of the calendar. At first the length of the year was fixed without precession. In that way the year was taken as somewhat too long (by about twenty minutes), for since the vernal point comes forward to meet the Sun, the duration of the year is shortened.

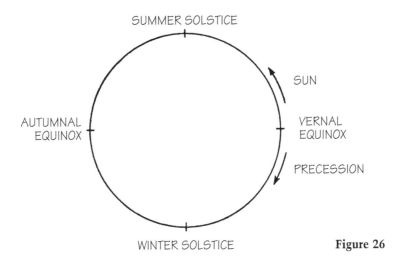

Figure 26

Now if one reckons without precession, then the beginning of spring each year comes a bit earlier, since astronomically it is not dependent on wind and weather, but on the moment of the Sun's crossing over the equator. That indeed happened in the Middle Ages, since people went by the Julian calendar, the calendar drawn up by Julius Caesar with the help of the Egyptian priest Sosigenes that was fully applied after the Council of Nicea. This used a year of 365 ¼ days, which was too long. Already at the time of the Council, 325 A.D., the entry of spring was on March 21 rather than on March 24; when at length in 1582 Pope Gregory XIII introduced a more accurate way of calculating time, which we still follow today, the first day of spring was March 11. The year was then so regulated that the vernal equinox must always fall on March 21, this being arrived at by means of omitting intercalary days at the turn of most of the centuries. From this one sees that the reckoning of time that had previously been an expression of divine lawfulness was increasingly transformed into a mere exercise in arithmetic. The intercalary days were inserted in such a way that the calculation tallied, and the very thing remains fixed that one wants to keep fixed fast, in this case, the beginning of spring on a certain date. In former times, at any rate in times preceding the Roman period, the intercalary days, weeks, or months were actually definite periods of a spiritual nature, in which the gods could manifest themselves to humankind. We have already spoken of this in the second Letter.

We will now pass over from the inexhaustible subject of precession to that of nutation. Here, in spite of the foreign-sounding name, we meet in fact with an old acquaintance. For the nutation is nothing but the reflection of the revolution of the Moon's nodes in a motion around the Earth's axis, exactly as the precession is a reflection (the word, naturally, is not used in a literal sense) of the revolution of the Earth's axis around the ecliptic axis, or the pole star around the Dragon point. But since the nutation movement is, in a sense, grafted onto the precessional movement of the Earth's axis, it can only be described in reference to it.

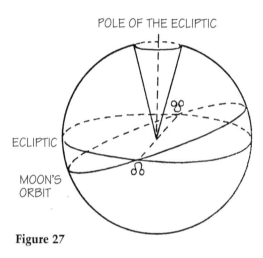

POLE OF THE ECLIPTIC

ECLIPTIC

MOON'S
ORBIT

Figure 27

Let us remember the retrogressive motion of the lunar nodes in eighteen years, seven months (Letter 9). Just as in the case of the precession, so here too we can pass from the description of the revolution of a point in the heavens (vernal point, or the Moon's nodes) to the revolution of one axis around another. It is, in fact, the axis of the Moon's orbit that in the stated time revolves around the ecliptic axis. The two axes enclose an angle of five degrees, just as the planes to which they are at right angles (the Moon plane and the ecliptic plane). The ecliptic axis meets the sky in the middle of the upper coil of the constellation of the Dragon, as was shown before (Letter 5). (This Dragon is not to be confused with the mythical dragon which, couched around the Moon's orbit, has its head in the ascending node and its tail in the descending node!) Now the axis of the Moon's orbit describes a small circle around the ecliptic pole in the course of eighteen years, seven months (18.6 years), while the Earth's axis, the equator pole, at a distance of 23 ½ degrees describes likewise a circle around the Dragon point, but in about 1,400 times the length of time, that is, in 25,920 years.

The accompanying diagram is a surface view of this. The small dotted circle indicates the positions to which the axis of the Moon's orbit points in the course of 18.6 years. The outer circle shows those points that one after another in the course of 25,920 years will be the pole star. This outer circle corresponds to the one marked $NP–N_1P_1$ of figure 22 in Letter 11, and the inner one to that in figure 29 of this Letter. The circles are actually the openings of two cones that are slipped one inside the other and whose apexes lie at the center of the Earth.

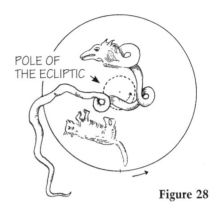

Figure 28

We should imagine clearly that the first circle will be traversed very many times faster than the second—almost 1,400 times as fast. The axis of the Moon's orbit revolves this many times faster than does Earth's axis. The one revolution manifests itself in the other in a peculiar way. While Earth's axis is engaged in the slow top-like motion that we have described, it is subject at the same time to a gentle oscillation, a slight trembling. It "nods," thus describing a light wave-like line instead of a pure circle. So the circle in the above drawing must also be represented as a sinuous line with 1,400 little "teeth." Each of these little waves or teeth actually represents a little circle, mirroring the inner circle again, which, owing only to the forward movement of Earth's axis, cannot become a complete circle, but merely a slight wave. This is what is called the nutation, the "nodding" of Earth's axis.

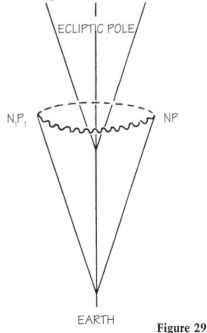

Figure 29

The movement, which is very slight—18.6 years being required to produce each tiny wave—was first discovered in the eighteenth century by Bradley, who simply proved the existence of such oscillations in the forward movement of the celestial north pole. Moreover, he soon found (in 1747) an explanation for this new movement of the Earth that must be added to all the previously mentioned movements. Since this is an oscillation of Earth's axis, we here find again a movement that we first saw as one of the orbit of the Moon to be in fact a movement of the Earth.

It was quite natural that Bradley could only give an explanation of this movement of the Earth on the lines of the Newtonian theory of gravitation, which was already highly elaborated at that time, and which had also been put forward as the explanation of the precession. The Moon's orbit, so Bradley said, takes up every possible position in relation to the Earth's orbit in 18.6 years, for its nodes move through the ecliptic in that time. The Moon therefore is always pulling, so to speak, upon the Earth from a different direction since it acts in a special way on the somewhat thickened "swelling" at the Earth's equator. (The Earth is to some extent flattened out at the poles; it has more *matter* toward the equator.) For that reason the Earth axis would begin to rotate around the Moon axis. Such a rotation would come about in 18.6 years were it not for the slight nodding or nutation that takes place in consequence of the already existing *top-like* movement of Earth—the precession.

This explanation is not put forward here so that people should especially rack their brains, but in order to call attention to something else. If one looks only at figure 29, one sees no reason there why the pole point, which moves in the outer circle that will travel around 1,400 times more slowly than the inner circle, has somehow or other to participate in the movement in this inner circle, has to "nod" with it. There is no causal relation to be found. Moreover, if one says that the axis of the Moon's orbit revolves around the axis of the ecliptic—the question can be asked: What has that to do with the axis of the Earth cone, why must that too revolve in the same time round the ecliptic axis? In other words, why do we find a movement of the Moon's nodes appearing again as a movement of Earth?

To this question the Newtonian doctrine of the gravitational force of the heavenly bodies gives, as we have seen, an answer of its own, in that it ascribes to the Moon an effect on the thickened Earth at the equator. But one can also disregard what is a grossly material causal relationship, and simply say: The nodes of the Moon's orbit go once around the zodiac in 18.6 years, and the Earth *accompanies* this movement with a gentle oscillation, a nodding, a greeting. It does not need a cause and effect relationship in order to exist.

These in fact are the expressions that Rudolf Steiner used for this movement, of which he spoke very often:

> It is not only that what the astronomers call the nutation, this trembling of the Earth's axis, this revolution of the axis of the Earth in a double cone around the central point of the Earth, it is not only that it travels around in eighteen years, but with it at the same time something else is happening. . . . You see, the nutation is connected with the passage of the Moon in the heavens. So that one can say: The nutation points to nothing more than the passage of the Moon through the sky. The nutation is only the projection of this movement of the Moon. (Lecture, April 16, 1920)

Through these words one feels oneself lifted out of the world of gravity, of the thickening at the equator, into a lighter, rhythmic world. Rudolf Steiner has also told us what that world is:

> We are able therefore actually to observe the breathing of the macrocosm. We have only to watch the course of the Moon during eighteen years, and respectively, the nutation of the Earth. The Earth dances. . . . This dancing reflects the breathing of the macrocosm, so that we can say: We look right into the breathing of the macrocosm. Through the movements of the nutation and of the Moon, we have what corresponds to breathing. . . . Thus it is impossible that we have only one world in our environment. We have the world that we can pursue as the world of the senses. But there is also another world that is based upon a different set of laws, that is related to our world as our breath is related to our consciousness, and that betrays its presence to us when we understand rightly how to contemplate the movement of the Moon—or its expression—the nutation of the Earth. . . . To each of the two worlds must be ascribed its own set of laws. As long as one thinks that a single kind of law is sufficient for our world, that everything is hanging on the thread of cause and effect, so

long does one give oneself up to an appalling error. Only when one can realize that in the nutation of the Earth and the movement of the Moon there is actually another world projecting in, does one come to a right conclusion. . . . One cannot say: the world that surrounds us is only interpenetrated, abstractly interpenetrated by the astral world. Rather one must say that it breathes the astral world through the movement of the Moon or through the nutation. We can look within, into its breathing process, its astral aspect.

A rhythmical process and a breath-like movement reveal themselves for us in the moving round of the Moon's nodes—in the rising and sinking of the Moon's path on the one hand, and on the other in the gentle rise and fall, like the breathing of a human being's chest, that the nutation appends to precession. We can thus understand why the rhythm of the revolution of the lunar node has to do with our subconsciousness, our dreams, as was discussed in Letter 10, and we can also understand that the breathing rhythm of the human being is bound up with this lawfulness.

We come here to that numerical relationship of which Rudolf Steiner spoke again and again, and mentioned emphatically in one of the last lectures that he gave, namely to the relation of the rhythm of the breath to the rhythm of the blood, and the relation of the nutation (or the Saros) to the precessional movement, as of one to four or eighteen to seventy-two. (Compare, among others, *Cosmic and Human Metamorphoses*, lecture 2.)

In seventy-two years the vernal point goes about one degree backward and indicates thereby the actual duration of a human life.

In eighteen years (we will here ignore the seven months) the Moon's nodes make one revolution. A human being takes on average eighteen breaths and has seventy-two pulse beats in a minute. At this average rate, a person takes 25,920 breaths in a day. But in a life of about 72 years a person has also lived through 25,920 days, has "breathed" the ego and astral body in and out in sleeping and waking more or less 25,920 times. So closely are cosmic and human rhythms bound together.

If one wants to explain things only by the principle of gravity, things will indeed become heavy and unwieldy. We have already shown it for nutation. In a peculiar way the precession too, according to the Newtonian system, is the result of attraction, a pulling of Sun and Moon on the thickened equator. In fact the Moon, being the heavenly body nearest to Earth, pulls most strongly, twice as strongly as the Sun! So in scientific literature one speaks of a lunar-solar precession and emphasizes that two-thirds of the attractive force proceeds from the Moon and only one-third from the Sun. The nutation is then only a slight variation of the powerful lunar pulling power of precession.

It is easy to make calculations on such an assumption, in spite of its being somewhat cumbersome. It corresponds to the point of view that sees in the human being only the physical body, which sees then in fact only the corpse.

In that reality which embraces more than the merely physical, the precession is also an expression of a quite different world from the one expressed by nutation. We have three worlds around us that interpenetrate each other:

> One world, the world we perceive around us; a second world that makes itself known within it through the movements of the Moon; a third world, which announces itself through the movements of the vernal point of the Sun, thus in a certain sense through the path of the Sun. There we look in upon a third world, which remains as unknown as the world of our will remains unknown to our ordinary consciousness (same lecture as above).

That is the world of the precession, of the successive periods of civilization, of the incarnation of the human spirit, which—through the human will that rests at first in deep unconsciousness—brings about the advance of civilization upon Earth.

This third world has nothing to do with the Moon, even though the Newtonian theory of gravitation strongly concludes that. In the Moon, in nutation, in the breath, Jehovah works. In the sense world, especially that of the visible starry heavens, Lucifer reveals his action. In the world of human incarnations, of the progressive civilizations, which in a manner is symbolized by the rising of the Sun in the east at the beginning of spring, the Christ enters in.

> In fact we must look for three kinds of law, not merely for a single one. It (the Moon) points to the breathing system of our universe, as the Sun points to permeation of the universe with ether. And the movements that come to expression in nutation are movements

that proceed from the astral world, not from something or other that may be looked for through Newtonian principles.

But the Christ lives within the world of sense perception following the laws of that other world.

First we must show that the Christ who lived in Jesus followed a law different from the law pertaining in the usual understanding of nature. If, however, one does not admit such a law, if one believes that the world is only dependent upon cause and effect, and that there is just one causally interrelated world, then there is no place for that which the Christ is. One must first prepare the place for the Christ by fixing our gaze upon the three worlds that are members one of another.

Three kinds of worlds—three kinds of laws! "And these three kinds of laws we shall have to seek for even in the human being himself."

This will be more and more our aim in the further studies that follow this first year.

YEAR TWO

September 1928–August 1929

September 1928

When Mercury Stood in Libra
The Writing of the Stars

THE APPROACHING OPENING of the Goetheanum at Michaelmas brings before the soul that September evening when the foundation stone of the house dedicated to spiritual science was laid at nightfall by Dr. Steiner in a solemn ritual. With an invocation of the hierarchies the foundation stone, the double dodecahedron, "symbol in its twofold twelvefoldedness of the striving human soul, was sunk as microcosm into the macrocosm," let down "into the condensed kingdom of the elements." To this stone was added the document that contained the solemn vow of humankind toward the spiritual world. This document closed with the words: "Laid by the Johannes Building Association . . . on the twentieth day of September 1880, after the Mystery of Golgotha, that is, 1913 after the birth of Christ, when Mercury as evening star stood in Libra, the Balance."

With these words the foundation stone was wedded also to the starry heavens. With a few words a definite constellation was indicated, a constellation that was considered so significant that it appeared in the foundation-stone document next to the names of the mighty hierarchies. In that moment, on that spot, as into the Earth the stone was sunk upon which the new Goetheanum will rise as if on its own foundation stone, this statement was made. We can now ask: What does it wish to tell us?

Let us proceed from the purely outer constellation that is mentioned: Mercury in Libra. If we consult an ephemeris for September 20, 1913, we find that on the same day toward eleven o'clock in the morning the planet Mercury had passed over the celestial equator in its descent, so that in the evening it still stood at one degree of the sign Libra. (We are concerned here with the astronomical Mercury, the little red planet that is always near to the Sun, and not with Venus who in common usage is called "the evening star." Also, here we are talking about the sign of Libra, not the constellation Libra. (Please see Letters 11 and 12.)

Not far from it stood the Sun, with which shortly before it had been in conjunction. As a result of this conjunction Mercury passed over from the west side of the Sun as morning star to the east side and became the evening star. It was invisible to the naked eye until it was three and one-half degrees from the Sun. Now since in Dornach the Sun on September 20 sets at about six-thirty (Mid-European Time), Mercury was actually setting directly on the horizon at the very moment when the laying of the foundation stone took place. Since, however, it had shortly before crossed the equator, it stood in the "autumnal point," the autumn equinox, which the Sun would not reach until September 23. The equator, however, meets the horizon at each specific place exactly in the east and the west. The east-west line always designates the inter-section points of the celestial equator and the horizon. Consequently, relative to the building, Mercury was standing exactly in the west, that is, it was lying directly in line with the major axis of our very accu-rately oriented Goetheanum, passing at the same time over the horizon, with the revolution of the Earth, and over the equator through its own descending motion. (See Figure 30.)

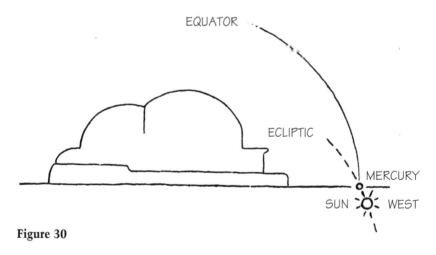

Figure 30

What we can thus discover from a purely astronomical point of view must become for us a symbol and a sign, as does the foundation stone itself in the consecration ceremony. Let us ask in the first place: Is the fact that "Mercury as evening star stood in Libra" anything very special in itself? In answering this question we must totally free ourselves from all that we have perhaps acquired from an outer "astrology." For in using the expression "Mercury in Libra" we are not pointing to a unique constellation or to an exceptional one, which one might consider very interesting, nor are we even speaking of a special aspect from which one might read quite particular perspectives concerning the future or links of destiny. The position as such is quite an ordinary one, always recurring in that particular time of year. Since the Sun itself always crosses the equator around September 23, and since Mercury can never be far from the Sun, it therefore almost always stands in the sign of Libra as evening star around September 20 (as morning star it would stand in Virgo).[1] The designation: Mercury as evening star in Libra would hold good on September 20 in almost one year out of two. We must rise to other ideas in order to see into the meaning of the constellation, and therefore we will distance our-

selves more and more from a popular astrology so as to rise to a spiritual-scientific imagination.

Already Figure 31, which is given here yet once more as a ground plan, speaks an imaginative language. We see the major axis of the building, the only symmetrical axis that passes from west to east and which is also the symmetrical axis of the foundation-stone (these relationships also apply in the second Goetheanum) directly pointing to Mercury, which is dipping under

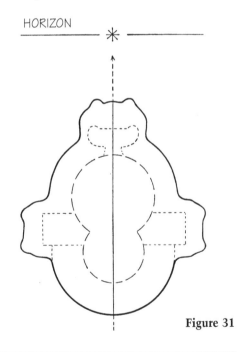

HORIZON

Figure 31

1. By evening star is meant, astronomically, that the planet follows the Sun, and therefore both rises and sets after it. At the time of sunset, it can naturally also be morning star, if it is placed just to the west of the Sun. It then sets before the Sun and is therefore quite invisible in the evening sky. (See letter 7 for the movements of Mercury and Venus.)

the horizon. Mercury has its position of equilibrium exactly between heaven and Earth—equator and ecliptic—and between the worlds above and below the Earth. This symmetrical axis is at the same time the "will axis" of the building. The impulse of word and will that flow down from stage and rostrum stream into space in this direction. In their turn they strike upon the sign inscribed in the world ether of Mercury standing on the horizon and the equator at the moment of the birth of the Goetheanum. This is a position of balance and equilibrium that could not be greater.

But what does Mercury in the balance between heaven and Earth tell us? It must be a symbol to us that we can decipher like a letter of the alphabet in the writing of the stars.

We find in Steiner's lecture cycle that was held in Torquay (England) in August 1924 (*True and False Paths in Spiritual Investigation,* lecture 10) the description of how a person who awakens inward spiritual consciousness at first feels an inner Moon arise within themselves. It is not the outer Moon that may influence such a person; otherwise he or she would become a somnambulist, and finally a medium. Rather, the Moon's night forces are magically brought into the day-waking consciousness. The spiritual begins to shine. The forces of the Moon sphere live in the human and develop a second human being within. The outer Moon is only a symbol for these spiritual forces of the Moon, whose light becomes a general elixir of life within which one feels oneself existing.

> Then the spiritual star of Mercury gradually rises in the night, which has been magically transformed into the day. Out of the sparkling twilight and fading radiance in which Mercury appears there arises the being whom we then call the divine being Mercury. We need him. We definitely need him; otherwise confusion will arise. . . . With knowledge of this being the human being can control at will the "second human being" who now lives within.

The Moon alone can transmit to us pure visions, imaginations, but one cannot tell from them if they represent a reality.

"But one enters into the sphere of the workings of Mercury, these imaginations turn into their beings. . . . And so you will become conscious of the Mercury influences and workings in such a way that your world of visions flows into a sphere where there is true perception of the spiritual." So, we can see, like an imagination of the cosmos itself, Mercury standing in Libra on the evening of the laying of the foundation stone. The messenger of the gods who leads us to true imagination is gleaming on the horizon, in the balance point between heaven and Earth! We are concerned here with a spiritual being who becomes visible to us in the planet Mercury, who outwardly has this planet for a divine body. The planet Mercury goes its preordained way; it is but a symbol for the active forces that rule in the entire sphere of Mercury. The planet itself indicates the course of these workings. In the "world of work" of the present earthly epoch, the planet itself does not manifest the deeds as was still the case in the time when the starry world manifested its own "activity." (Cf. Dr. Steiner's "Letter to the Members," *Newssheet,* November 2, 1924, and also Astronomical Letters 1 and 2, Year One.)

Mercury in occult tradition is considered the god of combining intellect. That, however, is only for the intellect that is bound to the brain. For the spiritual investigator it is the guide into the world of true imaginations. Thus did the ancient initiates know him, too, in their own way. For the Greeks, Mercury was Hermes, the same being whom the Egyptians named Thoth. He was the inventor of the arts and sciences that were spread among humanity in hoary antiquity by Osiris, the husband and brother of Isis. The nature and destiny of these gods were depicted by the ancient Egyptians with the help of the star script, "the writing that the heavenly bodies write in cosmic space" (see Rudolf Steiner's lecture on Hermes in *Anthroposophy,* vol. 2, no. 2). This star script portrayed for the ancient Egyptians quite real experiences. They knew that in the distant past clairvoyance was alive in humanity. That was the time when Hermes or Thoth educated humankind and when Osiris developed the writing that was patterned after the script of the stars. People felt in their souls the forces of Isis, Osiris, and of Hermes; these had been present from the very beginning. Sun, Moon, Mercury—each was an image, a symbol of one of the these forces, but an image that at the same time had something to do with what was represented. They were like the letters of a script, only not a script as we have today, but the heavenly script that was taught to humankind by Thoth. "As above, so below." When Sun and Moon circle round the sky and stand in a certain relation to the constellations, it is like a manifestation of spiritual-supersensible forces, which have called forth this position and have created for themselves in the heavenly script a means of expression for supersensible powers and impulses.

Osiris was the Sun in this heavenly script. The active outer Sun force of Osiris was felt by the Egyptians at the same time to be within themselves. In older times it lived in them as the power of clairvoyance. Humankind lived within a clairvoyant civilization in the times when Osiris and Hermes worked. They lived in atavistic imaginations. Osiris therefore understood how to form picture writing from the heavenly script, the hieroglyphs upon which the uninitiated gazed in dread and awe. But now took place what was later told as the Osiris-Isis legend.

Osiris had a brother, the wicked Typhon ("breath of air"). Typhon kills the beneficent Osiris by tricking him into lying down in a coffin, and then locking him in. Lead is then poured over the coffin and it is cast into the sea. It comes to Byblos in Phoenicia. Isis finds the coffin after long searching, and she brings it back to Egypt. Typhon again takes possession of Osiris and tears him in fourteen pieces. Only with the greatest difficulty does the sorrowing Isis succeed in finding the pieces and in burying them. She bequeaths the land to the priests and has an Osiris cult founded. Between Typhon and Isis, between her son Horus and Hermes, different events take place that need not be related here.

Important experiences of the human soul are hinted at in this legend. It is the disappearance of the old clairvoyance, and also the transition from the sacred hieroglyphs borrowed from the heavenly script to the abstract kind of writing of later times. Osiris does not represent a single being, but rather the whole period of clairvoyance. Typhon is that being—he corresponds to Ahriman—who kills the old clairvoyance. He wants to replace it with the intellect—at first in the form of cunning and craftiness. "The air breath kills the being of Light." In these images live reminiscences of the old Lemurian time when the breathing of light was succeeded by the breathing of air. For the Egyptian civilization was a recapitulation of the old Lemurian epoch. But now Osiris can no longer be the Sun. Now he can only ray back the sunlight in a diminished form. He has become the Moon, and the fourteen pieces in which he has been torn are the fourteen days around about full Moon. Isis again, the faithful wife, is the new Moon—always the dark, passive half as compared with Osiris.

Hermes too, in this celestial script, has a twofold nature. As Thoth he is the morning star, the god of wisdom, who descends to Earth with

winged feet. As evening star he is Hermes Psychopompos (Anubis or
Hermanubis, among the Egyptians), the guide of the soul into the underworld, bringing it to Osiris. For after his violent death Osiris is no more
to be found among the living in the upper world, but must be sought
in the underworld among the dead. From now on, only death—or initiation—leads to Osiris. In the *Egyptian Book of the Dead* one finds
the scene depicted where Thoth-Hermes—or the Jackal-headed Anubis
—brings the souls to Osiris for judgment since he, Thoth-Hermes, is the
scribe of the underworld.

In our fifth post-Atlantean period of civilization the old imaginations
must arise anew. Therefore we need Mercury as evening star in Libra,
we absolutely need him.

As Sun, Osiris has set; the time of the old clairvoyance is definitely
over. Later he is again present as Moon. This event, also, is expressed
through the writing of the stars. It is told that the death of Osiris took
place as the Sun stood in seventeen degrees of Scorpio and the full Moon
rose on the opposite side. We have here an assertion (it is to be found
in Plutarch, and elsewhere, "concerning Isis and Osiris") that is made
entirely according to the later astrological way of thinking and already
includes speculations, no longer the pure imagery of the actual legend.
Rudolf Steiner therefore said concerning this description: "So those, too,
who have turned their thoughts to the Osiris myth have referred back
to quite definite star constellations" (lecture, Jan. 5, 1918). In another
passage Plutarch applies the number seventeen to the age of the Moon,
which, two days after the full moon distinctly shows that it is in the
process of waning.

Let us consider the picture of the setting Sun in the sign of Scorpio,
which was the sign of the underworld and of death. The Sun stands not
far from the red-colored Antares. Osiris disappears in the underworld,
but soon afterward rises again as full Moon in the eastern sky. Hermes
accompanies him. Mercury is indeed like a Moon to the Sun, and even
the Egyptians understood Mercury and Venus as circling around the
Sun. In many respects Mercury acts in relation to the Sun just as our
Moon acts in relation to the Earth.

The constellation depicted here—the Sun at seventeen degrees in
Scorpio, the full Moon in Taurus by the Pleiades—is again not a unique
one, which, for example, could guide one to a definite historical date.
These relationships between Sun and Moon return again and again at

regular intervals. We have here an example of "rhythmical astronomy." Every nineteen years both Sun and Moon are to be found in almost exactly the same positions in the heavens as they were before this interval of time. This is what is called the "Metonic cycle," which like the Saros and other cycles is one of the rhythms of the Sun and Moon. In this way the death of Osiris by the hand of Typhon may also be looked upon as an ever recurring event that is having ever wider effects. Every nineteen years, one could say, when sometime in November the Sun stands in Scorpio at seventeen degrees and at the same time there is a full Moon, a fresh impulse is given for the dying away of clairvoyance. It was so at least during long stretches of time, but eventually it came to an end. Long after the Egyptian age and almost into our own there has been an atavistic clairvoyance—but then the effects alter and the same constellation must now be read in quite a different way.

For the ancient Egyptians, Osiris had disappeared from the side of Isis. A leaden coffin at Byblos in Phoenicia, the land where writing with letters was invented, remained upon the Earth. In a boat of papyrus, Isis traveled over swamps and rivers seeking Osiris. The old legend strikes us as a Typhonic foreshadowing of the art of printing that ushered in the fifth post-Atlantean period. Whoever desires to seek Osiris today without being torn in pieces by Typhon must themselves go to the dead. The dead, Rudolf Steiner said, are today the only human beings who can read the heavenly script. We can learn it from the dead if we can find a common form of experience with them.

Let us return to the constellation, the configuration of the heavens at the laying of our foundation stone! Outwardly it is somewhat reminiscent of the Osiris-Typhon-constellation: the setting Sun; the Moon not yet fully risen in Taurus between full Moon and the last quarter; Hermes-Mercury accompanying the Sun into the underworld; the descending lunar node not far from the Sun—for it is a few days after an eclipse of the Moon. We must not read the picture in the old way, for the experiences and the way of experiencing of the Egyptian age are definitely past. The fifth post-Atlantean age is the recapitulation, and must be the Christianized resurrection, of the third epoch. We have in effect the task of creating a new and opposite version of the Osiris-Isis legend. We must move away from the leaden coffin and the Typhonic artifices of earthly intellect to a newly arisen Osiris force, through a new heavenly script to a true cosmic experience. We must look up at the sky not in sorrow, as the Egyptians did. The new writing of the stars will not be written only by the gods, but will also be experienced by humanity in freedom, because between the tragic experience of destiny in pre-Christian times and the present-day experience of the star script there lies the event of Golgotha. To point to the constellation of the laying of the foundation stone is not to point to an inescapable fate, but rather it is to take a solemn vow!

Hermes-Mercury can again teach us arts and sciences when we are willing as scientists to follow Hermes-Psychopompus into the world of the true imaginations that may appear to us at first as a nether world. If we are not willing, he becomes Typhon or Seth. This was the name given by the Egyptians to the evening star Mercury when they looked on it as a separate being, not knowing its connection with Mercury as the morning star, the god of wisdom. The Greeks named him Apollo in this form. To the Egyptians he was Horus, the son of Isis and Osiris, who was in continual strife with Seth. But both lead to union with the Sun, by the inferior or superior conjunction. We can in this sense refer to them both together as the Archangel Raphael, who stands in the west.

And this can be our solemn vow in contemplation of the constellation at the laying of the foundation stone: May the divine being, Raphael-Mercury, lead us to the true imagination of a new science, a new art. Gabriel, the Moon messenger alone shall not suffice us. May Mercury guide us also past the dangers of the Venus being. May Lucifer not meet us when the imaginations pass over to their beings, and instead of the picture-filled world of the Mercury consciousness may there be rather an empty consciousness. Then we can push through to the experience of the Sun.

We have spiritually traveled over the path that for us, too, is depicted in a heavenly script through the planetary world from the Moon to the Sun. And when in spirit we have arrived at the Sun, then there is no glowing ball of gas, but a world of inspiration. There Michael meets us in his radiant robe of spiritual beings who have sprung from the powers of the Sun; Michael, whose word of light will one day stream forth to the waiting, hoping, and thirsting souls.

October 1928

The Nature of Astrology

WE ARE LIVING IN A TIME when among the various spiritual movements that are making their appearance, there is one that calls itself
astrology. It refers for its teachings to the treasures of knowledge of the
distant past. In this respect it differs from anthroposophical spiritual
science, in which we are dealing with the results of modern spiritual
research, not with the further development of old traditions. Yet a certain perplexity reigns even among members of the Anthroposophical
Society regarding the kind of phenomena that modern astrology presents
them with today. People do not feel justified in refuting them entirely yet
do not know how to relate them to the views found in anthroposophy.
We should attempt, therefore, to reach some clarity on this question.

Rudolf Steiner has himself indicated that there can be something of
the nature of an "astrology" beside astronomy, when he spoke of astronomy, astrology, and astrosophy as three branches of human knowledge
Where the actual effects of the heavenly bodies is considered, and not
merely their existence as such, there we have astrology. Such an astrology flourished in the time when human beings could feel themselves
especially connected to the world of the stars through their sentient
souls, their astral bodies. We know that this was the case during the
Egypto-Chaldean epoch. At the height of that civilization human beings,
especially in the condition of sleep during the night, had the experience
of being deeply connected to, bound-up with the starry worlds. The
constellations of the stars were like the signs, the letters of an occult
script. These told of the effective activities of the spiritual beings whom
humankind was less and less able to catch sight of. Humanity was perceived as entirely linked with the workings of the stars. How human
beings developed in body, soul, and spirit, what they did in the course of
their life, how the conditions of their earthly environment affected them,

all these without exception took place according to the laws of the stars. Outer social life was also regulated according to these laws.

The capacity of standing in such direct connection with the celestial world was lost comparatively early. It was gradually replaced, especially among the Chaldeans, by another newly awakened faculty—that of calculation. The Chaldeans first began to record the constellations so that later in the mystery schools one could afterward see on clay tablets how the planets had stood, and so on. From the sixth century B.C. on, this—in a modern sense—"calculated astronomy," although at first primitive, was practiced. And thereby an astronomy arose as a field of knowledge beside the old astrology. This method permitted the knowledge gained in the time of the ancient clairvoyance to be applied further, but calculation had interpolated itself between the cosmos and humankind.

The Greeks learned the art of astrology from the Chaldeans. It was flourishing among them just at the time of the Mystery of Golgotha and thereafter. Yet with the event of Golgotha astrology had lost its inner justification. For through the deed of the Christ human beings should gradually become free from the cosmos. By the death on the cross cosmic forces were implanted in the Earth itself that the human being can receive in freedom. Since then humankind no longer stands in the same relation to the world of the stars as before. The close interrelation of the physical body and the etheric body, which began with the "fall" and manifested itself especially strongly after the Atlantean period, had made it increasingly impossible for the cosmic forces to work rightly upon these lower aspects of the human being. One could say: The horoscope does not apply any longer to these aspects, and in the present age of Michael they are less and less valid. (Rudolf Steiner said once that from decade to decade this becomes more noticeable.) This phenomenon of a horoscope no longer fully in keeping with reality was changed through the Christ impulse from a phenomenon of decadence into a fact of human freedom. Indeed, the appearance of Christ was itself a "real symbol" for this fact. For, according to the astral conditions, Christ should have come much earlier, namely in the middle of Atlantean times. At that time, however, humankind had just received the first infusion of the Ego and would not have been able to receive [him] in freedom. The Christ came at a later time that was not determined primarily by the conditions of the cosmos, but rather by the needs of human evolution, according to what humankind must suffer, guiltlessly guilty, as a result of the Fall. So Christ Jesus with his appearance broke through astral law, even as in terms of the conditions of his environment he broke through the blood ties of the Hebrew people, for he was born from the mixed race of the Galileans. Also, with the raising of Lazarus before all peoples he superceded the old form of initiation. From the moment of this "mystical fact" the old initiation could no longer be effective, although for many centuries after human beings were still initiated more or less rightly in the old form. Thus, from the time of Christ the relation of humanity to the world of the stars has been a different one, a freer one.

It is not as if humanity were suddenly torn away from the star world! Things not only progress slowly and gradually—even if they are the result of a suddenly implanted new impulse, such as the Christ impulse—but besides, one might say, there is even care taken in the universe that continuity always be preserved. (Even today, not all people have taken the Christ impulse into their souls). So on the other hand the coming of Christ was inscribed in the heavens through a significant sign that indicated he could only come at that time in the fourth post-Atlantean period in which he actually came. It was the transition of the cultural impulse from the constellation of the Ram into that of Pisces, the Fishes, from the "light" into the "dark" signs of the zodiac. (See Letter 2, Year One.)

Egypto-Chaldean astrology, however, spread greatly just in the centuries that followed the Christ impulse. It was as if human beings for the first time really wanted to cling to that which more and more was to be taken from them. One might say that in the increasing darkness of the spiritual life in the succeeding centuries—into which only the young, germinating Christianity shed a clear ray of light—for many souls, occupying themselves with the laws of the stars provided at least some inner connection with the divine spiritual worlds. But astrology became more and more traditional, became more and more nothing but problems in arithmetic. And if one had the opportunity to compare, one would have found that what could be predicted of a person on the basis of a birth constellation or of his or her destiny on the basis of constellations arising later during their lifetime, these harmonized less and less with the actual facts.

Finally, in the fifteenth century a little group of people who were connected with the spiritual world came to the point of consciously sacrificing the old star wisdom, renouncing the higher knowledge that was concerned with the activity of the world of the stars. (See Rudolf Steiner's lecture, January 6, 1924.) And that offer was accepted by the spiritual world.

Since that time there is no longer a real knowledge of astrology. Despite this, we find in the following centuries even enlightened spirits who concerned themselves with it. They were—at least in the case of the truly enlightened, the others not being of much account—primarily persons who, in the time of approaching materialism, had still preserved an instinctive connection with the cosmos, whether out of a special organization of their nature or through the spiritual impulse streaming out from earlier incarnations. Rudolf Steiner pointed to three such spirits in a lecture (Nov. 9, 1911, "Prophecy—Its Nature and Meaning").

Nostradamus (1503–1566) was a physician driven out of his vocation. Able to devote himself for hours at a time to gazing into the starry heavens, he experiences pictures rising before him and clothes them in verse. The verses are certainly obscure, but they have a prophetic character. In fact the future proved that the prophecies were true not only concerning his immediate surroundings and immediate future, but for events right into our own time. It was not a matter of calculation—for he did not employ numbers at all—nor was it an interpretation of constellations he had observed. Rather, the stars themselves transformed the repressed forces of his prior vocation into visions of the future. The stars were only the means for releasing his visions. In this Nostradamus was an exceptional case, somewhat as Paracelsus was, or even Swedenborg, with whom he even shows a certain relationship in his life destiny.

It was different in the case of Tycho Brahe (1546–1601), who was a younger contemporary of Nostradamus by only a few decades. He, too, occupied himself with astrology, although for the most part by royal command. Indeed, his horoscopes for the little Danish princes (the sons of Frederick II) give the impression throughout that he took seriously the influence of the starry heavens upon human fate, and that he did not rely much on calculations to understand a birth constellation. Rather his interpretations drew upon an instinctive element of his being, that may have come from his earlier incarnation as Julian the Apostate [Roman emperor from 331–363 A.D. – author of *Hymn to King Helios*].

Brahe's later fellow worker and successor in practical star knowledge, Kepler, is distinctly more averse to astrology. He inveighs against it and yet he—a reincarnated former Egyptian initiate—must believe in it. He even handles it with great assurance. But he has to use many calculations and is entirely dependent on tradition for his interpretations. Thus in the brief period of some fifty years we see a transition from seeing to calculating, from direct knowledge to tradition, as if the transition from the Egypto-Chaldean period to the Greco-Latin period is being recapitulated. With Kepler one can say the astrology of enlightened spirits comes definitely to an end.

The three centuries that have elapsed since then have made human beings more and more into calculating beings, and have made them increasingly estranged inwardly from the cosmos. At the same time, in terms of the soul and even of the bodily functions, the human being has become ever more free from the cosmos. All these causes work together to predestine the human being of the present day to be a bad astrologer in the traditional sense. We can therefore understand it when we find Rudolf Steiner speaking in strong terms about what is today called astrology. As he said in the lecture of August 29, 1915, introducing the "Twelve Moods": "It is not a matter of imitating to some degree the method of those modern astrologers who transcend materialism only to add ignorant superstition to materialistic ignorance. It is a matter rather of entering into the lawful relationships of a spiritual world that manifests itself in the human even as in the cosmos. True spiritual science does not seek human laws in constellations of the stars, but seeks both human and natural laws out of the spiritual. Although spiritual science is constantly being associated with the meaningless mystical pursuits of modern times, it has nothing at all to do with them. If in certain statements, analogies of the human being with cosmic relationships have been used as the basis for a means of expression, it must be especially emphasized that spiritual science wants to have nothing to do with the dilettantism of modern astrologers and their crude pronouncements." I once heard Rudolf Steiner speak many years ago from another point of view against the aims of astrology in the reading of horoscopes. He pointed out the dangers that must arise for the very persons who are striving toward esoteric development. There lies, he said, a refined egoism in wishing to know something in such a way about oneself or one's fellow human being. And just when one strives for inner development one can easily arrive at such a subtle self-seeking, which is all the more dangerous since it works subtly. The knowledge of repeated Earth lives and of karma can, however, show us how little we can grasp of the true human being through the horoscope. For in the life the human soul goes through in the spiritual world before birth, it considers the experiences and practical knowledge it has brought out of the former incarnation and the faults and failings that still remain. According to this, the soul gives a direction to the new Earth life. It seeks out the opportunities that can lead to the strengthening or modification of its qualities. To this end definite events in the physical world are necessary, and the soul now chooses for itself rebirth at the time and in the surroundings in which such events can take place. Such resolutions made in the life before birth become deeds, events in the life upon Earth. The events can take the form of a catastrophe or of occurrences which, in terms of human concepts lead to an Earth life of discredit. Nevertheless, the soul has before birth wanted these experiences, and they cannot be averted simply because an incarnated human being has calculated from his or her horoscope the fact that they are about to occur. The more one may strive to escape from one's destiny—and it lies in the very nature of human egoism to want that—all the more surely would those endeavors lead to the destined goal. What the soul would lose by this, however, is the courage, the inner soul force to endure those experiences. This courage otherwise lives in the subconscious depths of the human soul and is a sure guide for it. All knowledge about these things that is reached by external means, as by the casting of a horoscope, can work only to weaken the prenatal will. These words of Rudolf Steiner are not to be understood to mean that human beings should not acquaint themselves with their destiny. Rudolf Steiner has given us, in 1924, the "practical karma exercises" for this very purpose. The deciphering of the celestial script will also lead more and more to an understanding of human destiny. Then, however, the calculated horoscope does not stand between a human being and his or her destiny.

It is another matter if one wants to penetrate the laws of the stars through observation of the past. In that case, egotism cannot make itself felt; we can have no influence upon the past. What Rudolf Steiner said about the constellation of the stars for the moment of death is also to be understood in this sense. For we can no longer work upon the soul that has entered into the spiritual world in the way we can upon the human being incarnated with us. One must, however, clearly understand that here also one cannot get anywhere with everyday astrology. Only the most experienced occultist, who stands at the end of his or her path, can really make use of astrology. Thus Rudolf Steiner ended his remarks.

Rudolf Steiner (in issue 28 of the journal *Lucifer-Gnosis*), in response to a question about astrology, gave an answer that is extraordinarily instructive. Because of its importance it shall be given here almost in full:

> How does Theosophy regard astrology? In the first place it must be said that at the present time people have little idea what astrology really is. For what often appears as astrology nowadays in handbooks is a purely external collection of rules whose deeper foundations are not anywhere explained. Methods of calculation are given, by which one can calculate the constellations of the stars for a person's moment of birth or for the time of another important event. Then it is stated that these constellations mean this or that, though one never learns from these indications why this should all be so, or even how it could be so. It is no wonder, therefore, that people today see all this as nonsense, swindle, and superstition. For it all appears to be quite arbitrary, to be assertions that are completely made up.
>
> The real astrology, however, is quite an intuitive science and demands of those who wish to practice it the development of higher supersensible powers of knowledge. These powers can be present today in very few persons. If one were to set forth the basic character of astrology, one would have to consider, in the light of spiritual science, the highest cosmological problems. For this reason only a few, ordinary aspects can be mentioned here. The star system to which we human beings belong is a whole, a unity. And the human being is connected to all the forces of this star-system. . . . For example, the Sun acts upon the human being through something quite different from what science calls gravitational force, light, and warmth. In the same way there are connections of a supersensible nature between Mars, Mercury, and other planets and humankind. Starting from such a view anyone who is gifted in this way may picture to themselves a fabric—a web—of supersensible connections between the heavenly bodies and the beings who dwell on them. But to clarify, to raise these connections into clear scientific knowledge, the development of quite high supersensible vision is necessary. Only the highest grades of intuition still open

to human beings can attain to that. And this is certainly not the vague presentiment and half-visionary dreams that people today usually call intuition, but rather the most positive inner sense faculty that can only be compared with mathematical thinking. Now there have been and still are people in occult schools who can work with astrology in this way. And what is to be found concerning astrology in the books accessible to us has come somehow or other from such secret teaching. At the same time, everything having to do with these matters is inaccessible to ordinary thought even though it is set down in books. For again, only a deep intuition can understand these statements. And those teachers' statements that have been written down later by people who didn't understand them are naturally not likely to give a favorable view of astrology to persons trapped in the way of thinking prevalent today. But still it must be said that such books about astrology are not without value. That is because the less people understand what they are copying, the better they copy it; they do not spoil it then through their own wisdom. So it happens that astrological writings, even though they are of such obscure origin, always contain pearls of wisdom to be found by the person capable of intuition—but indeed only by such a person.

Certainly astrological laws rest upon intuitions in comparison with which the knowledge of reincarnation and karma is still very elementary.

The work of Rudolf Steiner is filled with such deep knowledge necessary to a real understanding of astrology! One need in this connection only refer to his Letter "To All Members" in the first year of the *News-sheet,* no. 45 (November 16, 1924), "Michael's Mission in the World Age of Human Freedom." We find described there, in three concise columns preceding the actual "leading thoughts," the whole relationship of the human being with the surrounding cosmic world through the course of time.

Human beings have received their physical and etheric bodies from past world ages. These are entirely the result of cosmic activities and forces—although they are distorted by the luciferic temptation and, as already said, are too strongly joined to one another. The astral body is a younger creation, but it is in the ego itself—the "baby of the human aspects" that human beings experience their freedom. In earlier times cosmic activities streamed not only into the physical and etheric bodies, but through these into the astral body and the ego as well. The human being could not be free. While still today the human being must give over the physical and etheric bodies to divine-spiritual activity, we can lift ourselves with the ego into the spiritual worlds. For the sake of an independent life on Earth we must withdraw ourselves from the former cosmic assistance, and must now find support in the spiritual world in another way. In this way, freedom will not be a mere arbitrariness, or lawlessness, which would only work destructively in the spiritual world. And what meets human beings there, what gives them a real foundation for their action in freedom, is what Michael brings over again from the past, but out of a past that has been held back and guarded. These are forces that likewise come out of the cosmos, out of the system of the stars and planets, but that can no longer be compelling, for they do not penetrate into the world of nature. In the earliest times of earthly evolu- tion spiritual-moral forces from the cosmos were also taken up together with the outer material, with the sense-perceptions. They refined them- selves, so to speak, in their spiritual being and became knowledge. (Cf. also the end of Letter 8, Year One.)

Then came the time that lasted nearly to the Michael period, in which a kind of intermediary area formed. Here stream together what comes out of the organism, containing thus something cosmic, and what sinks down as half forgotten sense perceptions and memory pictures. These build a region of subconsciousness where cosmic lawfulness is mingled with undigested human soul workings. This is just the region that was much researched in the nineteenth century, although not always by fortunate methods, and where the researchers who cannot discern the signs of a new age are still looking today.

Today these relationships must be different, at any rate for those souls who wish to develop themselves in the terms of the Michaelic age. In the passage of Rudolf Steiner's already referred to, he says:

Human beings' position with respect to the world will in future become more and more incomprehensible to them if they are not prepared to recognize in addition to their relations to the beings and processes of nature, such relations as that to the mission of Michael. . . . Human beings thrust away from themselves cosmic forces that want to form and mold them further—that want to give their ego organization the necessary physical supports as they did before the age of Michael. . . . He (Michael) devotes himself in the manner here described, to the task of bringing to the human being from the spiritual part of the cosmos forces that can replace those from the realm of nature that have been suppressed. He accomplishes this by bringing his activity into the most perfect accord with the Mystery of Golgotha.

It is then described how human beings, even as they receive light and warmth from the physical Sun, can feel themselves permeated with warmth from the spiritual Sun, the Christ.

Feeling themselves thus permeated, they will say to themselves: This warmth liberates your humanity from the bonds of the cosmos in which it must not remain. "Christ gives me my humanity." This will well up in the soul as a fundamental feeling and pervade it. Once this feeling is present another comes, in which the human being feels raised by Christ beyond mere earthly existence, feels one with the starry firmament around the Earth and with all that can be recognized in this firmament as spiritual and divine.

It is the same with the spiritual light. . . . Human beings unite themselves in the present with the spiritual cosmic forces of light that belong to the past, when they were not yet free individuals.

There we have an activity quite contrary to the fatalistic activity that certainly exists in present-day astrology. To turn our minds to this activity shall be an ideal above all else. Not until we strive for this shall we have a right relation to what now actually seems determined by the cosmos—like the star constellation at birth. This right relation will be a free relation, permeated with knowledge. We find the foundation of this knowledge in a previous passage (*Anthroposophical Movement,* October 25, 1924):

It is a deep source of satisfaction to Michael that through human beings themselves he has succeeded in keeping the world of the stars in direct union with the divine and spiritual. For when human beings, having fulfilled their life between death and a new birth, start on the way to a new Earth life, in their descent they seek to establish a harmony between the course of the stars and

their coming life on Earth. In old times this harmony existed as
a matter of course, because the divine-spiritual was active in the
stars, where human life, too, had its source. But today, when the
course of the stars only continues the manner in which the divine-
spiritual worked in the past, this harmony would not exist unless
human beings sought it. Human beings bring their divine-spiritual
portion—which they have preserved from the past—into relation
with the stars, which only now bear their divine-spiritual nature
within as an "after-working" from an earlier time.

In this way there comes into the human being a relationship to
the world, something of the divine, that is appropriate for former
ages and yet appears in these latter times. That this is so is the deed
of Michael. And this deed gives him such deep satisfaction that
in it he finds a portion of his very life, a portion of his Sun-like
living energy.

The whole work-world is spread out around us for the sake of our
freedom. It cannot compel humanity in its spiritual nature. To this world
of work, this world of maya, of illusion, there belongs also the external maya-appearance of the starry heavens at the moment of a birth.
It merely points to what the human soul in the spiritual world before
birth has experienced together with the "spiritual-cosmic light-forces of
the past." All realities, all activities, take place beforehand in a purely
spiritual existence. That this activity still creates its pictorial impression
in the star world (which is expressed in the birth-constellations of the
horoscope)—in spite of its being no longer "necessary" in this stage of
world evolution—this in fact is the deed of Michael!

In this knowledge lies hidden the insight into why so many people
today strive after a renewal of astrology. They, too, are unconsciously
seeking Michael. As they lack the needed knowledge, however, that has
been bequeathed to us in, for instance, the "Letters to the Members"
and in the whole life work of Rudolf Steiner, they are inevitably misled.
They cannot distinguish between the workings of the past and the present, between pre-natal will and earthly determination, between spiritual
cosmic light forces and earthly shining starlight. A way so traversed can
never lead to the Christ, for:

The divine-spiritual of former ages shines no more. In the light that
the Christ brings to the human ego the primal light is there once

more. . . . and in this light human beings can find ways that truly guide our human nature if we unite ourselves in full soul understanding with the mission of Michael. (November 9, 1924)

In the next Letter we will speak further and more concretely of these matters.

More About Astrology in the Light of Spiritual Science

IN THE LAST LETTER the human being's twofold relation to the world of the stars was mentioned. In their bodily processes, human beings experience stellar influences that at first remain in their subconscious nature. These influences are concerned with the part of the human being that is not free, cannot be free, since we are subject to the laws of nature. Indeed, it is a portion of just these forces that has withdrawn and has left human beings free for spiritual activity. From the other side, we meet again with cosmic forces that were brought to humanity through the power of Michael, as has been described.

We can consider as yet a third province, an intermediary one already hinted at, that works from the stellar world in a determining way upon the fate of the human being, insofar as it is conditioned not merely by the body but rather more by the soul and spirit. It can be said that an expression of this province is being created in the world of stars through the activity of Michael. This is the horoscope of the human being, from which one may read one's destiny more or less clearly if one possesses the necessary intuition. It was necessary to utter a warning from the standpoint of spiritual science about thus construing destiny. Rudolf Steiner says in lecture 3 of *The Spiritual Guidance of the Individual and Humanity:*

> Thus is a human being put into his place within physical existence, and it is in accordance with his horoscope that he guides himself before entering earthly existence. This subject, which in our time seems such a risky one, should not be touched upon without our attention being called to the fact that almost everything carried on in this area today is simply dilettantism—a pure superstition—and that for the external world the true science of these matters has

been for the most part completely lost. Consequently, one should not judge the principal things said here according to that which nowadays in many cases leads a questionable existence under the name of astrology. . . .

It is the active forces of the stellar world that impel a human being into physical incarnation.

For a knowledge of these forces we must describe from this standpoint the life of the human being between death and a new birth. That shall be done on another occasion. (See Letters 5–7, Year Two.)

Now, however, we must turn our attention to the activity mentioned first. This is primarily one common to all humankind. For the Sun as well as the stars shine for all human beings in the same way, although it is only in the course of twenty-four hours that the various separate parts of the firmament pass over the different continents of the Earth. The planets are in particular relationships to one another. These change from day to day, but pertain to the whole Earth. So the activities by which the whole machinery of the human organism is kept going are always present. They may even exercise an influence on the human being's soul functioning as well, insofar as the soul nature of the human being works also into the physical and etheric bodies. If a person in their soul and spirit is still bound to the bodily nature, then these direct stellar influences will still also affect the soul life. One thinks, for instance, of the changes of the Moon!

In anthroposophical teachings we find a good deal about such general workings, which belong just as much to humanity's life in common as what has been brought over from the evolutionary stages of Old Saturn, Old Sun, and Old Moon. They are presented to us as not being of an individual moral nature but rather as working like a purely natural law.

Let us take Saturn as an example of such activity. It has a strong connection with the human astral body, especially in the head region. It incorporates this astral body into the human being's physical body. Now Saturn is the outermost planet, the one furthest from the Earth and nearest to the fixed stars. It is the creator of lead, not only what is found on the Earth as a relic of long past ages, but also the lead found in a finely dispersed, more etheric form in the Earth's atmosphere. It thus brings weight to the human organism. In the old traditional astrology, which arose at a time when human beings were not yet willing to bind themselves to the heaviness of Earth, Saturn was represented as the "Great Malefactor," as that planet that brings disaster upon humanity. It makes its children melancholy, avaricious, and cold. Saturn is the planet that permeates the human sense organs with heaviness, so that the human being can make proper use of them. It subdues the overexuberant life that the senses would otherwise have. This life comes from the Sun, and had the Sun alone worked upon the human being, we could not have used our eyes, even though they are created, as Goethe said, "by the light for the light." They would have become muscles or vessels, not the crystalline entities that they are today. Through the working together of Saturn and the Sun, through the lead process that Saturn mingles with the sight, the eye receives the slight heaviness that deadens the too-exuberant life.

Now this interworking did not merely happen once in the distant past. The balancing between life and death must continuously take place, otherwise even today the human being would come into disharmony. The Sun and Saturn both traverse the heavens, the Sun in one year, Saturn in thirty years, so that once every year the Sun overtakes Saturn, though each time twelve days later. (Cf. Letter 8, Year One.) In this way there is a conjunction (σ) and an opposition (σ^o) between the Sun and Saturn every year.

Once a year, therefore, the Sun covers Saturn with its rays. That planet becomes inactive, while the life-giving force of the Sun is able to unfold powerfully. After six months and six days when the opposition occurs, Saturn shines in the night sky while the Sun must work through the Earth. Saturn culminates at midnight, will stand highest in the sky, and stimulates the lead process in the environment of the Earth, and thus influences the human sense organs. If we could suddenly "think" Saturn out of the sky, the human being would after a time become a quite different being who could no longer use the sense organs rightly. Thus we have to be thankful for this constant change in the relationship between Saturn and the Sun constellation (between the opposition and the conjunction there are also two squared aspects, when the Sun and Saturn are ninety degrees apart), for the balance between an overly strong and a too-weak sense life. The world of finished work with its regular, apparently mechanical course of the heavenly bodies, takes care that the mechanism of the human organism is kept going.

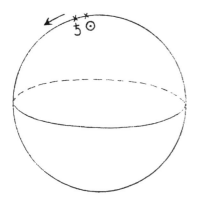

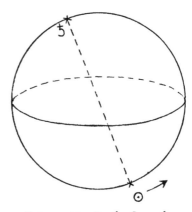

Saturn in conjunction
with the Sun

Saturn opposite the Sun after
six months and six days

Figure 32

The same is true of Jupiter and the other planets of the solar system. They all come at determined times into relation with the Sun and with each other. Jupiter, for instance, which passes through the entire zodiac once in twelve years, meets the Sun at intervals of one year and one month. Its activity during this time gradually increases and come to a high point in order to be again effaced by the Sun. In the course of twelve years (or in the case of Saturn, thirty years) this event takes place in each constellation of the zodiac, and thereby also undergoes a differentiation.

As Saturn works upon the sense organs to tone them down, as it were, Jupiter acts in the same way upon the human nerve life. Jupiter makes the existence of the nerves possible, inasmuch as it tones down the Sun life in a particular way. If the Sun places itself before Jupiter, the nerve-life becomes especially stimulated. If Jupiter is in opposition and works by itself a toning-down sets in. The periods in which the nerve-life is stimulated and again subdued correspond almost exactly to those in which Saturn works on the life of the senses (one year, thirty days; one year, twelve days, respectively). One must not imagine that every time, for instance, the conjunction of Saturn and Sun takes place, people would be able to experience a palpable stimulation of their sense-life. These workings remain too strongly in the subconscious for that, and human beings with their ego-consciousness are already too emancipated. But the contrasting conditions of Saturn in conjunction with the Sun and Saturn in opposition to the Sun work in the whole course of the year in an equalizing way upon the sense-life of humanity as a whole. To have too strong a conscious or semiconscious experiencing of these positions would only indicate that the person who experienced them in this way had not yet freed themselves sufficiently from the workings of the cosmos upon the body, in accordance with the present state of world evolution.

The planets naturally have many other effects besides the toning-down of which we have just spoken. We must always bear in mind that what occurs visibly or invisibly as a constellation in the heavens is only an indication of the influence that the spheres in question exercise upon each other during the constellation. It is not therefore a matter of the apparent "magnitude" of the planet. Tiny Mercury, for instance, stands before the Sun several times a year (in the so-called "inferior conjunction"), and thereby each time somewhat weakens the life coming from the Sun. It works upon the metabolism, and therefore the processes of stimulation and diminution must be more frequent and must occur at intervals of only a few months. Without Mercury and its aspects to the Sun, human beings would not be able to retain their food.

All this works upon humanity as a whole, and in the way in which it is manifested in the heavens. The individual human being, however, gives these general aspects a definite basis through his or her horoscope, through the positions of the planets and fixed stars in the heavens at the moment of birth. There the starry sky fixes itself for the individual as if on a photographic plate. It is in reality the spiritual world that to a certain degree he or she has left behind at the moment of his or her first breath that reproduces itself thus within, in the aura and even physically in the brain (see Rudolf Steiner's *The Spiritual Guidance of the Individual and Humanity*). And just as one can trace on the photographic plate the movement of the planets as contrasted with the relatively stationary fixed stars, if the exposure is long enough, so do the movements and positions of the planets inscribe themselves in contrast to the birth constellation. Even as the ego of the human being at birth actually remains outside the earthly realm and does not enter in during the course of the lifetime, so does the configuration of the starry heavens over the place and at the time of birth remain stationary, a background for the whole future life upon which are projected the further movements and workings of the planetary system.

Every thirty years, therefore, the relationship between Saturn and the Sun that existed at a person's moment of birth occurs again. Once in this period of time Saturn will come into conjunction, once into opposition, and twice into square with the Sun's position at birth. However, the Sun need not be in the constellation of the zodiac in which it was at birth. It can be in a different position, but the actual position of Saturn at the moment under consideration projected onto the birth horoscope gives the actual aspect. Such effective activities of Saturn as described above (Saturn is here always taken only as a representative example for the planetary world) can then come about, but they take on a more individual character, connected with personal karma. There we have that sphere of stellar activity which (on the first page of this Letter) we have called the third, a middle sphere, between the bodily-physical domain and the sphere of the human being's free spiritual relationship vis-à-vis the cosmos. It is just in this domain that the karma of the human being finds expression, the karma that comes from former Earth lives, and has been shaped in the life between death and rebirth, and that with the help of Michael he or she has expressed in their birth horoscope.

The warning that must be given concerning the casting of a horoscope and following it up over the years applies to just this sphere.

When a person is fifty-nine to sixty years old the same Saturn constellation occurs as at the time of birth—supposing that at birth there was an actual aspect between Saturn and another planet. If there were, for instance, a conjunction of Saturn and the Sun (to keep the same example) then at about age sixty, a strong cosmic stimulation of the sense life would come about. It would be a fortunate time for a painter, for instance, who might be able just at that time to be sensitive to "the many colored light" of Saturn in the surrounding atmosphere.

All these effects, however, will be more significant if human beings can release themselves from the planetary forces bound to their organism and at work in it, and can rise to the free handling of cosmic forces. Then Saturn, for example, will discard its outer, fateful, hindrance-bringing nature and become for the human being something like a doorkeeper of the spiritual, cosmic world. If we take human memory as an example, we can see clearly how the nature of Saturn is altered if it penetrates neither the organic processes nor matters relating to the soul and to destiny.

Saturn, as we know, calls forth human memory. It is a soul faculty that expresses itself generally in the bodily-physical nature of human beings. What occurs in the creation of a memory picture is a kind of weighing-down and at the same time a rendering selfless of a sense impression. Instead of an impression flitting past, it becomes somewhat fixed. Instead of the sensations and emotions called up by the immediate event the memory spreads a calmness over the experience. Saturn takes care of all of this. Just as Saturn closes off the solar system from the heavens of the fixed stars, so do human beings in memory shut themselves off from the surrounding world. That is no mere comparison, but a deep peculiarity of the Saturn sphere that human beings experience when they enter it in the life between death and a rebirth.

If a person starts on the path of inner development, he or she brings about a change in their memory. It becomes a faculty of knowledge. And now Saturn meets such a person as that being who provides him or her with those qualities that are very specially needed by the spiritual investigator. Saturn lives in the past, within the history of our solar system. It knows how to portray this in a wonderful way to one who can raise oneself to the Saturn being. Then Saturn is no longer "the great malefactor" of traditional astrology, but confers on the human being just those qualities that replace ordinary memory. Through an ever-renewed experience the spiritual researcher creates those forces that take the place of the old mechanical memory. This experiencing, the necessary concentration and meditation, must, however, come from human beings themselves out of their free spiritual activity. Then the Saturn forces come to meet them, and support them spiritually in the way they have supported themselves as human beings in ordinary life through the soul and bodily memory. And then Saturn can disclose to us the cosmic past, as we find it described in Rudolf Steiner's *An Outline of Esoteric Science* (compare also end of Letter 8, Year One).

In ancient times it was known that Saturn binds the soul nature (the astral body) to the human physical body, and that this connection must be a proper one if a person is to be guided to initiation. Therefore in the Egyptian mysteries, when someone was to go through initiation the position of Saturn at his birth was taken into account. If the position was an unfavorable one according to the conditions of those times, then the person was rejected. No one would have considered this to be a special hardship, but rather something like a law of nature. One felt oneself to be entirely a part of the cosmos. Today no one need be denied the right to tread the path described in Rudolf Steiner's *How to Know Higher Worlds,* regardless of their horoscope, provided they are sound and healthy in their soul-life. By this fact alone we can appreciate the whole transformation of outlook that has occurred since pre-Christian times.

A person who tries, for example, to do a concentration exercise by focusing on a pin will experience the difficulty in mastering these free forces of Saturn, but will enter a relationship with the cosmic world in a "sense-free" manner and without an external compulsion of destiny. For this purpose one can advantageously make use of the Saturn forces that are not weakened by the Sun forces—those forces that radiate freely down to the Earth at night when the Sun and Saturn are in opposition. The very position that is so feared in traditional astrology—Saturn in opposition to the Sun, especially when the planet is at its zenith at midnight—is the one that opens the door to the spiritual world, if a person can call on the free Saturn forces. This position is one adapted to the occultist, to the spiritual investigator, though in the outer world it can call forth much opposition fraught with destiny. We find it strikingly in evidence in the case of Rudolf Steiner; and we see how when this constellation was repeated a second time, there was a very special occupation with cosmic questions. Just at that time also, Rudolf Steiner referred to the idea of the recurrence of the Saturn constellation, which we have been considering. So, to the modern human being, ways stand open to a free grasp of the cosmic forces, which work, however, according to law, according to the higher laws of the spiritual world. In order that modern humanity might come to this stage, people had for a while to be as free as possible from cosmic forces in their spiritual life. This period began in the fifteenth century. If one observes the development of astronomical and other conceptions of the world in the significant decades (during which a Copernicus, a Tycho Brahe, and a Kepler were working), one sees this process of becoming free from the cosmos very quickly complete itself. But since the rulership of Michael (from the last third of the nineteenth century) it has begun to be possible to bind oneself anew to the universe.

Again, in Christ Jesus we find this free and yet regulated relation to the cosmos lived in advance. In Rudolf Steiner's book, *The Spiritual Guidance of the Individual and Humanity,* it is clearly stated how that projecting back of the configuration of the heavens at the exact moment of birth, through which karma expresses itself in an individual manner, was not present in the case of the Christ. Rather, "the Christ always stood under the influence of the whole cosmos. He made no step without the cosmic forces working in Him. What came to pass here in Jesus of Nazareth was a continuous realization of the horoscope, for at every moment there occurred what otherwise only happens at a person's birth" (lecture 3).

Therewith a new ideal for humanity has been lived out beforehand. This could only be realized at that time and with that being who as Christ Jesus lived in Palestine at the beginning of our era. Yet the image has been placed before humankind of the perfect human being who has overcome the karma that expresses itself in the horoscope—the "moral legacy" of the previous Earth life, as Rudolf Steiner once called it- and who is only the expression of the cosmic Father-forces. "I and the Father are one."

For present-day humanity the realization of such a relationship begins only gradually. And here as everywhere, two paths of error stand open. One is to stay with the old astrology that likes to read something from the stars in a "human, far-too-human" way and apply this to human life, we have spoken of this enough. It is the luciferic temptation to hold to the ancient traditions, not to recognize the freedom that has become possible through the impulse of the Christ. On the other hand, Ahriman wants to take the human being as a cosmic being without considering the individuality, the legitimately unique personality. We find an impressive representation of this fact in Rudolf Steiner's third mystery drama, *The Guardian of the Threshold.* Strader, sent in the spirit by Benedictus, enters Ahriman's realm consciously and there finds twelve human souls whose bodies are sleeping. Their souls, in a condition of deeply dulled consciousness, speak out all sorts of beautiful-sounding phrases. These do not really arise out of their own ego, but are something through which they let the cosmic spirit of the zodiac speak, stammering, through them. For Ahriman this is a great joke, and he mocks at the poor souls. To Strader it is terribly painful that they must go through such an experience. For although what they speak is in part beautiful, and moral, he senses the being of their true humanity is not present. Indeed Ahriman says to him:

> *From time to time I take account of men*
> *And see both what they are and what they can do.*
> *And when I once have chosen out my twelve*
> *I do not need to search for any more.*
> *For if I come in number to thirteen*
> *The last is just exactly like the first.*

One sees that Ahriman knows very well that there are twelve signs in the zodiac and that people are formed according to them. Therefore the thirteenth is of equal value to him as the first. It is the same story all over again! Ahriman takes account of human beings only according to number, not according to individuality. He looks at them solely and entirely from the point of view of the horoscope! Strader, who stands within the world of technical science, must recognize just by this horrifying experience where the power of number lies. So when Strader speaks to Benedictus of his painful experience, Benedictus tells him that Ahriman has wanted to bind these human souls to Strader's own soul-nature "according to the measure and number" that have been taken from the course of the Sun through the twelve signs of the zodiac:

> *It was through Ahriman's power that you had to learn*
> *The meaning of number in the universe*
> *It was necessary for your own soul's course.*

Between the personal determining influences from the cosmos that work into the organic and soul-life (which present-day astrology would still like to consider) and Ahriman who on the basis of cosmic technology completely disregards the personality, we must seek the Christ who stands in the middle and who binds human beings and the universe together in freedom.

December 1928

Isis-Sophia

THE CHRISTMAS FESTIVAL that now again draws near turns the gaze of the aspiring human being in two directions: toward the inner nature of the human being with its wants and needs and toward the starry heavens in their majesty. From these heavens sounded the message of peace to the shepherds and shone the star that the wise men of the East saw, which guided them to Bethlehem. We know that the two manifestations point to two different birth events, events that lay months apart in time, but we will not occupy ourselves with that now. Rather we will consider the contrast between the wisdom that comes to the shepherds in the field and that possessed by the Magi who see the star in the East. Rudolf Steiner, in the Christmas lectures of 1920, has pointed to these two streams of wisdom and linked them with the mystery of Isis-Sophia. This is very closely connected with the evolution of mathematics and astronomy, right into our time and into the future, to the extent that the future lets itself be fructified by spiritual science. Therefore our Christmas considerations shall be devoted to just this mystery.

In ancient times a primal wisdom was spread over the whole inhabited Earth bound up with a primitive dreamlike clairvoyance. In the centuries that preceded the appearance of Christ Jesus this clairvoyance rapidly disappeared. At the time when the Jesus child, or the two Jesus boys [e.g., see Rudolf Steiner's *The Fifth Gospel*] were born, only in exceptional cases could human beings have direct experiences of the spiritual world. That indeed was the terrible pain of Jesus of Nazareth as he grew up, that the people around him could no longer hear the voices that could be heard by their fathers, and that the lofty spirit powers descended no more upon the altars that deserted, or even possessed by demons, still stood on the ancient religious sites.

Human beings in ancient times were gifted in two different ways. Some human souls—among them, as a last echo, the Magi—saw a starry world permeated with spirit and also experienced the minerals and plants in a world of color filled with visual images. A deeply spiritual astrology was peculiar to these ancient people, an astronomy that as yet did not calculate, but saw and heard, because "stars spoke once upon a time to human beings." That primal wisdom dwelt in Hermes [Trismegistus]—the reincarnated student of Zarathustra—who bore the astral body of Zarathustra and from whom such deep pronouncements have been handed to us, such as that concerning the creation of the source of all things: "The Sun is its father, the Moon its mother, and the Wind has borne it in its womb." The stars, and the mineral and plant worlds stirred a wisdom in these ancient people that was not intellectual, but that through a later metamorphosis has become our own present-day intellectual knowledge. In its original form it was imagination, a pictorial knowledge. That is one side of the divine Sophia, the side that is directed toward the outer world, and allows the human spirit to be kindled to wisdom by this outer world.

There was a different impulse at work in that stream which we see represented by the shepherds, who are its last remnants. These human beings are connected with the depths of Earth, with that which ascends from the Earth as forces, fluids, and as clouds of color, and binds itself with the human soul and also with animal life. These stream into human beings' souls and inspire them, fructifying especially the will and the life of feeling. Fervor, piety is the characteristic expression of persons of this stream, a wisdom of the heart, just as sublimity and majesty are characteristic of those who possess the cosmic wisdom.

The qualities that hold sway in the shepherds who experienced the message of peace from the heights are of a germinative nature. They belong to the part of the human will that can first come to complete unfoldment after death. In incarnated human beings they are especially active during childhood, then gradually withdraw in the course of life in order to light up again at death. In especially gifted persons only, they are also active in later life. If no childlike quality is preserved into old age, there is no geniality! Therefore the shepherds are childlike souls, taking the angelic message into their hearts with piety and reverence.

The cosmic wisdom of the Magi, in contrast, is an after-experience of what the human being passes through during the life in the spiritual world before birth. As one goes through the cosmic spheres, building up according to the stellar and planetary constellations the seed of a new physical body, a faculty remains that first appears in later life, when a person has become "old and wise." Before birth, human existence is bound to the cosmic realms. Cosmic realms were seen by the spiritual ancestors of the Magi. For them the stars were not points of light. Rather, even by day from the dark skies—for the blue color was at that time not yet visible—something spiritual streamed forth that the ancients referred to by name. These are names we still use to a great extent, though for the most part we do not understand them. This spirituality spoke to them of human destiny, and in particular the descent of the human soul to Earth through birth. This faculty was present particularly in ancient Persia among the Iranian people. It was cultivated until the sixth century B.C. when Nazaratos, the reincarnated Zarathustra, was the teacher of Pythagoras in Chaldea—right up to the threshold of that time when, because of the withdrawal of the ancient gift, the astronomy of calculation began to arise. One can say: In the child after the seventh year of life the power of calculation appears to the extent that the formative forces of earliest childhood are withdrawn inwardly. In the same way, at a certain point in history, to the extent that the old prenatal powers of imagination waned, there awoke in humankind the power of using mathematics and scientific astronomy, later even mechanics. Magi perception kindled from outside changed into a knowledge arising from the human being's own inner powers. The colorful outer world, the spiritual hosts in the dark vault of heaven, vanished from human sight. When human beings on Earth began to perceive the firmament as blue in color, the old clairvoyance was at an end. Instead of this there arises within the human being a colorless mathematics that is applied to an abstract astronomy, which treats the stars as mere points of light. Then, almost two thousand years later, out of this now fully intellectualized inner life, humanity developed the laws of physics and mathematics, and applied them to the starry heavens that had been emptied of spirit. This is the way that one stream of Sophia, the primal wisdom, has taken: from without to within, from seeing the mysteries of the stars to the bringing forth of abstract geometry, phoronomy [the purely geometrical theory of motion], and the like. In contrast, those human souls to whom the shepherd's souls belong as last descendants, experienced the counterpart of the starry heavens—the qualities of the Earth that make themselves known to an inner power of perception. Peculiarities of climate, of the soil, became known to these souls through the uprising fluidity, as well as by the aura of their fellow human beings and of the animals, everything in which the warmth of the Earth lives. This faculty as such vanished also. It changed because it could no longer act as an intermediary for the spiritual. It became external sensory perception that conjures before our eyes a nature devoid of spirit and soul. It went from the inner human being to the surface, into the sense organs, and became, many centuries later, the modern perception of nature—the present-day, abstract sense perception that has become the natural science of our day. The world of the investigator of nature is gray and colorless: behind all manifestations of color and all objects of sensory perception he or she surmises vibrations and atoms.

When Christ Jesus was to be born, there were still "in the East" the three wise men, formerly pupils of the great Zarathustra, who had pre-served the prenatal faculty, who were therefore still especially gifted to observe births, to judge from the constellations of the stars the approach of a soul about to incarnate. (It is significant that the Roman writer Cicero relates a Persian legend according to which the birth of Alexander the Great, as the future destroyer of Asia and Persia, was foretold from the stars by Magi.) The Magi at the beginning of our era see the star in the East. They follow it and it guides them to Bethlehem, stopping over the house in which lies the newborn child. We must not under-stand by this either an ordinary star or a new star or even a comet, or a planet, as well-meaning people sometimes do. What the Magi saw was in fact a definite celestial configuration, connected with the sign of the Virgin, in relation to that of Gemini, the Twins. From this experience emanated for them the last force of the prenatal clairvoyant power, in order that they might recognize the spiritual star of the reincarnating Zarathustra, and the path this "golden star" (for that is the meaning of the name Zarathustra) took in its etheric form to the place of the birth. The writers of the Gospels, with a final summoning of all the forces of the ancient wisdom—the ancient clairvoyance, were able to describe the history of Christ Jesus. In the same way the birth of the Solomon Jesus child—which was a preparation for the Christ event—was recognized through a final exertion of the ancient holy human forces. At this late date, probably only because of the unique nature of this event, these forces were still completely present and available for a few karmically preordained souls. They know, these wise men from the East, that with them this faculty will come completely to an end. So they offer to the newborn Jesus child as gifts the gold of wisdom, the frankincense of purified feeling, and the myrrh of pure will—all that had been, and that must become changed, in order to arise again in Christianized form. The offer of the ancient wisdom symbolized by the gifts of the kings out of the East was that ancient wisdom that was so great, so mighty that Rudolf Steiner said of it that the present day with its knowledge could blush with shame over it.

That is the Sophia, which has fallen into the abyss, as the Gnostic document the *Pistis Sophia* describes in such moving words. It is at the same time the ancient Isis who once mourned for Osiris. The destiny of the pre-Christian world, experienced in cosmic pictures, unites itself with what has come into the world through the Christ. Tragedy holds sway over this destiny, holds sway even into our time.

We have already examined the Isis-Osiris legend and seen how this relates to our time. Osiris was killed by Typhon-Ahriman, torn in pieces, and was then sought by Isis, who later became the mother of the child Horus. For the Egyptians, Osiris was a Sun god during his life and rule; they looked up to him as to a Sun being. In this respect he was for them a precursor of the Christ. The Christ cannot be slain for the Earth like Osiris. He lives on in the Earth's aura, even though the bearer of the Christ, the child born of the Virgin Mother at Christmas, died on the cross. For the human soul, Christ is always here. But the Mother, Mary Sophia, the Isis of olden times, becomes Sophia, and it is actually she who has vanished for humanity today. She it is who has been slain. And when we ask who has killed her, the answer is given in the Isis-Sophia meditation [by Rudolf Steiner] that was also given at Christmas 1920:

> *Isis Sophia,*
> *Wisdom of God,*
> *Lucifer has slain her*
> *And upon the wings of the forces of the world*
> *Has carried her away to distant realms.*

Until the time of the Mystery of Golgotha, Isis-Sophia worked in a twofold manner—through the shepherds and through the Magi, as ancient heavenly and as ancient earthly knowledge. We still find the last remnants of this wisdom working throughout the first pre-Christian centuries. It was used for the purpose of being able to penetrate more deeply into Christianity. So when, for instance, the Christ was

designated as the "Sun of Righteousness," John the Baptist was considered the Moon ("He must increase, but I must decrease"). And just
as Christ must have twelve apostles because there are twelve signs of
the zodiac, so the Baptist must have twenty-nine and one-half disciples,
since the Moon requires that many days to return to the Sun. The com-
mentator Clement Romanus explains that there were twenty-nine male
disciples and one woman named Helena, who as a woman only represented "half a man." One sees that here as in quite later times, human
history is ordered according to astrology. The celestial realm with its
laws is what is primary, and what comes to pass in history can only be
an expression of those laws.

All that formerly lived in this way and then, as in the example above,
became rigid and dogmatic or degenerated into superstition or fantasy
—all that has died out. It was killed by that other side of Christianity itself that believed the old must be destroyed in order for the new
to take root. The conflict of the Christian church with the gnosis is
well known—for the knowledge we are speaking of is the gnosis. Even
Origen, the Church Father who wished to bring a cosmic world conception into Christendom, was banished. Of the Isis of ancient times only
a coffin remains.

We can recognize today that there is a necessity in this conflict, that
it had to happen for the sake of our freedom. The human being would
not have become free of the old cosmic dependence had not the old
wisdom been forcibly withdrawn. The Christ-impulse was there, but at
first it was living only feebly and dimly in humankind. It was anchored
in the feeling nature of the human being. It did not yet live in human
knowledge, except indeed through the gnosis. And this itself had taken
on luciferic characteristics. The heavenly world was more familiar to
it than the earthly world. Some Gnostic sects even held the view that
Christ was not actually crucified, for he had not really and truly been
incarnated—that the life of Christ had only been an etheric phenomenon! The Church had to take a stand against such an outlook that
nullified the holy deed of Christ. She did this cruelly and thoroughly,
ruthlessly rooting out all that could call to mind the ancient wisdom.
Still today, clerics of the most diverse views shudder when the word
"gnosis" is heard.

But what has died must rise again. Even Lucifer will some day evolve
himself into a sanctified spirit. Out of the old Isis-Sophia shall the new

Isis-Sophia emerge. As the shepherds and the Magi, each in their own way, reverenced the Virgin along with the child and lay their gifts before her, there was the beginning of the new Isis-Sophia, Maria-Sophia. What today has developed out of the powers of the shepherds and the Magi merely works at making the coffin of the ancient Isis. Today we must seek this coffin. We do not need to look for the coffin of Osiris, for he who was bequeathed to us in place of Osiris is with us "to the end of the world." The coffin of Isis is not to be found on Earth, it is spread out in the heavens. It is modern natural science (astronomy and mathematics above all) that—arising only from the inner nature of the human being and then applied to a celestial realm—is void of spirit, and abstract laws are empty of spirit, too.

So we see how evolution passes through a zero point and must be reversed and come to a point of intersection. The power through which formerly the depths of Earth spoke to human beings, with which the shepherds could still receive the tidings of the angelic host, has become inactive and has now metamorphosed into human observation of the tapestry of the sense world, the external world of illusion or maya. It has become the view of outer nature held by physicians and scientific researchers, and lives as the basis of present-day natural science. What in early times was the astrology and astronomy of the wise—and was directed to the outer world, the heavenly spaces and the reaches of the stars—has gone inward and lives on as mathematics in those peculiar creations that are indeed once free but are as yet unable to grasp the concrete spirit.

Rudolf Steiner has remarked that a certain merging of the two streams of forces took place in ancient times and that this was among the Jewish prophets. They were men of the inner life in whom the qualities of the after-death experience were strong. But they did not only use these in their prophetic gift. They were exceptional men and in them the prenatal faculties also were active—the capacity of the Magi to see and predict the future. Thus they could point prophetically to the future of their people.

One could say that today a similar interpenetration exists. However, as long as Isis-Sophia has not arisen from her coffin, it cannot be wholesome. Scientific research does not stop before the tapestry of the sense world, but fantasizes behind it a material and mathematical world of atoms, vibrations of the ether, electromagnetic equations, and so on. All this is what lives inwardly as the abstracted Magi stream, and constitutes the present-day luciferic picture of the world. If mathematics penetrates through the tapestry of the sense world, it becomes technology. It manipulates the forces of the depths of the Earth, but in such a way that they degenerate into the ahrimanic—into the subsensible. Modern evolution calls out to us from all sides: Seek the Isis-Sophia, seek her coffin in celestial realms and in the netherworlds, and raise the coffin's lid with the strength that the Christ can lend! Then the inner life, which has become dried up mathematics, "will intensify itself in picture-form to become imagination."

Therein lives the progress of the ancient wisdom of the Magi. The Magi—the pre-Christians up to the time of the worshippers of the Christ, the three wise men from the East—used to see the heavens in mighty pictures. In the future human beings, if they transform abstract mathematics, will experience the recapitulation of these celestial imaginations. It is precisely with the mathematical faculty that human beings will understand the imaginations.

That which has become outer sense perception, which was formerly the heart-wisdom of the shepherds, must go further outward, not remain fixed on the surface of the body. It must leave it, become "body-free" knowledge, and then it will become inspiration. A new faculty of perception will be able to bring about for the people of the future what once the shepherds in the fields experienced in their simple hearts. Human beings will again "hear the angels sing." The whole of nature shall proclaim to us: God shows himself in the heights and peace can come to those who are of good will.

The simplistic understanding of space has dismembered Isis. She is poured out into the universe, shining in beauty, but dead.

We must seek her in the heavens. And in the materialistic nineteenth century, human beings mostly looked for her in the heavens. But they knew nothing of the new Isis, did not know that she has become Sophia and that she can be found only with the power of the Christ. And so developed that conception of the world which still prevails today and which is infinitely more widespread than one would assume. This is the mathematical-mechanical worldview, the prime example and model of which is an understanding of the starry heavens that is bereft of spirit.

Let us look at this nineteenth-century picture of the world. On the one hand, there is atomism, which sees the explanation of natural processes in the movements of the tiniest particles. On the other hand, there is in astronomy the mechanical way of forming concepts. This reached a certain conclusion after Laplace wrote his *Heavenly Mechanics,* and Le Verrier discovered Neptune using calculations based on this celestial mechanics. At the same time the "uniformity of matter in the universe" was presented by means of spectroanalysis.

One now thought: if one could follow and calculate the movements that ultimately take place in the human brain at the moment when a person experiences a sense impression in the same way that one follows and calculates the movements of the celestial bodies, then one would know exactly how the soul and the spirit work in the human being. Against this expectation du Bois-Reymond had to thrust his concept of ignorabimus—"we will not know." He explained that even if this ideal were realized and the movements of the smallest parts of the brain could be "astronomically" calculated, still we would never be able to know why, for us, these movements are transmuted into soul experiences.

In a lecture held in Berlin titled "What Has Astronomy to Say about the Origin of the Earth?" (March 16, 1911), Rudolf Steiner pointed out that exactly the same must apply for the whole starry heavens as for the human brain, namely, that one cannot ascertain from the movements the soul-spiritual reality that stand behind them.

> Imagine the human brain enlarged in the sense of Leibnitz and du Bois-Reymond to such an extent that we could walk about in it and look at the movements in it in the same way as we look at the movements of the celestial bodies. If in these movements of our brain we do not perceive anything of the psychic counterparts of these movements, we need not be surprised that when standing within such an enlarged brain—namely, in the universe—we cannot find the bridge between the movements of the stars in the heavenly spaces and the possible activities of soul and spirit which extend throughout the world spaces. These have the same relation to the movements of the stars as our thoughts, feelings, and soul experiences have to the movements of our own brain substance.

It is no wonder, then, that in the universe the astronomer can find nothing of a spiritual-soul nature that fills all space. Such a reality cannot be deduced from mere movements. In this way the astronomer is confronted with his or her limitations. One should have asked a question much different than that asked by du Bois Reymond: "Is it possible to proceed in another way to find the soul- and spirit-beings who fill cosmic space?" The answer is, yes, spiritual science and the knowledge gained through it; that is the new Isis, the new Isis-Sophia!

> Only then, when these forces of knowledge have been lifted to a higher stage, will it be possible to find in space and time something different from what was considered in the nineteenth century as the optimal realization of space and time: the movements of forces and atoms in space ascertained in an astronomical way.

A mathematics arising out of imagination! A natural science receiving inspiration! They can only arise from the human being. If we take such a simple truth as that of the interrelationship of the three dimensions in our ordinary space, with the structure and functions of the human form with its division into left-right, above-below, front and back, we shall see the human form itself as the prototype of mathematics. Such an enlivened mathematics, raised to imagination, will also be able to penetrate the starry heavens.

Rudolf Steiner said, "The astronomer of today sees of the starry heavens what a modern anatomist sees of the human being. And to the same small degree that a corpse is a human being does the content of modern astronomy encompass the starry heavens." If, however, we take what is given us in his *An Outline of Esoteric Science* regarding the origin of the universe through the Saturn, Sun, and Moon stages of development, we do not have a corpse-like astronomy. Then we have the other side of Sophia, of the new Isis, who today, invisibly to outer sight but plainly legible to imaginative vision, bears the inscription: "I am the human being. I am the past, the present and future. My veil shall every mortal lift." [See lecture of January 6, 1918, in *Ancient Myths*.]

But Rudolf Steiner says on another occasion:

> One must understand how Isis, the living, the divine Sophia had to be lost for the sake of that development which has driven astrology into the realm of mathematics, geometry, and of mechanics. But one will also understand that when out of this corpse-like realm, out of mathematics, mechanics, and geometry, living imagination is awakened, this betokens the finding of the new Isis. Human

beings must find this divine Sophia if the Christ-forces they possess since the Mystery of Golgotha are to become living within them, fully living—that is to say, permeated with light. [From lecture 3 in *The Search for the New Isis*, December 25, 1920.]

We are standing before a new event of the Christ:

The Christ in the course of the twentieth century will not appear again in his spirit-form simply because something external comes to pass, but only when humanity finds that strength represented by the Holy Sophia. . . .

"We look upon the crib in the right sense today only if we deeply experience with a unique sensitivity that which flows through space and then look to that being who entered the world through the child. We know that we bear him in us but we must approach him with understanding. Therefore, just as the Egyptian turned from his Osiris to Isis, so must we again learn to look to the new Isis, to the Holy Sophia." [From lecture 2 in *The Search for the New Isis*, December 24, 1920.]

Finally, we are again directed to the crib in which the shepherds found the Christ child. It is always the image of the infant lying in the crib between the ox and the ass that touches the human heart most deeply.

Ancient knowledge has vanished, and we have passed through a field littered with corpses. We are struggling for a new science, for the revivifying, the unveiling of Isis.

The will of Christ
Working in the human being,
Will wrest from Lucifer
And on the boats of spiritual knowledge
Awaken in human souls
Isis-Sophia,
The wisdom of God.

January 1929

The Life Between Death and Rebirth in the Light of Astrology I

WE WILL NOW ENDEAVOR to depict the path of the human soul between death and a new birth as it takes its course through the world of the planets and the stars and back again to Earth. What the soul experiences in processing its karma, and what it brings to expression in the germ of the new human body—this forms the foundation of a true astrology. In undertaking such a depiction we are of course entirely dependent on what the spiritual researcher Rudolf Steiner has shared with us. All the supersensible insights he brought down from the spiritual worlds over the years form a body of knowledge that shall guide our search for an astrology of the future. Naturally only a little of this can be considered here.

The human being who passes through the gate of death leaves the physical body and, as we know, lives on for a few days linked with the etheric body. During this time a person is still connected with the physical world, but particularly with the configuration of the planets at the moment of death. (In Letter 2, Year Two, this was referred to briefly.) At the time of birth a kind of fixing of the configuration of the starry heavens at that moment occurs, upon which everything later is projected. In the same way, the moment of death is something that remains fixed for further life in the spiritual world. The constellation— principally of the planets ruling at that moment—is like a summing-up of the previous life, of the karma of the incarnation just ended. And while the human being experiences the life-tableau in the etheric body, the retrospective pictorial remembering of the past life, the interrelated working of the planetary forces, continue to resonate within. Rudolf Steiner described this as something like swimming in embryonic water before physical birth, only the embryonic swimming goes on for a longer time. The forces that work in the embryonic existence are also etheric (working in fluids), but they are interpenetrated with Earth forces, strongly defined by the place on Earth where the embryonic life takes place.

The constellation that is present at the time of death imprints itself in the soul during the days of the retrospection and remains present for the first half of the life after death. When the soul returns again to be born, it must in some way adapt itself to this constellation or else the new life will not be properly related to the earlier karma or to the cosmos. It strives therefore to come back again with a constellation similar to the one under which it left the Earth, or at any rate to seek again an essential feature of the death constellation for the new birth. Of course, the aspects of the heavens at a certain moment are never repeated exactly. And what the soul goes through in the life between death and rebirth causes it to seek out other constellations that express, for the new incarnation, the karma that has been worked out. Perhaps one characteristic aspect (the relation between two planets) of the death-horoscope will be found in the new birth horoscope. If, for example, a soul has left the Earth under the constellation Saturn opposition Sun, as the most prominent of the aspects ruling at the moment of death, the next birth will take place under the same constellation (which occurs once a year), while the remaining planets will be differently situated than at the moment of death. Moreover, the place of birth will usually be a quite different one. A certain place leaves its mark on the person born there during the embryonic period and then especially at the moment of birth, through the configuration of the starry heavens in relation to the horizon.

It is of course difficult to study the connections between a death horoscope and the horoscope of the following birth; Rudolf Steiner's "karma lectures," however, make it possible to test a number of cases. They corroborate what has been stated and open up prospects for a historical investigation of the future.

What the soul next experiences after death is the laying aside of the etheric body—it has expanded into infinity and apparently dissolved—and the leaving of the Earth. One could even say that the soul leaves space and enters into time. And indeed it does so in a specific way that has a last touch of spatiality namely, it departs the Earth toward the east. For every place on Earth the east is that direction in which what is earthly (the horizon, the equator) meets the heavenly (the zodiac) in a special way. The celestial bodies rise in the east; toward the rays of the rising sun the soul leaves the Earth as the domain of space.

Rudolf Steiner has pointed out that in certain occult societies one uses the expression, "Brother So-and-So has entered into the eternal east," when a person has died. We have in this a valid expression of reality. The "gate of death," through which a human being leaves the physical plane in order to enter the spiritual world, is to be found in the geographical east. It is not relevant that one can conceive the east as a relative concept (because what is east to one person lies in the west for another). Rather this is a matter of a quite definite direction that coincides with the direction of the Earth's rotation, for the Earth rotates from west to east. (We will return to this subject on another occasion.) The rotation of the Earth—of which the human being, possessing four aspects, is completely unconscious—becomes, in the first days after death, a consciously experienced phenomenon. Thus, after death, human beings set themselves free from the physical world, then from the etheric world, and then enter the elementary world, into the sphere of the Moon. That sphere has the Moon's orbit as its outermost border. The soul gradually expands to the extent of this entire sphere. It encompasses all that lies within the circle described by the Moon. It has now arrived in the "land of soul," which in its lower regions is identical with the Moon-sphere. (Cf. April 1, 1913.) There the soul deals immediately with effects of its karma from the Earth life that has just ended. In the ether world of the Moon-sphere all that we have failed to carry to completion on Earth is inscribed as an actual record in the Akashic record. What a person has undertaken to do but has not completed, what he or she ought especially to have done in terms of self-development but has neglected—all this engraves itself into the Moon-sphere in the life after death. The faults and characteristics of human beings engrave themselves into the other spheres in the same way. This fact also has a strong connection with the free will allotted to us. If this engraving did not take place in the ether world of the spheres, the errors would express themselves directly in a person's physical body. A lie, for instance, would immediately blind a person. We are spared this direct punishment of our sins by the beneficent gods, so that we may do in freedom what is good. The force, however, that would otherwise work in the physical dimension gets repressed, and engraves itself in the cosmic ether. In the life between death and rebirth one confronts for the first time the consequences of one's earthly deeds, and especially of one's failings. There, the vision of these consequences in the ether cleanses the human soul, and awakens within it the will to atone for these deeds under the same conditions in which the deeds were performed—namely, when one has once more taken on a physical body. Indeed, the longing to again take on a physical body—"the thirst for existence"—arises through experiencing one's imperfections after death. Out of this longing the germ for the new Earth life is formed. Later, when one reaches the sphere of the Moon on the way to incarnation, this longing makes use of the appropriate configuration of the planets.

Moral faults are rarely inscribed in the Moon sphere. These are of a social, or rather unsocial nature, and are connected with other human beings. In the Moon sphere we must deal largely with what relates to oneself. If, for example, someone had not lived up to their talents, or had manifested imperfections that, according to the conditions of their life, they ought not to have, and that had not been eliminated right up to the time of death, these would be dealt with in the Moon sphere. There can also, however, be what Rudolf Steiner called a noble imperfection—ideals, intentions that the person had cherished but that, because of their magnitude, he or she had not been able to realize. An unfinished work of art, such as Goethe's [play] *Pandora*, is an example of this. Obviously the completion of *Pandora* would not be inscribed in the Akashic records, "but the fact—corresponding to the astral body of Goethe that he had the far-reaching design but had only carried out a portion of it. All that is inscribed between the Earth and the Moon" (lecture, March 12, 1913).

If there are many such entries from one soul, they do not remain bound to the karma of the single personality who has made them, who could not possibly balance them all karmically in a future Earth life. Rather, they become the common property of humanity. Rudolf Steiner pointed this out in the case of Leonardo da Vinci. Although this spirit accomplished many great deeds on Earth, the plans and aims that he did not realize and the plans that had to remain incomplete because the times were unfavorable or simply because of earthly conditions were much more numerous. What such a spirit inscribes in the etheric world detaches itself from him and becomes an inspiration for other souls who live upon Earth after his departure. While what a genius leaves behind in a completed state remains in a certain isolation within the earthly world, in his or her imperfect or unfinished works there lies the germ of continuing evolution. Something is lifted up out of the personal fate of a human being and is transposed from the sphere of necessity and karmic destiny to that of freedom. Instead of the unfulfilled goals of a Leonardo da Vinci appearing as karma in his next horoscope, they bring a new relation to the cosmos for those human beings who can receive them in freedom as inspirations.

We have discussed those things that affect the human being most closely and are therefore inscribed in the nearest sphere, the etheric sphere between Earth and the Moon. The first period of the after-death life—for those strongly bound to the Earth by desires, ambition, and so on—takes place much nearer to the Earth than to the orbit of the Moon. Distances that are apparently spatial correspond in the spheres of the universe to the gradual withdrawing of the soul from earthly relations, until in the real world of the stars it performs—with the help of the higher hierarchies—those exalted deeds that create the seed of a new human being. The immense distances of the stars from the Earth that modern science fantasizes—although the fantasy has a mathematical basis—expresses nothing more than the fact that human beings of the last few centuries have been estranged from such lofty spiritual activities. When human beings once more—while on Earth—understand the concrete tasks of the human spirit, especially in the middle period of the life between death and a new birth, then the heavenly worlds will again appear nearer to humankind.

In the sphere of Mercury, human beings after death are subject to other conditions. There they experience what they have become as moral beings, or—and this in terrible loneliness—what was unmoral (cf. *Life Between Death and Rebirth,* lecture 1, Nov. 5, 1912). Inscriptions are made here also, although not nearly so many as in the Moon sphere. There, what was inscribed were the unrealized plans, the neglected deeds, everything that wasn't brought to completion; everything that—as long as it remains uncompleted—concerns only the person themselves. In the sphere of Mercury, however, is inscribed what occurs between human beings but has not come to a proper conclusion—unfulfilled promises, for example.

In the sphere of Venus we experience all that unites humanity on Earth in groups that have a spiritual link, as in religious communities. The person who has been an atheist until death will live in this sphere in utter solitude. Lack of understanding for religious life is engraved here and forms karma for the next life.

We must now picture to ourselves that the soul on its return journey to a new incarnation again passes through the planetary spheres. What has been recorded there helps form our destiny, as something external that (apparently!) happens to us, or as new qualities woven into our new physical or soul nature. That which during life on Earth is repressed, that does not act as a moral force affecting the physical body, and then becomes inscribed in the universal ether, now emerges as an impulse of destiny. The human being cannot extinguish it, but must inscribe it into his or her own being.

Rudolf Steiner has given an example of a man who had inscribed an imperfection in the sphere of the Moon—and every human being records many things there every time—and afterward, in the sphere of Mars, inscribed a characteristic connected with his aggressive nature. When he then appeared again on Earth he had taken into his karma the imperfection engraved in the Moon-sphere, but Mars now stood in a definite aspect with the Moon—since the spheres revolve and various configurations of the planets come about. So Mars would work with the Moon, for example, through their conjunction—one placed behind the other—and the man would seek—through his combative forces—to overcome that which remained within him of the imperfection inscribed in the Moon-sphere.

So the positions of the planets actually show what human beings themselves have previously engraved in those spheres. When we consider the position of the planets astronomically, and also the position of the planets in relation to the fixed stars, these are a kind of indication of what we have ourselves inscribed there. The actual planets are not of consequence; what affects us is what we ourselves have inscribed in each sphere. Here we have the real reason why the constellations of the planets do indeed work upon the human being. It is because the human being passes through the spheres. When the Moon stands in a particular position relative to Mars and to a fixed star, the members of this configuration work together. This means the qualities of Mars together with those of the Moon and the fixed star work upon the person, and thereby occurs what can come about through their working together. So it is actually our moral legacy, deposited during the life between death and birth, that appears karmically in the new life as star configurations in our destiny. That is the deeper basis for the constellation of the stars and its connection with human karma (lecture, March 3, 1913).

The outer and inner planets differ in that with the outer planets, it is more the virtues of human beings that are inscribed, the positive soul qualities they have developed. Thus they give human beings forces for their new bodily nature, and these are important for their future karma, since they endow them with special faculties. In this respect the passage through the sphere of Saturn is of especial significance.

Let us say that a person has taken up during his or her life certain spiritual concepts, such as those of spiritual science. Then, for such a person passage through the Saturn-sphere—which for most people, since they can inscribe nothing there, is not consciously experienced, will be of deep purport. Saturn, which we know to be the planet of the spiritual investigator, will transform the inscriptions of the spiritually aware human being into bodily faculties in the next life, so that he or she will be gifted with spirituality by nature, will be born a person attuned to things of the spirit. The natural Christianity of the painter Raphael, for instance, his quite natural relation to the Christ impulse, is the disposition given him from the Saturn-sphere. This in turn issues naturally from his karma as John the Baptist, out of his many inscriptions in the Saturn-sphere as John the Baptist.

It will also be understandable that many souls cannot consciously enter the spheres of the outer planets, especially of Jupiter and Saturn, because they have nothing relevant to inscribe there. In the lectures held at Penmaenmawr (*The Evolution of Consciousness*, lecture 10, August 28, 1923), Rudolf Steiner has explained that such souls, instead of experiencing these planets, become the spiritual inhabitants of the planetoids, those small celestial bodies that lie between the orbits of Mars and Jupiter and which, looked upon spiritually, are colonies of Jupiter and Saturn. In the fourth mystery drama (*The Soul's Awakening*, scene 6), the soul of Felix Balde provides an example of inability to fully experience the Saturn region. He finds himself there in his spiritual life that lies between his incarnation as Joseph Kuhne (in *The Soul's Probation*) and his coming incarnation as Felix Balde. Saturn is described during this time as pouring out a multicolored radiance over the spirit region. The soul of the future Felix Balde must wander in solitude, repeating only empty words of destiny out of his last Earth life, for the spirituality of his incarnation during the Middle Ages does not lead to a "cosmic midnight in wakefulness of soul." The soul of Joseph Kuhne can be awake only in relation to the time determined by the Sun, and even then only becomes freed from its solitude under the spell of Lucifer.

We have not yet considered the passage through the sphere of the Sun, which is of immense significance for the life between death and a new birth. Here as everywhere else, the Sun places itself so as to separate and yet to unite the inner and the outer planets. Human beings live in the heart of the solar system—have themselves become heart—and there their relation, not only to other human beings and groups of human beings as in the spheres of Mercury and Venus, but to the entire human race, is what is decisive. And most decisive is the relation that they themselves have achieved on Earth to the Representative of Humanity, to the Christ, and also to Lucifer, that spirit who has encroached so powerfully upon the evolution of humankind.

It is during life on Earth that the human being must come to know the Christ impulse, because after the Mystery of Golgotha, the Christ dwells no more upon the Sun. In the Sun sphere a human being can only have an understanding for all humankind, only through the fact that Christ died for all human beings, regardless of race and religion. Because Joseph Kuhne lacked this understanding, he lived in the Sun sphere in dismal solitude until Lucifer became his deliverer (*The Soul's Awakening,* scene 5). Lucifer is the spirit who guides the soul's wanderings through the spheres of the outer planets. There he has his rightful mission. But he can only work in a wholesome way if Christ has first kindled the consciousness. Just as the Christ—that is to say, what we have taken up of the Christ impulse—leads us through the lower planets up to the sphere of the Sun, so does Lucifer lead us, insofar as we can maintain our consciousness, up to the Saturn sphere, yes, even to the spheres of the stars.

Then comes the moment that has been called the cosmic midnight, the middle of the life between death and a new birth, when the previous Earth life and its results have entirely gone into the cosmos, and the path of return to Earth is entered upon once more. For the soul who lives through this in wakefulness, this is an experience of the deepest meaning. We can regard this cosmic midnight as experienced in the Saturn-sphere (as depicted in scene 6 of the fourth drama), or as taking place in the Sun sphere (as described by Rudolf Steiner in many other places). In a certain sense the Sun sphere contains the other spheres within itself, so that one does not actually leave the Sun sphere even when one enters the Saturn period. For with the Sun sphere begins the "spirit-land" that also includes the spheres of the upper planets, where the human being has left behind as corpse the astral body of the last incarnation, whereas the spheres of Mercury and Venus represent the higher parts of the soul world.

In our next Letter we will consider how, from the moment of cosmic midnight, the new life on Earth is prepared and how karma shapes itself in connection with the world of the planets and stars.

The Life Between Death and Rebirth
in the Light of Astrology II

THE PATH OF A HUMAN SOUL toward a new incarnation leads especially into those regions that are important for the observation of karma as it comes to expression in the birth horoscope.

The "midnight hour of existence" is that time when the soul turns away completely from the last incarnation and faces the one to come. (In one of the glass windows of the Goetheanum, that depicting "Birth," the soul is represented in the upper part with a Janus-like double head. One countenance looks back to the life on Earth that has passed, while the other looks down upon the new parents who are to prepare the body for the soul.) All the experiences of the last life are metamorphosed into qualities and faculties for the next incarnation. They must now be incorporated into what is called the spirit-seed of the new life on Earth.

We generally picture a seed as something very small. That is only the physical seed. The spiritual seed, which must be present if anything is to grow, is bound up with the macrocosm; is first of all immensely large, as large as the universe. The human spirit has expanded itself out to the Saturn sphere and beyond. It lives in the world of the stars, in fact beyond the starry firmament, and looks back from there to the world of the planets. It passes through the zodiac, and together with the beings of the hierarchies that are active in the zodiac it forms the spirit-seeds of the single organs and limbs of the human physical body. The cosmic consonants, the images of the constellations of the zodiac, unite with the cosmic vowels that resound from the planets. The spirit-seed is formed according to how each zodiacal constellation works in conjunction with the planets. While the human soul resides in the constellation of Aries the head is perfected, but the "uprightness" that distinguishes the human being from the animal is also acquired. In Taurus we acquire the vocal cords, or the "capacity of sound creation," another thing that raises the human being above the animals. (Cf. Rudolf Steiner's *Man in the Light of Occultism, Theosophy and Philosophy,* lectures 5, 6.) (We are dealing here with the actual constellations, not with the "signs.")

Here, too, the imprints made by the human being in the various spheres work as actual factors in the formation of the spirit-seed. The planets shine spiritually, "from the other side," into the various zodiacal spheres precisely according to their movements. These planetary motions, simultaneously "heard" as the music of the spheres, function as cosmic-script and cosmic-speech, revealing to the human soul what it has done well and what it has done badly. The movements themselves are naturally the same for all those human beings who pass together through the experience of, let us say, Mars in Aries. However, the cosmic speech sounds different according to how the spheres to which the planets belong—Mars-sphere, Venus-sphere—have been differently prepared by the inscriptions that the human being has made there. (Cf. Rudolf Steiner's London lecture, November 19, 1922; *Goetheanum,* 6.50.) These tones are then interwoven in the formation of the future physical body. Thus, the physical body becomes an expression of karma.

All this happens under the guidance of spiritual beings; the human being would not be able to accomplish it alone. During this period the human being exists in the cosmic condition of "substantiality" that once characterized the entire world order. (See Letter 1, Year One.)

It is only the beings there, beings of the planetary and stellar worlds, among them also luciferic beings of the most varied grades, and those beings who extend even beyond the zodiac, who carry out the highest functions in the cosmos. But now comes the time when these beings begin to obscure themselves from the consciousness of the human soul. Indeed, the return to birth means that the purely spiritual withdraws more and more from the human being, and that he or she is led more and more toward their future sphere of work. Rudolf Steiner said that the planetary world lays hold of the incarnating human being with its "weight." (See Letter 8, Year One, where these relations were briefly referred to.) It is no longer just the upbuilding, organ-forming forces that especially work at this stage, but rather what, understood spiritually, corresponds to earthly gravity. Earthly gravity alone stands only at the foot of the ladder that leads from the cosmic-moral realm, represented to us by the starry world, down to the amoral heaviness of earthly nature.

Indeed it is the longing for this heaviness that seizes human beings when the world of spiritual beings closes itself to them and the revelations from that world become ever darker. The human being would be unable to endure life forever in the light of the spiritual world and thus has a hunger for the heaviness of the physical world. Thus in incarnated life, human beings are always drawn back after sleep to the physical body. The same is true of the human being between death and rebirth. The human being longs for the reassuring solidity that the Earth with its gravity provides, which at the same time renders possible the experience of freedom.

This longing for gravity streams out from Saturn, whose sphere the soul must now pass through again. Jupiter when its sphere is traversed bestows a certain joyousness upon this longing for weight, so that human beings can contemplate their new and perhaps difficult earthly tasks with even a feeling of joy. Mars gives a forceful, active grasp of the earthly tasks, an ability to courageously meet and deal with what awaits the human being. Venus, with her own weight, adds "a loving acceptance of the earthly mission to the forceful and joyful longing that has been bestowed by the other planets." (lecture by Steiner, December 10, 1920.) Once on Earth the human being experiences gravity and must first overcome it in standing upright and in walking. But gravity then becomes the foundation of our experience of freedom. It offers us a resistance that is only a "natural" one, and therefore leaves the soul free within the limits it — through its karma—established for itself.

In this passage through the spheres back toward Earth, the constellation in which a planet stands when the human being passes plays a role. If Saturn is in Leo, for instance, its influence is strengthened through the zodiacal Lion. Then the "longing for heaviness" will be modified in such a way that Saturn will give the human being the ability to "deal skillfully with external accidents of life" if this has been otherwise determined by prior karma. If Saturn stands at that time in Capricornus or Aquarius the planet will make the human being weak, a person who is easily cast down by the outer events of life (lecture by Steiner, November 5, 1922). These circumstances will also be expressed in the horoscope.

Until now we have dealt principally with general human characteristics (with the exception of the above remarks about Saturn). We must now consider what has more to do with the individual personality that is incarnating. This individuality has quite definite karma to work out, must be born in quite definite conditions. We come here to those realms that, on the one hand, are ruled by those beings of the hierarchies who have evolved in the proper way—the "good gods"—but who, on the other hand, could not be at all what they are without the luciferic impulse. This means particularly the nation into which one is born, whereby one also speaks a definite language; and the family, the line of ancestry; and finally, the parents who give us a physical body and with this draw us at the same time into the stream of heredity. Therein plays that human element which can never be excluded from an incarnation, that separates groups of human beings from other groups, through nationality and speech, or as in heredity, forces the soul to enter a body that can never be the full expression of its being. Rudolf Steiner relates to us the remarkable fact that very early in the process of rebirth, just after the "midnight hour of existence," when the spirit-seed has not as yet begun to form, it is already determined in what part of the Earth and into what nation a human being will be born. This decision has nothing to do yet with the direct working of the folk soul, who is an archangel belonging to the Mercury sphere. (We will come back to this later.) But it is Lucifer who in the higher spheres beyond the Sun must, as we have heard, play a large and also a justified role in seeking out for a human being the nation to which he or she will belong. If a person has taken the Christ into themselves upon Earth, he or she can assuredly preserve in their soul what they have acquired; they need not lose the fruit of their life after death. However, as a rule a person cannot yet, at the present stage of human evolution, determine his or her future karma out of their own being. People must let themselves be helped by Lucifer. That is a rightful task of "the bearer of light."

Lucifer seeks out the nation for our next incarnation. The decision requires that various things must come to pass in that nation so that there will be the right environment—historic, political and so on—for the soul when it is incarnated there, perhaps centuries later. Naturally, those souls destined through their karma to play an important role for their nation or for humanity through their nation, receive special consideration. One sees therein, one might say, the hand of Lucifer at work. The battles, wars, and revolutions that must take place through the centuries so that a soul may find its place prepared on Earth, these cannot happen without the activity of Lucifer. In a sense all that goes to bring this about is far removed from the lawful workings of the stars.

What rules there is the intervening hand of Lucifer. In the decision that comes later concerning the family into which one will be born something similar occurs. One cannot yet speak of definite parents, for those individualities who will be the parents are, as a rule, not yet incarnated themselves this early in the return to Earth; nor are the second, third, and fourth preceding generations. But a definite stream of inheritance is there, a "family tree," and this is worked upon in a preparatory way. When one thinks that things must be worked out, not only for the parents but also for the as-yet unborn grandparents and the great-grandparents, then one gets a picture of a whole weaving, ruling world of active forces that must be directed and guided by whole hosts of beings who belong to the hierarchies, but who are supported by Lucifer in this. The complicated, many-branched genealogical tree of an old family, gives but a static picture of the immense spiritual activity that streams out over the centuries to make possible the conditions for a single human life.

> If you imagine the greatest complexity that can be created here on Earth, it is primitive and simple compared with the mighty web of cosmic greatness and grandeur that is woven there, that is then pressed together, densified, through conception and birth, and that permeated with physical Earth material becomes the physical human body. [Lecture of November 5, 1922, as above.]

Rudolf Steiner once gave a concrete example of this activity. The appearance of Martin Luther had to be prepared for in the eighth and ninth centuries. Already the forces had to be directed to the nation where he was to work.

> Then again a time elapses. And next the question must be decided—and this is an awe-inspiring activity, although one can describe these things only with ordinary words—the question must be decided what characteristics should the parents have who are actually to produce the human being who is to be born at a definite place, at a definite time? That must all be settled already long before. . . . It had to be settled for Luther already in the tenth, eleventh century who his forefathers were to be, in whose family line he would be born so that the right parents could be there. (Lecture, April 27, 1913)

Luther himself was born in the fifteenth century. Here we can see the mighty activity required so that a single person can be born in accordance with his karma.

When the nation and the line of generation have been chosen for a human being in this way, the moment also comes later when the parents are chosen—when a link, at first still of a soul and spiritual nature, is formed with the parents. The human soul takes much more part in this than in the working upon the stream of heredity in general. We have actually chosen our parents. That happens when—after the passage through the sphere of the Sun—the human being prepares to enter the sphere of Venus. There he or she must clothe themselves again with an astral body. This astral body with lightning speed rushes together from all sides, in the way iron shavings collect around a magnet. It is an exact expression of the karma that has been worked out, and it has the form—as Rudolf Steiner describes it—of a bell, open at the bottom, which exactly mirrors the being of the soul in many nuances of color. Such bell formations shoot here and there in the astral world with terrific speed during a time that is only measured by hours, and thus seek out a parental pair within the limits of the previously determined family line. (Cf. *At the Gates of Spiritual Science,* lecture 5.) Here the soul's link with the parents is now established. In the Venus sphere, the sphere of work of the archai, the extent of the connection of the person with his or her family is decided—the freedom of the soul or its dependence on the family.

Here the inner planets, with their direct relation to the Sun and Earth, begin to play a role. For someone will take a different position in their family if, as they pass through the Venus sphere, they encounter the planet Venus on this side or on the other side of the Sun. If Venus is situated so that it sends its beams to Earth—that is, if it shines as a morning or an evening star—then the person will become someone who feels very bound up with the family. If Venus is in conjunction with the Sun, especially in superior conjunction (in transition from morning star to evening-star (see Letter 7, Year One), then the person's progress will be but slightly affected by the planet; he or she will not be very much bound up with the family. (See lecture, November 12, 1922; *Goetheanum,* 6.44.)

Then follows the passage through the Mercury sphere. There human beings are connected to the nation to which they will belong, by that nation's archangel. One does not choose here. This has happened much earlier with the collaboration of Lucifer, and moreover, a choice would no longer be possible, for the incarnating soul has already in the Venus sphere been connected with a definite human pair—and the family usually belongs to a definite nation. A distinction must be made between the choice or assignment of the nation and then of the family that has occurred earlier, and this establishment of a soul connection first with the parents in the Venus sphere and then with the folk soul in the Mercury sphere. In the latter, in which the forces of the folk soul are mediated by a people's respective archangel, the astronomical position of Mercury plays a role. The position of Mercury in relation to the Sun and Earth at the time of a person's passage through the Mercury sphere determines the extent of their connection during life with the folk soul.

Naturally, all these relations are extraordinarily complicated and not to be expressed in a simple model. One need only recall that according to the researches of spiritual science the planet Venus is actually within the Mercury sphere, and that Mercury is in the Venus sphere, to see how here, too, the linking with nation and family is crossed and blended in a remarkable way. For instance, Venus gives the ability for a particular language to be spoken on Earth; through Mercury, the planet of the folk soul, this language is directly determined. And Mars bestows speech in general, the universal word, which is transformed through the power of Venus to the human word. (In Letter 8, Year One, brief reference was also made to these cosmic metamorphoses.)

For human beings this is a time when they themselves can only perceive the ever-weaker revelations of the spiritual beings; they no longer have a direct interaction with them. They appear to human beings only in pictures. The consciousness of the spiritual world becomes ever more dim. The new incarnation approaches ever nearer. The human being lacks at this time not only the physical body, but also the etheric body. He or she is a being of soul and spirit, which draws itself more and more together. The already formed spirit-seed of the future physical body becomes smaller and smaller, and the attention of the soul is increasingly directed to the mighty task that lies before it: out of the spirit-seed to make a human being who can experience his or her destiny on Earth.

The most important things in this connection take place in the Moon sphere, which the human being now enters. This is the moment of the incorporation of the etheric body. This process is completed out of a feeling of desertion, of forlornness. The spirit-seed, which has been built up through long periods of time, is lost to the soul in the Moon sphere. Suddenly it is no longer there. The fruit of life and work since the cosmic midnight seems lost. In fact, the spirit-seed fruit has begun its journey to Earth, to conception. Through this, in a brief and definite time the etheric body is incorporated into the human being. This event is immensely significant just for the astral connections. The etheric body is not added in as a separate entity itself, as was the case with the astral body. Rather, with the help of supersensible beings, it is formed out of the etheric forces in the whole planetary system. In this the spiritual inhabitants of the Moon are especially active. The Moon is a true mirror of the universe. It not only reflects the light of the Sun, but really gathers all cosmic influences within itself. And the Moon-beings observe all that goes on in the planetary system. They observe what the human being has experienced with Saturn, Jupiter, Mars, and so on, and prepare the etheric body accordingly. The etheric formative forces are drawn from the planets, the "moral ether," as well as from the four kinds of ether— above all, the light-ether, "the flowing light of the cosmos." Sunlight, however, which would work destructively, is excepted. It can only be included in the human etheric body in the form of moonlight, the light of the Sun rayed back from the Moon. And when at new Moon there is no moonlight, the whole remaining cosmos works upon the forming of the etheric body. It is then that what Rudolf Steiner called the "moral ether," or the "inner side of the etheric body," is incorporated, while the outer side is formed at full moon (lecture, April 21, 1924). The Moon-beings from their lunar viewpoint observe the configurations that are present and the location and movement of the planets, and read from this a person's fate insofar as it should come to expression in an etheric body. There a person actually encounters his or her whole destiny as they had brought it with them through death in the previous Earth life. But at the same time, he or she meets it with all that they themselves have become in the meantime. The Moon-beings create the true balance according to their cosmic observations. Through the etheric body they combine the previous life with the future one and weave karma into the soul.

We will break off our considerations at this important point, and will continue them next time.

March 1929

The Life Between Death and Rebirth in the Light of Astrology III

THE PASSAGE THROUGH the Moon sphere of which we were speaking last time is characterized at its beginning by an important event that takes place a long time—or perhaps a short time—before the incorporation of the etheric body. Again a decision is involved. After the decisions as to parents and race there comes, just at the passage into the Moon sphere, the decision as to sex. Now the question of which sex is most appropriate for the karmic circumstances of the coming incarnation is decided. And here again the phases of the Moon play a role. (The London lecture previously quoted refers to this also.) For a man to be born, the passage to Earth, passing by the Moon, must take place when, as seen from the Earth, the Moon is new. Viewed from the other side of the Moon, the Moon is actually full. The full Moon that sheds its light on Earth is not meant. Rather, it is the other side, the side always turned away from Earth, that sends the reflected light of the Sun out into the universe. Such light and the forces bound up with it shine toward the human soul which, since it wants to accomplish its next Earth life as a man, is approaching the Moon at this time. For a woman it is the opposite. When the light of the full Moon rays down on to Earth the soul draws near the Moon, which has its dark side turned toward it. For when we here on Earth have the full Moon turned toward the Earth, the other side of the Moon is then steeped in darkness.

The side of the Moon turned away from Earth has fourteen daily phases from new Moon through the first quarter to full Moon, and so on, as does the side turned toward us.

Think of the Sun as being above Earth and the Moon, and of Earth as being in the center of the Moon's orbit. The Moon goes around

Earth in one month. (Earth and Sun are here regarded as stationary since their movements in relation to each other are not a factor.) We human beings on Earth always see but one side of the Moon. The far side remains for the most part always invisible, presenting itself only to the descending soul. In the drawing then, we must imagine that whoever is to become a man comes from "above" so that the illumined side of the Moon shines toward him, while Earth is having a new Moon. The woman will approach the Moon, in terms of the drawing,

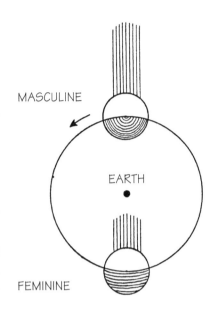

MASCULINE

EARTH

FEMININE

Figure 33

from "below," and thereby be permeated by the forces that radiate their activity into the universe from the dark side of the Moon. On Earth it is then the time of the full Moon. These observations show how we enter more and more into relations of space, which already have a connection to Earth.

It was Kepler—if we may allow ourselves a little historical digression—who first had the courage to consider these lunar relationships in a quite concrete way. Stimulated by the Copernican system, which he entirely supported, he had to perceive the Moon as a celestial body that moved freely in space just as did Earth, but that because of its deficient axial revolution (it is dependent in this movement entirely upon Earth) has something like a near side and a back side. The far side is distinguished from the near side in that it can never be "shone on" from Earth. It knows neither "full Earth" nor "new Earth," only a fourteen-day period of unbroken sunshine, alternating with a fourteen-day period of complete darkness. In a charming, richly imaginative, and also fully scientific way, Kepler has described these relationships in his *Moon Dream*—or rather, he lets a Moon-demon, conjured up by a wise woman in Iceland, describe them to the woman's son, a former student of Tycho Brahe. It was a courageous act to make clear

to himself with all the details the astronomical realities of both the
Moon's hemispheres. Later astronomers, building on this description,
have from time to time wished—bemoaning their fate—to have an
observatory upon the side of the Moon turned away from Earth. There
the disturbing conditions of our Earth environment are absent, the sky
is never clouded, and for fourteen days there is neither the disturbance
of daylight nor of night light, just an unbroken, blackest darkness in
which only the planets and fixed stars shine. One cannot help thinking
that such a Moon observatory, from which one looks out into the vast
cosmos, exists in a spiritual sense, and that the Moon beings of whom
we spoke last time are the observers there. Kepler depicts what the
human soul encounters in passing through the Moon sphere, though we
must, of course, conceive the actual situation in a more spiritual way.
Even what was described as the new Moon here, full Moon over there,
and so on, concern light-ether and astral realities; it is not so much a
matter of the physical nature of the Moon.

When one considers the human being in this stage one must remember that here, as in the choice of nationality and family, it is above
all a question of soul and spirit relations, not at all anything physical. Although a person at this point already has a connection with a
folk spirit, he or she can in no way be looked upon as "German" or
"English." In the same way, sexuality is only characterized by what
distinguishes man from woman in terms of soul quality. This soul
nature is then incorporated into the spirit-seed of the physical body,
and later, in the embryonic life, the physical differentiation according
to sex occurs. In this peculiar double aspect of the Moon with its contrasting phases depending on whether one observes the near or the far
side, there is a reference to the double sexuality of the human being—an
individual with a female physical body having a male etheric body and
vice versa. One must think that in this stage the human being has not
yet incorporated the etheric body, and is thus still only a being of soul
and spirit.

Rudolf Steiner has given further details about the activity of the
Moon during the human being's descent. For example, it can happen
that one who is to become a man and therefore is drawing near Earth at
new Moon (or at full Moon, as seen from the cosmos) remains above in
the Moon sphere for half a Moon period. In other words, he waits for
the next full Moon before he proceeds into the Earth sphere. If he does

wait he will have black hair and dark eyes. The woman who waits for the next new moon phase (again observed from Earth) will have fair hair and blue eyes. The second half of the revolution of the Moon around Earth therefore brings another decision, but now one that is connected even less with the "whole man" than the decision of sex. It is a matter of the color of hair and eyes. Of course, it is not physical hair that grows on a person at this time. What forms itself as a predisposition at this point is what one experiences of a soul quality in the dark or light eyes and hair of an incarnated human being.

We can now say that the new human being, prepared to this degree, leaves the Moon sphere and enters into the Earth sphere, or what was called in earlier times the sub-lunar or elementary world. Accordingly, conditions of Earth begin to have an ever-increasing meaning for him or her. We must still not consider these from their physical aspect. Rather, they manifest themselves from the cosmic-astral or even from the elemental aspect. For Earth, the descent of souls is something like an insemination. It is part of the course of the year. Just as the plant seeds are placed in the Earth at a definite time of year, where they must go through their waiting and maturing time, so must the human seed, the spiritual archetype of the future human being, likewise enter at a definite time into the aura of the Earth. This period in northern Europe corresponds to winter, from Christmas to the beginning of spring—namely, that space of time in which Gabriel works as cosmic archangel. (See lecture 5 on the archangels, *Newssheet,* Michaelmas, 1926.) There-by, astronomically we have a definite relation between the Sun and Earth. There is no longer a direct relation to the zodiacal constellations or to their spiritual beings as there was in the more central time between death and a new birth. One can say: the human seed makes the transition from the astral to the etheric, from the "constellations" to the "signs." For the beginning of winter means astronomically that the Sun stands in relation to Earth at the deepest point of its yearly path. It is in that part of its path that has always been designated by the sign of Capricorn. At the beginning of spring the Sun crosses the equator; day and night at that point have equal length, and the Sun is in Aries, the sign of the Ram. Solar-earthly relations! It is not a matter of the weather that first makes itself felt at the time of year when a human being is born but what, astronomically and in terms of soul and spirit, is connected to the seasons, in this case to the winter.

The final uniting of the spiritual human germ with the fertilized egg in the mother can indeed take place anytime during the year. It is not connected to the course of the seasons, yet the uniting with Earth, the descent into the Earth sphere, only occurs during the three months mentioned.

At one time in the evolution of humanity, at least among those peoples who worshipped Hertha or Nerthus, human fructification could take place only in the period that immediately follows the beginning of spring (the beginning of spring marking the end of the time of year when human souls could enter the Earth's aura). From the day of the [first full Moon after the] vernal equinox—which today we call the Easter full Moon—was the time for the propagation of humanity. [Cf. Endnote 78 in the 1980 edition of the Letter.] All this was regulated through the mysteries, and humankind experienced the event in holy visions. The births occurred then only in the time of the Twelve Holy Nights or a bit later. It was a great transformation in human evolution when—about 3000 B.C.—this cosmic order broke down and human conception (and hence of course human birth) began to take place throughout the year. Through this, human beings were set free from the old dreamlike clairvoyance. Nevertheless, even today the Earth is fructified by the instreaming human seeds only during the period from winter to spring. If the conception takes place later in the year, then the soul must wait for a long time in the area surrounding the Earth. The destiny of a soul is affected by this. The strength of a person's connection to the Earth is determined by the length of time he or she has to wait for the uniting of the spirit-seed with the earthly seed that proceeds from the parents.

With this description we have arrived again at the point where we broke off last time, at the moment when the fruit of the most exalted spiritual activity, the created spirit seed, departs from the soul. This spirit seed arrives earlier on Earth than the human being. It unites itself with the heredity substance that comes from the parents. The consequence of this loss of the spirit-seed to the soul is the incorporation of the etheric body. This event still takes place entirely in the Moon-sphere, which completely encircles the Earth and to a very slight degree also interpenetrates it, although the human soul is already within the "Earth environment" in which the active workings of the planets are reflected in a special way. It is just these planetary influences that are woven into the etheric body.

At this point there is another dramatic moment that mirrors a process that occurs immediately after death. When the etheric body is about to be laid aside, there is a tableau of the life just ended, and in powerful, solemn pictures the whole life presents itself once more to the watching soul. In the same way the soul, at the moment when below on Earth the fructification is taking place, experiences a preview of the life to come. Again that life shows itself in pictures, but of course not in the detail possible with an Earth life that has already run its course. Nevertheless, the destiny that awaits a person in the coming life reveals itself in a broad way. The life-tableau after death is received in a deeply earnest condition, quite undisturbed by personal feelings. The vision before birth, however, has a powerful, unsettling effect on the soul and this explains much concerning presentiments and premonitions of destiny that people have during their lives on Earth. Rudolf Steiner, in referring to this life preview (lecture, May 28, 1907), tells how a soul seeing the difficult life that awaits it, can receive a shock, and to a certain degree can draw back from the incarnation. This creates the possibility that the incarnation will be one of extreme mental retardation or of an epileptic. This information lets us peer deeply into the mighty workings of karma, which in its details certainly is not determined by the incarnating soul or by its preferences, but by mighty spiritual beings to whom human karma is like an open book.

This plainly shows a parallel between prenatal life and the life after death, which we will find in other connections. For example, just as a human being leaves the Earth in the direction of the east after the dissolution of the etheric body, so in a certain connection does the return to Earth again come from the direction of the east.

During the life in the spiritual world the human being has become a sphere, a planetary, celestial sphere, and out of this forms his or her head. When human beings descend to Earth, they are essentially head-organization, and since the head comprehends the whole sphere, we cannot speak of a definite direction in regard to it. The head is the transformation, the metamorphosis of the whole organism of the previous life on Earth. One can say: Human beings bring the head, which has a tendency to roundness, out of the spheres. The limbs and the entire metabolic system are first formed by Earth itself at a later period, and attached to the head during the embryonic time. The particular district where the mother happens to be before the birth takes place has a great influence upon just this "lower" aspect of the human being. The forces

for it come from the center of the Earth and are differentiated by the
different terrestrial regions. Between the head system and the metabolic-
limb system lies the chest system, consisting of the heart, lungs, and
the circulation of the blood. These organs of the chest are not brought
from the sphere of the farthest spaces of the cosmos nor are they formed
on Earth—but rather, as Rudolf Steiner put it, out of the half-sphere.
They are a hemisphere whose central point in terms of ordinary earthly
geometry is at an infinite distance, but lies in the direction of the east.
(See lecture, January 21, 1917.)

Here again we see emerge the concept of the east, which in a
remarkable way binds together a spiritual concept with a geographical,
astronomical one. The east is a definite direction for the whole Earth—
and at the same time, for a definite place on Earth it is a direction that
disappears on the horizon. From there the east seems to go further into

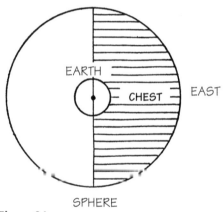

Figure 34

the endless indefinite, but
it is in this direction that
the Sun appears daily and
the stars and planets rise.
In this direction the dead
disappear into the spiritual
world, leaving the three-
dimensional world behind.
Human beings come from
this direction insofar as
they bear within them the
rhythmic system, insofar
as they carry their destiny
with them in their breast—their "beat of heart and lung." We find this
significance of the easterly direction again in the birth horoscope, where
the precise eastern point—the so-called ascendant—is considered the
most important point in the whole horoscope.

The human being at this stage exists as a threefold being in another
way. There is soul itself, clothed in the etheric body and about to reunite
with the lost spirit-seed. The spirit-seed is there as a second entity and
works as the stimulating, form-giving factor in the ovum, whose substance, thrown into chaos by fertilization, lets in the cosmic forces of the
spirit-seed. In the ovum itself the third element is active—the substance
of heredity which, given by the parents and forefathers, comes from

the whole stream of generations. Because this stream of heredity comes originally from the spiritual world, it has a cosmic connection with the soul that also has come from the spiritual world.

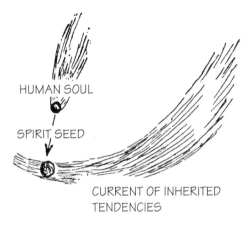

HUMAN SOUL

SPIRIT SEED

CURRENT OF INHERITED
TENDENCIES

Figure 35

The union of the soul—or the ego—with the fructified seed occurs very soon, in the third or fourth week of embryonic development. Only in the case of great initiates is there a connection at an earlier stage. In such a case, right at the beginning the seed is taken hold of by the ego so that nothing happens without the activity of the spirit itself. It is not possible for us to describe the quite wonderful development of the embryo life that runs its course according to the laws of the cosmos. We refer for that to the articles by Dr. Koenig in *Natura*. The laws of the Old Moon existence live in what forms there. The soul itself experiences in wonderful living images the work of the etheric body, of the astral body, and of the ego in the construction of the new physical body. These images, however, escape the consciousness like dreams.

We have followed the human soul on its path—in the sketchy and incomplete way that alone was possible—and seen how, going through death, it enters the spiritual world, travels through and experiences the heavenly realms, and finally returns to Earth. This description applies to the time that comes after the Mystery of Golgotha. If one wishes to describe pre-Christian times various things must be represented differently. That has already been mentioned in the description of the Sun sphere. Christ no longer lives in the Sun sphere. His throne stands empty, and the throne of Lucifer towers high and mighty. Indeed, since the Mystery of Golgotha, the human soul can find Christ on the Earth itself. The Christ lives in the aura of the Earth and he meets the soul in the moment of death. But one can also say that souls meet the Christ in birth. When they incarnate they make themselves at home in that world which, since Christ lives among us today, is nearest to the Christ. Earth is just that world where the message of the Christ can penetrate into human souls. They no longer need to prepare themselves in mystery-places to seek for the Sun-God in the sphere of the Sun. The Christ is with us always, until the end of the world. Our life on Earth becomes immeasurably important. Although very short compared to the life between death and rebirth, our earthly life creates the conditions for the whole of spiritual existence. One can understand much of the one-sidedness in the historical development of Christendom. This development was based on the idea of communicating to humanity the unique significance of life on Earth, which moreover was understood as a non-recurring event. This sowing has had a rich harvest. We live in a time when the Earth as never before is taken to be real and important; yet for the most part that is not on account of the Christ. And so we see again that it was only out of the mystery wisdom that humanity of our time could be taught why the Earth must be for us a place that is sacred and full of meaning. Rudolf Steiner had to reveal to us that the Earth is the body of the Christ who has come down to us from heaven, that the power of Christ penetrates and indwells the whole of the Earth, and that in bread and in all the things of the Earth we should experience this power of the Christ springing forth. It was also Rudolf Steiner who bestowed upon us the knowledge of death and rebirth.

So we look to Good Friday of Holy Week, when "in Christ we die" was prepared. We look to Easter Sunday of the resurrection, where the event took place that has sanctified the body of the Earth for the human soul, and has given the Earth its meaning, so that the soul returns ever and again through birth in order to find the Christ, in order to be able to take the power of Christ with it into the spiritual world when the hour of death strikes once more.

April 1929

The Horoscope

THE HUMAN BEING who is building up a new body in the ten lunar months before birth lives in an environment that is still entirely per-meated with the activity of the cosmic world. The environment is not entirely the "world-of-finished-work," although the earthly body is being prepared for that world. Cosmic forces are directly involved in the formation of the body. The Moon, for instance, participates especially in the building of the head. At every full Moon the back of the head is worked on, at every new Moon the front, and at the quarters the two sides. Just as an artist cannot complete one portion of a work and leave the rest unfinished, so the cosmic forces—working directly—build up the human body gradually during the embryonic period. The later physical body after birth, adapted through birth to conditions on Earth, also experiences these forces (see Letters 2 and 3, Year Two), but they no longer penetrate directly into the structure of the organism, and, most importantly, they withhold themselves from the person's consciousness. Between these two conditions lies birth, which in a very powerful way represents an incision into the entire human life. With the first drawing of breath the earthly world enters the human being. At that moment we free ourselves to a certain extent from the cosmos, but in the same moment the cosmos leaves a permanent image of itself imprinted in the brain. Rudolf Steiner speaks of this in *The Spiritual Guidance of the Individual and Humanity*:

> If a person's physical brain were extracted and its structure clair-voyantly examined, so that it might be seen how certain parts are situated in certain places and send out appendages, it would be found that the brain of each individual is different. No two people have an identical brain. Then let us imagine further that this brain

could be photographed in its complete structure so that one would have a kind of half-sphere in which every detail is visible, then this would make a different picture in the case of each person. And if one were to photograph a person's brain at the moment of birth and photograph also the heavens exactly over the person's birthplace, then this latter picture would have exactly the same appearance as that of the human brain. How in the human brain certain parts are arranged, so are the stars situated in the heavens. The human being has within himself an image of the heavens and each has a different one, depending on the time and place of birth. That is an indication that the human being is born out of the whole world.

Perhaps it will be possible some day to prove this anatomically and physiologically. While the building-up of the brain proceeds in the way described during the entire embryonic period, the moment of birth brings an imprint that corresponds with the starry heavens. The passage quoted makes it clear that the Earth is also a factor in this image that the human being carries throughout life. The Earth plays its part through the exact geographical spot and the exact moment of the day or night at which the birth occurs—in other words, through the appearance of the horizon and the meridian. The horizon divides the zodiac and the whole remaining starry heavens into two parts, one above the Earth and visible, the other concealed by the Earth. The constellations and the planets below the horizon can work only through the Earth—and therefore can only exercise an influence that on one hand is weakened, but on the other is even more spiritual ("The Sun at Midnight"). The part of the heavens to be found exactly above the horizon depends upon the time of birth. This also determines which of the zodiacal constellations lies on the eastern horizon, at the point where the zodiac (or ecliptic) and the horizon intersect. This is the so-called ascendant—the constellation rising just at that moment. The degree of latitude of the place, which denotes at the same time the altitude of the celestial pole under which one is born, also changes the view of the heavens as seen from the Earth. The place of the Sun in the celestial picture is dependent on earthly circumstances, not only the time of day, but also the time of year. The Sun is situated at a definite point of its yearly path. It receives the human being at birth into its circular path. Whether it is summer or winter, a cold or a warm time of year, is a destiny, a reality for the newborn, something that suddenly crystallizes and then remains fixed at its starting point. The "sign" in which the person is born expresses itself in the month as part of the yearly course of the Sun in relation to the planet Earth.

In order to make this clear we include here a chart representing the heavens for six o'clock (local time) at Dornach on March 21, 1929. The eastern point is on the left, the western on the right. (This is opposite to the arrangement of Figure 34 in the last letter, which was made by Rudolf Steiner. He used to draw the zodiac as one often finds it on old star maps, in a clockwise manner. Here we adhere to the way of presentation now in common use, except that—we are taking no account of the so-called houses of ordinary astrology.)

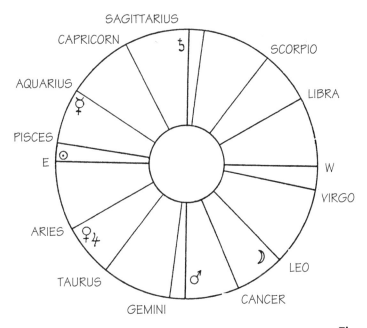

Figure 36

The plane of the diagram is that of the zodiac. The east-west line represents the intersection of the horizon, and the vertical represents the meridian of Dornach, 47 $\frac{1}{2}$° north latitude. For the moment chosen (the crossing of the equator by the Sun, which therefore stands exactly at the vernal point) the meridian must be vertical, that is, cutting the ecliptic into two equal parts. When, however, the zodiac no longer passes through exactly at the east and west points, but has its starting point more to the south or to the north, then the meridian line must be drawn as inclined to the horizon. This results of course not from the position of the meridian itself, which for every place has an invariable direction—going from north to south through the pole and the zenith. Rather it comes from the changing position of the zodiac, which at one time is less and at another is more inclined to the horizon according to the time of day and year and in this way has a position that also changes in relation to the meridian of the place. (Cf. Letter 5, Year One.)

What is imprinted in the human being in the way described has an influence through the whole of life as a foundation in what one calls the horoscope (literally, "a viewing of time"). What can be calculated and drawn even though it cannot, as in ancient times, be actually seen or glimpsed—that is what the human being receives for life as a kind of imprinted seal from the spiritual world. In *The Spiritual Guidance of the Individual and Humanity,* Dr. Steiner expresses this in the following words:

> If a comparison were to be used, we might think of each human being as a kind of a spherical mirror. This, if it were set up, reflects all the surroundings. Let us suppose we trace with a pencil the outline of all that is shown from the surroundings. We could then take the mirror and carry the picture about with us wherever we went. This symbol indicates the fact that when a person is born, he brings with him a copy of the cosmos in himself, and afterwards carries about with him all through his life the effect of this one picture.

This picture then depicts nothing irrelevant to the human soul. Rather, in a truly wonderful way it is a summing-up of the whole cosmic prenatal life of the soul being born into the world. What the soul has gone through with the planets, namely the outer planets in relation to the stars in its descent through the spheres, all that is contained in this image of the heavens in the birth horoscope. What the ego, the immortal essence of the human being, has experienced by way of forces in the long period of cosmic spiritual existence, creates its expression in the position of stars and planets in relation to Earth at the time of birth. This circumstance, too, was clearly described in the little work that has been quoted: *The Spiritual Guidance of the Individual and Humanity.*

(Together with the *Leading Thoughts,* this book offers a real foundation for a new astrology.)

> . . . With these spiritual powers of the cosmos the human being is connected—each person in a special manner according to his own individuality. If he is born in Europe, he lives in a different relation to warmth conditions, and so on, than if he had been born, let us say, in Australia. Similarly, during the life between death and a new birth, one person may stand more closely related to the spiritual powers of Mars, another to those of Jupiter, and others to those of the whole planetary system in general, and so on. These forces also bring the human being back to Earth. Thus before we are born we are living in connection with the collective whole of stellar space.
>
> According to these particular relationships of a person to the cosmic system, the forces are determined that lead him to different parents and to this or that locality. The impetus, the inclination to incarnate here or there, in this or that family, in a special people, at a special time, depends on how the person was connected with the cosmos before birth. (Lecture 3)

We find here briefly mentioned what was more fully described and explained in the last letter. The human being has, especially in the last period of prenatal life, an individual relation to the world of the stars and in particular to certain planets that are specially significant for his or her karma, and it is these that guide one down into physical existence. "And it is according to his horoscope that he guides himself before entering earthly existence." (Cf. Letter 3, Year Two.) That means that the birth must take place so that the celestial configuration corresponds to what has been previously lived through.

Let us suppose that the human being has worked at the forming of the head at the time when Mars was standing before Aries, and that therefore "certain Aries forces are obstructed by Mars, so that they become weakened"—or that he or she had experienced Saturn in a particular way in Leo—then these celestial configurations would show themselves at birth. (As we know, some constellations of the last death will also appear again in the horoscope of the new birth.) The forces of Aries-Mars, and of Leo-Saturn will lead these souls toward birth. They are the real forces, and what displays itself in the sky as a constellation is, in a sense, only a photographic image of the active forces. We have already discussed (Letter 2, Year Two) how theoretically, the human being could come to Earth without this "photograph," without a horoscope that can be read from the stars. The cosmic forces do not, in fact, work directly into the "world-of-finished-work" through the outer manifestations of the planets and stars. That this connection is there, that the human being is permitted to catch a glimpse of his or her cosmic pre-existence when they observe the aspect of the starry heavens at their birth, that—so Rudolf Steiner taught us—is due to the deed of the archangel Michael. Today, this deed is recognized in what the world knows as ordinary astrology, but in a way that is more zealous than spiritual. This deed likewise implies that the hour of birth must be prepared, one might say, far in advance. First, it goes back to the time of conception, although this may vary. We are thus led back further into the spiritual prenatal existence, for the moment of conception is connected with the experience of the soul in the Moon sphere. Before this came the passage through the Mercury sphere, which in turn was connected with a definite position of Mercury in relation to the Sun, and so on. We must then wait for the changing relationships of Sun, Moon, and planets to the zodiacal constellations to create a configuration that expresses the essential characteristics of one's cosmic experiences. One could see here just as great a complexity—though springing from different sources—as in the determination of the streams of heredity over successive generations, which we have discussed. We know, indeed, that planetary constellations, if measured to the exact degree, never repeat themselves. A general constellation predetermined in all its details would appear perhaps only after thousands of years.

However, we must conceive of these relationships not only in an abstract, schematic way, but in a really living way. One finds, for example, that the soul expresses its relation to the outer planets in the horoscope in a different way from how it expresses the relationship to the Sun and the lower planets. If Mars, Jupiter, or Saturn has had a special relationship to one of the zodiacal constellations, this would be found in the horoscope, for example, as Mars in Aries, Jupiter in Leo, and so on. Now it can happen, and indeed it is generally the case, that the human being has developed a special relation to only one of these outer planets. Then he or she will be led to birth when this planet stands exactly in the appropriate constellation and, indeed, as we have seen, by the forces of the planet itself. If, for example, the planet is Saturn, it stays in each zodiacal constellation for two and one-half years, and thus will return to a constellation after thirty years. Thus, when the conditions for birth are present, and when Saturn "shines" again in the Lion, the planet's forces can lead the person back to Earth. It can also happen that two of the outer planets are decisive, for example, Saturn and Jupiter, or even all three, even when Mars, perhaps, is standing before Aries, and works only to weaken it. Then the three planets in the three constellations would together send the human being to the earthly plane. Any given combination of the three outer planets, each in a certain constellation of the zodiac, recurs as a rule every 118 years. Hence, the birth in this case could perhaps take place only a fairly long time after the cosmic experiences in question had been passed through. But such a strong working of all the three outer planets could only happen in the case of a specially gifted, important soul whose new incarnation must always be prepared over a long period of time. (These rules probably won't be applicable in a simple way to the exceptional case of a rapid reincarnation at the end of the century about which Rudolf Steiner spoke. In fact, he also said that this must take place with the breaking of many laws of reincarnation (August 14, 1924).

From an abstractly calculated horoscope, it cannot always be determined whether and to what extent one, two, or three of the outer planets must be seen as specially active. That is just where the individuality plays its role. Each person, according to his or her stage of evolution, must have a quite different relation to his or her horoscope. Calculations are not of use here, only true intuition.

Here we can consider the relation the individual characters in Rudolf Steiner's mystery dramas have to the three "soul powers," Philia, Astrid, and Luna. In the last three dramas they are called "the spirit beings who mediate the binding of the human soul powers with the cosmos." To these is added the other Philia—"the spirit being who retards the binding of the soul powers with the cosmos." (In *The Soul's Awakening* she is called "the bearer into the world of the element of love that belongs to the spiritual personality.") Rudolf Steiner has pointed out in the lecture "The Secrets of the Threshold" (August 24, 1913), that Maria in scene 9 of *The Soul's Awakening* experienced both Astrid and Luna as objective beings, as soul powers; for Johannes it is the other Philia, and for Capesius (scene 13) Philia herself. From what Rudolf Steiner says we know that it points to something important that two of the three soul powers appear to Maria, and only one soul power to the other two.

Maria, in her recollection of the "cosmic midnight" of the foregoing spiritual life, is led to two planets, and Johannes and Capesius each to only one. The spirit beings, Philia, Astrid, and Luna, by virtue of their own natures point to the inner planets, Venus, Mercury, and the Moon. The other Philia, too, is a being related to Venus, but in a more luciferic way. They mediate the relationship of the soul powers to the cosmic, that is to say, with the Sun and the outer planets, in whose realm the cosmic midnight comes to pass. So Philia says to Capesius in scene 13 of *The Soul's Awakening:*

> *What your own self's Sun nature radiates on you*
> *By Saturn's ripened wisdom will be dulled;*
>
> .   .   .
>
> *Then I myself will lead you to the guardian*
> *Who on the spirit threshold keeps his watch.*

In terms of the horoscope, the essential relationship of the inner planets to the Sun must be considered. The position of Mercury and of Venus in relation to the Sun—whether a conjunction or elongation, whether as morning or evening star—determines a soul's national and family feelings. Many things connected with our organism—temperament and the like, and the outer faculties of understanding and love—are, in any incarnation, connected with these inner planets. For Mercury and Venus, the constellations in which they are situated are not so important as for the outer planets. The greater or lesser distance they have from the Sun in the birth horoscope essentially reflects the experiences the soul had in passing through the spheres in question. The Moon also has a strong connection with the different constellations of the zodiac. It is related to stars in its basic nature. On the other hand, its phases, its relation to the Sun, are of great significance. It is actually the Moon that finally brings about a human birth.

In the horoscope the Sun expresses its double relationship—to the inner planets with which it is closely connected, and to the outer planets, which are more free from it in their movements. The "sign" in which it stands, and which is the object of such one-sided interest today, if one constructs a horoscope according to the ordinary rules, points to the Earth below. It indicates the human soul that is descending to Earth from the Sun-sphere through the Venus, Mercury, and Moon spheres. If, however, one considers the Sun in relation to the actual zodiacal constellation in which it stands at birth, then we have something of the experience of the human being who as pure spirit-being has descended out of the stellar worlds through the Saturn, Jupiter, and Mars spheres—a being who has not yet built up a new astral body. Insights into destiny reveal themselves when the "sign" is observed, and individual spiritual experiences when one looks at the constellation. The difference between these two was indicated in Letters 11 and 12 of Year One, and also briefly in the introduction to the new calendar, "Easter, 1929–Easter, 1930."

The direct relation of the planets to Earth at the moment of birth is still to be considered. It differs, as we have already said, according to whether the planets are below or above the horizon. Rudolf Steiner once gave an example of what it signifies when at birth and in the time following a person has Jupiter shining in the night sky—in other words, in opposition to the Sun:

> Consider, that because the human being is incorporated into the cosmos it makes a difference whether he or she stands at some point on the Earth, and let us say, Jupiter shines from the heavens, or whether he or she stands here on Earth and Jupiter is hidden by the Earth. The effects in the one case are directly upon the human being. The effects in the other are of such a nature that the Earth stands between. That makes a significant difference. Jupiter, as we have said, is connected with thinking. Let us suppose that when the human physical organ of thought is gradually unfolding, that is, soon after birth, the human being from his or her birth on is experiencing the effective radiance of Jupiter. The human being receives the direct effect of Jupiter. His or her brain becomes exceptionally well organized for thinking. He or she receives a certain foundation for thought. Let us suppose that a person lives through this time with Jupiter on the other side of the Earth, that the Jupiter effects are therefore checked by the Earth; then that person's brain is less well adapted to be an organ of thought. On the other hand the Earth works in this individual with its substance and forces, and all that proceeds from the substance of Earth is perhaps even molded

by the workings of the Moon, which in a certain way are always present. The person then becomes a dull dreamer, a person of dull consciousness, and thinking withdraws. In between lies every conceivable degree. Let us suppose that a person has forces from the former incarnation that predestine his or her thinking to be especially cultivated in the life on Earth life that he or she must now enter upon. Then that person prepares to descend to Earth. Since Jupiter has a definite time of revolution, the individual chooses a time for birth when Jupiter is shining upon the Earth and sending its rays down directly. In this way a constellation provides what allows the person to be born according to the conditions of his or her former Earth life. (Lecture, May 5, 1921)

So we see how the karma of the preceding life expresses itself in the horoscope, in that it becomes forces that induce a human being to be born. And equally true is what Rudolf Steiner stated in his lecture immediately following the preceding passage:

To be sure, today, in the age of consciousness, human beings must free themselves more and more from what is shown you here. But it is a matter of freeing themselves in the right way. . . . What we develop through spiritual science, as I have represented it in *Knowledge of Higher Worlds*, is at the same time a directive that human beings become independent (in the right way) of the cosmic forces that nevertheless affect them. In that human beings let themselves be born, they find themselves at home on Earth according to their individual constellation of the stars. But they must equip themselves with the forces that in the proper way make them independent of this constellation of the stars.

The source of these powers has been indicated over and over again. It is to be found in that being who for the sake of human freedom passed through the Mystery of Golgotha. We are led to him through a rightly understood spiritual science. We unite ourselves anew with the cosmos, in that we free ourselves from the old fetters through the power of knowledge and love that we can attain through the Christ.

May 1929

The Future of Astrology

The Life of Christ Viewed in Terms of Astrology

THE OBSERVATIONS CONCERNING ASTROLOGY in the preceding letters should serve to awaken a new consciousness of the relation of the human being to the world of the stars. This new consciousness can arise when one really "lives into" the laws of the spiritual world. Therefore, much more stress must be laid upon bringing to consciousness the facts regarding the cosmic life of the human being than upon giving new rules (or even ancient rules that have been preserved) for the reading of horoscopes and such. Astrological principles that are truly suited to our time and are based on the spirit can in future be framed only through collaborative work on the basis of spiritual experience, and on what has already been given us in this domain by Rudolf Steiner, who had planned to give us more information. Take, for example, what is said in his *Man in the Light of Occultism, Theosophy and Philosophy* (lectures 5 and 6) about the connection between the constellations of the zodiac and the human form, and especially what was said in lecture 9 regarding the working together of Sun, Moon, and Venus in the threefold human being; or in *Christ and the Spiritual World*. Such statements are based on an astrological wisdom of the human being that in its further elaboration must replace what is now done in the reading of horoscopes and the like.

We need not repeat here what has been said about the dubiousness of reading horoscopes. All that can be gathered about this from the rich store of anthroposophical teaching shows us how particular the understanding must become in a person who wants be able to read something of true value from a horoscope. "Only the highest grades of intuition still open to the human being are adequate for that," wrote Rudolf Steiner in the journal *Lucifer-Gnosis* in 1905. We can perhaps add that such an intuition will in essence make the calculation of a horoscope superfluous. One could experience that in the case of Rudolf Steiner himself. Rudolf Steiner could give information to someone about his or her birth-constellations without having seen that person's horoscope at all. This advice was not at all given as is usual in astrology. From what has been said about the imprinting of the horoscope at birth, we can understand what faculties were at work there.

For many centuries there has not been a real astrological science that could take its place in the civilization of the age, as, for instance, natural science and technology fully do today. Nevertheless, there has always been a real and concrete connection between the human being and the world of the stars. However, with the rise of the new natural science there could be no appropriate expression for this, because materialism could grasp nothing of this connection, and also because human beings in the age of the consciousness soul had the task of emancipating themselves as much as possible from the cosmos. That we have also already indicated (Letter 2, Year Two). Archangel Michael preserved the connection—through the birth-constellation— between the human being and the star world throughout the time when humanity was most completely shut off from the spiritual worlds, through the whole period when the rulership of the cosmic intelligence slipped away from Michael. Through this a connection between humanity and the divine world was maintained. Thus even in the time of greatest materialism a sense of this connection lives in humankind. Although referred to aphoristically, such an idea lives in the well-known observation of Kant:

> Two things fill the mind with ever-newer and continually increasing wonderment and awe: the starry heaven above me and the moral law within me.

Here Kant names, although he probably would never have admitted the concrete connection, two regions of the universe that are bound to each other by deep inner laws, and one could say that more true astrology lies in this statement than in many popular modern astrology books. And Kant's contemporary, the somewhat homespun poet Matthias Claudius, has his "stargazer" Lise, a simple child of the common people, express the same sentiment when after finishing her work at midnight she allows the grandeur of the stars to work upon her:

Then, under the vault of heaven, the heart says to me
There is a better world than all your pain and desire
I throw myself down upon my bed and lie awake a long time
And seek it in my mind, and long for it.

This presentiment and longing could only be satisfied through a new
spiritual science, not through the reheating of old astrological laws! But
this spiritual science is at the same time one that brings human beings
quite definitely into a different relation to the star world and its laws.
The knowledge it imparts accelerates when the soul really allows spiritual science to work upon it, a process which—since the dawn of the
new Michaelic age—has been increasing, and of which an indication
was given at the end of the last letter with the words of Rudolf Steiner:
"Human beings must equip themselves with the forces that, in the
proper way, make them independent of this constellation of the stars.

This does not so much mean the birth constellation, the horoscope
itself, which as we know remains constant as the cosmic expression
of karma. Rather, what is meant is the continuing influence of the
"aspects" during the lifetime, the determination of the further course
of life by the aspects or constellations that arise later and that, as we
stated in Letter 3, always refers back to the birth constellation. People
who have evolved themselves spiritually are not under the compulsion of these constellations, although they may work upon the more
external circumstances of the physical body. The so-called "progressed
horoscope," as exoteric astrology calls it, is no longer valid. If people
compare their real destiny with what it should be according to the usual
astrological principles, they see that what these principles give is a kind
of caricature of true experience. It is something like the way in which
the contents of the drama *Outcasts in Body and Soul* relate to what is
experienced by the principal characters in *The Portal of Initiation* and
the succeeding mystery dramas by Rudolf Steiner. It was also briefly
noted that a person can come to Earth with a horoscope that is not a
full expression of his or her previous karma, under certain circumstances
necessitated by world evolution.

From all this we can see how much the progress of astrology depends
upon whether human beings will succeed in raising themselves to a
concrete spiritual knowledge. Otherwise we merely bring harm into the
world. With earnest words Rudolf Steiner has also pointed to this:

Today astrology is obviously dead, a mere calculation. It will only become living again when things are once more grasped in a living way, when the birth year of Christ Jesus, for instance, is not somehow calculated from the stars, but is seen with the clairvoyance that can be gained today in the way described. Then things become alive. There is no such vitality today when it is simply calculated that one star stands in opposition, conjunction, and so on, to another. These relationships are to be experienced in a living way—are to be grasped inwardly, not as one understands scientific mathematics. No particular objection to scientific mathematics is intended. It can, of course, shed light upon many things—although to be sure, it may also cast darkness upon many things, too. But this is not what is truly necessary for humanity today. Things cannot be transmitted in the old way; that would only bring a desiccation and paralysis to human evolution (lecture, December 28, 1918).

Astrology will have a significant future as soon as it can become a truly social science. It is certainly not that today, although sometimes people suggest otherwise. For our age one must say that social life can only be advanced through the knowledge given by spiritual science. Rudolf Steiner expressed this in the last sentences of his answer to questions on astrology, which was reproduced almost in its entirety in Letter 2, Year Two.

One should not regard the understanding for such things as a worthless, impractical activity without connection with real practical life. Through becoming familiar with the supersensible worlds human beings grow not only in terms of knowledge but above all in their moral and soul nature. Even a faint idea of the place we occupy in connection with the world of the stars affects our character, mode of dealing with things, and the direction we give to our whole being. And much more than many today imagine, the further development of our social life depends upon the progress of humanity on the path to supersensible knowledge. For the insightful person, our present social situation is only an expression of materialism in our understanding of the world. When this way of looking at the world is replaced by a spiritual one, then external conditions of life will also become better.

To this spiritual view of the world belong most importantly the sublime and grand cosmology that Rudolf Steiner has developed and an understanding of the life between death and rebirth. These are the basis for an understanding of karma and thereby of the horoscope. If one succeeded in transposing this knowledge into an astrological science, in connecting it with a true science of the human being—which is also the basis of our anthroposophical pedagogy and medicine—astrology could become a real social science. One must be clear, however, that this is an anticipated future development. Not until the next period of civilization in the sixth post-Atlantean epoch will astrology actually be appropriate to the time, will be not merely knowledge, but a direct human faculty—at least for a portion of humanity alive at that time. We find it thus represented in the lecture about the three kinds of forces that will be evolved in the future "out of human nature itself in a quite elementary way" (*The Challenge of the Times.*) These are the forces of occultism applied to mechanics, hygiene, and eugenics; we will concern ourselves here only with eugenics. It is the faculty that in human beings of the East (reckoned from Russia onward) will lead to a wonderful, practical, and above all, in the deepest sense, social astrology—not to one that is personally egoistic.

> What I call the eugenic faculty is the elevation of human propagation above mere human arbitrariness and chance. An intense and clear knowledge will be developed in the people of the East, from which will come an understanding of how certain cosmic phenomena must run parallel with the laws of population, and of how to regulate conception in harmony with certain constellations of the stars. Thus it will be possible to make earthly incarnation accessible to souls of either a good or evil tendency. . . . To express this simply: the human being will know how, in concrete individual cases, to bring conception and birth—which today work chaotically and arbitrarily over the whole Earth—into harmony with the great laws of the cosmos. Abstract laws are of no use in such cases. What will be acquired is a concrete individual faculty, which in individual cases will know that conception must or must not take place at a given time. (December 1, 1918)

We see that here it is not a matter of calculating a birth horoscope. It is still less a matter of setting up a horoscope in advance in a self-seeking and presumptuous way, with "favorable aspects for the moment of conception"—an abuse already practiced here and there today. A faculty is spoken of here that will evolve in human beings of the East. That will be in an epoch that will be a reflection of the era that lay just as far before the Mystery of Golgotha as our present one will come after it, and which has already been referred to. Among the tribes of the Ingavonen in ancient Germany of the third and fourth pre-Christian millennia, propagation could only happen at a definite time of year, so that all births fell between our modern Christmas and Easter. Then followed the period of freedom and randomness in this domain. This will not be replaced by a new rule of the priesthood, but human beings themselves will regulate the laws in harmony with the cosmos. For this, the human being will have to establish an intimate connection with the souls that are on the way to rebirth, and also with the actual spiritual-cosmic realities that express themselves in a given celestial constellation. This must still seem premature to us today. We are just beginning to try to establish a connection with the realm of the dead in a truly spiritual way. Rudolf Steiner has given the most beautiful and varied suggestions regarding this aspiration, but he did not teach us how to approach the realm of the unborn. It is moreover a realm that relates in quite a different way to earthly human egotism than does the realm of the dead. Still, we must always look forward to a future evolution. The faculties that are to come later must be evolved in advance by individuals. Thus, consideration of astrological laws in harmony with the spirit, insofar as they are accessible to us today, may contribute to the creation of a more conscious and pure relation to the cosmic realms than was possible before now. It may be permitted now to connect these thoughts to others I was able to present at the Goetheanum during the last Easter festival. These also lead back to the being of the Christ, whose life and death signify a revolution of the whole relation of humanity to the world of the stars. We will also give the configuration of the heavens—although only a calculated one—at the moment of the Mystery of Golgotha. In the first edition of the *Calendar of the Soul* in 1912, Rudolf Steiner wrote in the historical remarks: "April 3, 33, is the day of the death of Jesus Christ according to the researches of spiritual science." This was, of course, not a calculation, but in the sense of a truly living astrology a "seeing." Still, the subsequent casting of the horoscope—this was many years ago—seemed to give Rudolf Steiner much pleasure.

In the lectures whose contents he designated as "the fifth Gospel," Rudolf Steiner has drawn a comparison between the life of Christ and that of the rest of humankind that can show us how the life and death of Christ were at the same time the conception and the birth of the Christ-impulse. If we do not regard only the being who died on the cross at Golgotha, but him who rose from the grave on Easter Sunday, then we have the picture of a birth, preceded by a kind of embryonic life, followed by an Earth life that endures "even unto the end of the world." If we can regard the life of Christ from this point of view then we shall find throughout conformity with the course of a human life.

The human being descends before birth from the Sun sphere through the planetary spheres, passes through the Moon sphere, and enters into the sphere of Earth. So too, Christ came from the Sun in order to bind himself with a body prepared upon Earth. This, however, was not in the germ-condition in which the human soul at the moment of incarnation—in the third week—finds the human seed. Rather it had passed through a long, careful, and complicated process of preparation for thirty years. We know from the lectures on the Gospels and from other cycles how the body of Jesus of Nazareth had come about: The Nathan-Jesus child was for a number of years the bearer of the Zarathustra ego, and the Zarathustra ego left him just before the baptism in the Jordan River. In the descent of Christ to Earth the moment of the baptism corresponds with the moment of human conception.

This comparison and those following must not be forced so that they lead to impossibilities, but they themselves point to profound interconnections when we look for correspondences in a spiritual way.

The baptism by John took place in the element of water, and was not a mere baptism in the modern sense but a complete immersion in the water of the river. The human being lives in the watery element during the embryonic period. The cosmic impulses are mediated through the water. Therefore the embryo has no horoscope, but swings around with all the planetary constellations. It stands in a continuous connection with them. We know of Christ Jesus that he continuously actualized in himself the planetary and starry constellations occurring at the moment, and could transmit these to his surroundings. This we find as well in *The Spiritual Guidance of the Individual and Humanity* (based upon Whitsuntide lectures), and Rudolf Steiner himself later described these lectures as belonging to the fifth Gospel.

In the case of any other human being, the cosmic-spiritual laws work upon him only in that they give him a start in earthly life. Thereafter there appear in opposition to these laws others that arise out of the conditions of the evolution of the Earth. In the case of Christ-Jesus, after the baptism by John the cosmic-spiritual forces alone remained effective, and were not influenced in any way by the laws of the evolution of the Earth.

The Christ actually had the same relation to the universe that the unborn human being has, who, protected from the actual earthly conditions, lives in the tiny space where the cosmic forces can dominate. The correspondence is truly more than a merely superficial one. One might say that the words of the Christ must be taken as real to this degree: "Unless you become as little children—even like the infant in the mother's womb—you cannot enter the kingdom of heaven." The human being ascending to spiritual freedom, the human being linked through Christ to the spiritual world, lives in the kingdom of heaven as a child lives in the body of the mother.

The child is surrounded there with its sheaths. In the course of embryonic life it transforms these three sheaths into what is, after birth, the expression of the etheric body, the astral body, and the ego. In the case of the Christ, one can also speak of the three sheaths into which he entered, and which he transformed. They are the physical body, the etheric body, and the astral body of Jesus of Nazareth. The transformation, however, in this case, is a breaking-up of the physical body, a gradual destruction of the physical body—just as in the embryo, processes of actual decay occur in the sheaths during the first weeks. The power of the Christ consumed this pure and unique human body, just as a flame consumes pure wax. Therefore, what took place at the end of this embryonic life of three years was, externally considered, a death. This death was of that physical body which, "for the salvation of the Earth and the progress of humanity," had to be forcibly led through the terrible act of crucifixion. Not until the words "It is finished" sounded from the cross did the birth of the Christ impulse for the Earth occur. One can also say that in this moment the horoscope appears—the horoscope of both the death and the birth—the celestial constellation at the Mystery of Golgotha, the configuration of the heavens on that afternoon of April 3, 33 A.D.

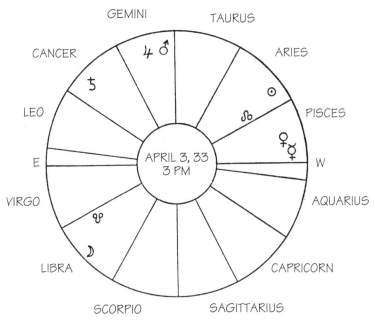

Figure 37

The horoscope reproduced here has in fact much of the nature of death in it. United with it were the elemental events that came forth with such mighty force that they were like cosmic events. There was darkness over the land that for retrospective sight, as Rudolf Steiner said, seemed like an eclipse of the Sun, and yet cannot have been one, since the Jewish Passover falls at the full Moon. In fact, calculations show that there was an eclipse of the Sun fourteen days before, at the new Moon, as it must be. On the day of the crucifixion a partial lunar eclipse took place, so that the Moon rose partially eclipsed as the Sun was setting. The deep, hours-long darkness over the land of Palestine was a darkening of the Sun from the Earth. This was a powerful reminiscence of the time of the cosmic "effective-working" in the midst of "the world of finished work," so that the Earth brought to expression in terms of weather what was a spiritual reality.

The actual "birth" was then accomplished on the third day, on Easter Sunday in the early morning, as the Risen One appeared for the first time to Mary Magdalene. A delicate morning mood surrounds this appearance. Although we meet again with essentially the constellation of Good Friday—only the Moon has noticeably progressed—yet how different this picture looks!

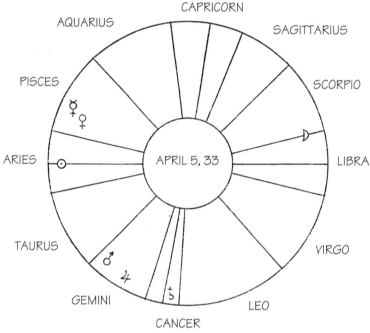

Figure 38

The Sun according to the account of the Evangelists is about to rise or has just risen, and is depicted directly on the eastern horizon. It is preceded by Venus and Mercury, which on Friday evening, since they were both morning stars, were not shining, but are now both radiantly bright. Mercury is even in its greatest elongation, and thus in that part of the world is as plainly visible as Venus. The Moon, somewhat past full, is just about to set. Saturn is at its lowest point, as if pointing to the underworld, just as when at its zenith it opens the way for earthly humanity to enter the spiritual world. It symbolizes the passage of the Christ to the souls of the dead in the underworld, which takes place in the time between the death and resurrection—"Christ's descent into hell."

It must be pointed out again that we need not concern ourselves with "exceptional positions" of the planets and so on, but with reading this constellation in its uniqueness as the letters of a script. As we know, the number of these letters was originally not more than the combined number of the planets and signs of the zodiac together with Sun and Moon in the starry heavens.

If the "birth" of the Christ has been accomplished in this way for the earthly world, now follows what corresponds to the earthly life of the human being. That is the forty days from the Resurrection to the Ascension—that time in which the Christ appeared to his disciples in his resurrection body and taught them about the kingdom of God. Much of what has passed into Christian "gnosis" has its origin in the super-sensible teachings that Christ communicated to his disciples during this "Earth life" of forty days. Then at the Ascension he disappeared from their sight, just as a human being who dies is withdrawn from the sight of his or her family. The Ascension therefore corresponds to the death of the ordinary mortal, and the ten days from Ascension to Pentecost to the life in the soul world, or "kamaloca." Then the human being enters into the spiritual world, into the Sun sphere. But for the rest of his Earth-life the Christ has renounced his existence in the Sun sphere, that is to say, in "heaven." He remains near the Earth and enters into the Earth sphere on the day of Pentecost, as the Holy Spirit comes to the disciples. "He set up his heaven upon Earth" as it is expressed in the *Fifth Gospel*. The human soul in the Sun sphere, and what comes after it, experiences the midnight hour of spirit existence, which also represents the first beginnings of a new Earth life. However, the Christ evermore remains with human beings upon Earth. His path, which can be compared to the human path through conception, birth, and death, diverges sharply at the point where a human being enters into the bliss of the spiritually creative existence. Christ's path becomes rather an earthly one. Since then, Christ has been bound up with the destiny of the Earth and humanity; and when in the near future he will be able to show himself still more intimately and more clearly to human beings, then he will appear as the comforter and counselor, as the one who stands by us, the Paraclete. Then he will—just as directly after his Ascension he breathed upon his disciples the Holy Spirit—himself bestow upon us the Holy Ghost, which proceeds not only from the Father alone, but from the Father and from the Son.

June 1929

Comets I

NOW THAT OUR CONSIDERATION of astrology has come to a certain conclusion for the present, this second year shall end with a few astronomical reflections, bearing especially upon the nature of comets, meteors, and stars, as was stated to be our intention at the end of the first year.

Although comets are among the astronomical phenomena that have received great attention, they least of any can be approached with the standard materialistic concepts. Indeed, in the history of humanity they have even been viewed with certain notions and feelings that point to a connection between the comets and the divine spiritual world, to a moral element that they embody in a special way. In ancient times people even connected them with the souls of the dead. Thus in Ovid we find the description of how immediately after the murder of Julius Caesar, his soul was born aloft to the stars by the goddess Venus, and: "As she bore him the spirit became bright and fiery, and from her bosom she let it go free. High over the Moon now she mounted in flight, and with flaming hair streaming behind, shone as a star."

In the Middle Ages there was a fear of comets as the "scourge of God," as omens of every kind of evil. There has certainly been much superstition linked with this point of view, which we do not want to revive today. In a deeper sense, however, that way of understanding comets points more to reality than the modern scientific viewpoint, which tries to include the comets as far as possible in the system of the ordinary planetary laws. Thus Rudolf Steiner compared science in this domain with a fly crawling over a painting by Raphael, and then describing what it perceives of single flecks of color and so on. It is precisely the special characteristic of comets that they do not follow the laws of the rest of the solar system, least of all in the prejudiced form these laws take in the Newtonian theory of gravitation. We must therefore approach the nature of the comet in the light of spiritual science.

In the first Letter we spoke of the exceptional position of comets in the solar system, and of the apparent contradiction that they—actually a laggard creation in evolution—are governed by beings of the highest hierarchy, the seraphim and cherubim, are ruled by higher beings than even the stars and planets. (Cf. *The Spiritual Beings in the Heavenly Bodies and in the Kingdoms of Nature,* lecture 7, April 10, 1912, which was referred to in the same Letter.)

Our solar system has a long and complicated history, and all the things that exist within it stand therefore at different stages of evolution or of "staying behind." The comets are beings who are still at the stage of the ancient Moon existence and cannot behave completely in accord with the laws of the planetary system of today. Rudolf Steiner has repeatedly emphasized that in 1906, he had already pointed out that nitrogen, and nitrogen compounds like cyanide, must be important for comets in a way that corresponds to the special role of nitrogen on the Old Moon. When, in 1910, Halley's comet could be observed by the spectroscope, this fact of spiritual science was fully confirmed, inasmuch as prussic acid—cyanide—was proved to be in the spectrum of the comet.

Comets form the exact opposite pole of the Moon of today. The Moon in a different way is not quite in accordance with the times. It has gone ahead in its evolution, has gone too soon into the stage of hardening. Meanwhile, the comets have remained fugitive, elemental, and certainly spiritual, but with a corporeality that does not correspond to the other conditions of the cosmos.

Rudolf Steiner, especially at the time Halley's comet appeared again (spring 1910, see *The Christ Impulse and the Development of Ego Consciousness,* lecture 5) repeatedly pointed to the contrast between the lunar and the cometary as being the cosmic image of another contrast, a human one, namely, in a physical sense, that of male and female. Just as the Moon has overstepped its phase of evolution, has entered too soon into the Jupiter stage and therefore has had to harden, the male body shot past the appropriate point of evolution, and has hardened, has descended too far into matter. The female body, on the contrary, has remained behind the true point of evolution; it is too soft, has remained too spiritual, has not joined itself enough to matter. It corresponds to the comet. In the cosmos, the Sun and the Earth provide a normal, middle stage between the two extremes of the Moon and the comets. For the human body, no true mean is represented; there are only the two extremes. One can point to the time when the comets remained behind in the evolution of the planetary system. It was only in the middle of the Atlantean age that our solar system actually received the laws that apply today. There, at a celestial council of spiritual beings, it was decided that in future the planets should move in definite paths according to special periods of revolution. This revolution was henceforth to be in the charge of the "spirits of the revolution of time," offspring of the seraphim and cherubim. Thus, since that time we have a predictable planetary system. Only the comets were not included. They were to describe no definite orbits in definite periods of time like the planets. They were dispatched directly by the seraphim and cherubim into the physical world in order to effect quite definite impulses.

> Something of an elemental nature, something that stirs up, and in a certain condition is necessary in order to rightly maintain the progress of evolution in the cosmos—that is the nature of the comets (lecture, March 5, 1910).

Rudolf Steiner thus compares the appearance of a comet with the arrival of a newborn infant into a family. It is something new, something fundamentally incalculable that breaks into the usual everyday routine and creates within the family new circumstances that at first cannot at all be envisaged. The comets likewise have definite tasks to perform in the solar system.

When we consider the eclipses of the Sun and Moon, we have there, too, phenomena that have special tasks to fulfill in regard to Earth. The task of an eclipse of the Sun is not unrelated to that of a comet (cf. lecture, June 25, 1922, and Letter 10, Year One). Just as eclipses of the Sun release evil from Earth into the universe, so comets work to purify the astral forces in the planetary system. They are "an outer sign of an inner law," Rudolf Steiner said. Only they do not follow a strict rhythmic law like the eclipses. To begin with, comets make their appearance quite arbitrarily, as a purely spiritual center of force. They draw the bad astrality to themselves, and after they have completed their journey, they unload these bad forces into the universal cosmos. For this task they must be sent forth into the solar system by the highest spirits, by the seraphim and the cherubim, who are able to work directly into physical matter. Although only a few become visible, especially for the naked eye, we know since the time of Kepler—and the present-day possibilities of observation have fully corroborated this—that comets are as numerous as fish in the sea. There is thus ample provision made for the purification of the astral atmosphere.

When we speak of this general mission of the comets, we are referring to the non-periodic comets, to those that make a single appearance. These in fact appear anywhere, at any time, and their appearance cannot be predicted, is not linked to a definite time nor bound to a definite place in the zodiac where all the planets describe their paths. They may make their first appearance at any point of the heavens, at the North Pole, at the South Pole, at the equator, or anywhere in between. The periodic comets have different tasks. One can often predict their reappearance with some, but never with complete, exactness. We will do well to first say something about the orbits, the outer form, and the peculiarity of comets before we speak about the mission and history of individual comets.

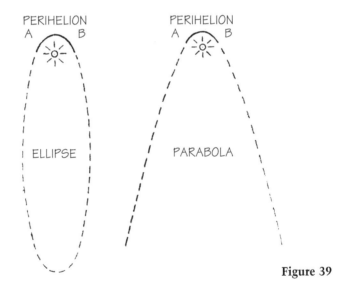

Figure 39

Comets move in the path of a conic section around the Sun, which stands in one of the foci. Modern astronomy since Kepler assumes for the planets as well an elliptical path, which, however, scarcely differs from a circle. Cometary ellipses, however, have a much more oval, and in the case of some, even an extraordinarily extended, form. The ellipse appears as a cometary orbit only in the case of the periodic comets, for among conic sections it is the only enclosed form except for the circle. The periodic comets—at least apparently—always traverse the same path, as is the case with the planets. Sometimes even the orbits of the non-returning comets are looked upon as elliptical. We must remember, though, that the comet can really only be seen physically on quite a small portion of its path—where the path is near the Earth. Then the Sun with its brilliance again quickly renders invisible that part of the path in the neighborhood of the Sun—the perihelion. The part of the path on which the comet can be observed is so small that from the calculations founded upon it, it is difficult to tell whether the orbit is elliptical (periodic) or parabolic (non-periodic). Figure 39 makes this clear. AB represents the part of the path that can be actually observed.

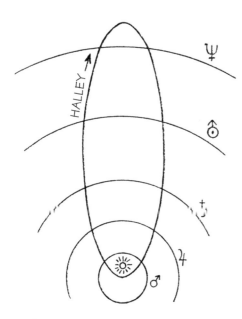

Figure 40

What Rudolf Steiner said about this sheds another light on the question. He often stated that in fact a comet—with very few exceptions—always dissolves when it disappears from physical sight (See *The Spiritual Beings in the Heavenly Bodies and in the Kingdoms of Nature*, lecture 7). If a comet returns, apparently on the same path, then it has formed itself again. In the time between appearances (indicated by the dotted line of the orbit) the comet is not present in our three-dimensional world. It comes to exist anew as a center of spiritual force "on the other side." We can thus imagine that a comet that has disappeared into "nothingness" (although this nothingness is the spiritual world) along a certain parabolic path, later comes into existence upon another parabolic path. In this case, the identity of the two comets can no more be established than the identity between the individuality of Raphael and that of Novalis can be established by purely external means. The underlying unity is a spiritual impulse in the supersensible world. From this point of view the distinction between elliptic and parabolic cometary orbits is not very significant. An orbit such as the one that, according to calculation, Halley's comet must have, would extend beyond the orbit of Neptune, would actually leave the planetary system. The elliptical form of this orbit corresponds roughly to that of the first diagram. Figure 40 shows this same orbit, but intersected by the various planetary orbits starting with the orbit of Mars.

When one remembers that when the "periodicity" of this comet was discovered by Halley—the contemporary and colleague of Newton, the solar system was only known as far as Saturn, then one sees what a mighty "leap into the void" this cometary path then signified. One also understands the suspense with which its return in 1759—the first predicted and precalculated return of a comet—was awaited. We will come back to this comet again later.

Altogether about seventy comets are regarded as elliptical. In fact, the "return" has only actually been observed for two dozen, and, as we now know, this really is equivalent to a new formation of the comet. A very few comets are believed to have a hyperbolic orbit, while almost all are believed to have an orbit that is a parabola. As we have said, though, this difference doesn't mean much. It is interesting, however, to establish the fact that the appearance of a comet is never actually observed before it enters the neighborhood of the orbit of Mars. As comets travel out again, one can follow them only to a certain distance, corresponding to that of the asteroids, the little planets between Mars and Jupiter. The comets then disappear even to the telescope. (The distances meant here are the distances of the planets that have been calculated astronomically, and the distance, derived from the same assumptions, of a comet at a certain point of its path. From these figures the foregoing remarks can be implied. We are not here concerned with the assumptions upon which these calculations have been made nor with the exact magnitude of the numbers, but only with the comparison of the magnitudes. The same applies to further statements that are based upon astronomical calculations.) There is perhaps a single known exception. A comet, appearing in 1889, was visible beyond the orbit of Jupiter, and almost to the region of Saturn. It is the *Mars sphere* that has a great significance for comets and meteors.

When a comet first becomes visible it usually looks like a little nebula, but soon shows by its rapid change of position that it is no such thing. At that time it does not yet have a nucleus or a tail. It consists only of a shining, nebulous envelope (*coma,* hence the name comet) which must be regarded as the actual original being of the comet, a real "astral entity"—for in this form the comet leaves the field of vision after its journey around the Sun. From remarks of Rudolf Steiner we know that the formation of the nucleus and the tail is connected with the comet's mission to work in a purifying way on the astral realm. Later the nucleus will reflect the light of the Sun as do the Moon and the planets. However, from the coma, from the actual comet, there must stream out a light of its own, as is the case with stars, nebulae, and the Sun. These facts will seem comprehensible to us when we think of the cosmic hierarchical origin of the comets and the role that Lucifer plays there.

The appearance of a comet can take place at any point in the heavens, in the Great Bear, in Orion or also in the zodiac. Then the comet always moves toward the zodiac, for it is approaching the Sun around which—with immense velocity and usually at a relatively small distance—it then describes its curve. Figure 41 gives a rendering (from Flammarion) of such a cometary movement in the year 1882. From this one can grasp the rapid change of position and the peculiar curve described in the firmament that corresponds to the theoretical parabola.

The comet, sighted first in the constellation of the Sextant not far from Leo, reached the Sun in a very short time, the Sun then (September 17)

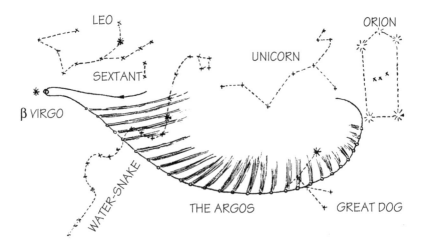

Figure 41

being near the star (β) in Virgo. The comet was at that point in perihelion, and was visible in bright daylight. After that, as seen from Earth, it passed first in front of and then behind the Sun's disk, continued its path, traversing the Water-Serpent, went through the Great Dog in a wide bend around Sirius, and after nine months vanished in the region between Orion and the Unicorn. Other comets would be seen as taking a very different path.

The tail of the comet, which for human sensibilities is its chief characteristic and even for science presents a great riddle, usually forms later, although occasionally it forms earlier, and sometimes not at all. The comet, which ought to obey the laws of gravity, contradicts these laws with its most essential part. The tail is always directed away from the Sun, instead of being drawn toward the Sun (cf. Figure 42, and compare with Figure 41, in which the changing directions of the tail correspond to the progression of the Sun in the zodiac). In such a case one overcomes the difficulty easily by thinking in terms of "electric" or similar forces, which can work with a repelling action. Indeed, all the usual ideas lead in this case to impossibilities. The comet represented below [Figure 42], which appeared in 1843, at its perihelion must have had a tail so long that it reached from the Sun beyond the orbit of Mars (in terms of astronomy 150 million miles). But when the comet came to the region of the Sun it increased its velocity terrifically so that the nucleus must have been traveling at nearly 400 miles per second. (One may calculate or try to imagine with what velocity then the end of the tail had to make its turn around the Sun!) Besides, some comets pass extremely close to the Sun so that they pass through the sphere of the so-called "solar flares" that extend out from it. One can trace, though, no influence of the Sun on the comet—nucleus or tail—nor a disturbances of its path, or an alteration in its structure, except in most instances a noticeable increase in the size and brilliance of its tail. The 1882 comet represented in Figure 43 required four and one-half hours for its passage around the Sun. In other words, it traveled across the disk of the Sun in one and one-quarter hours. Its revolution around the Sun, until it disappeared behind it, lasted two hours. Another hour or so passed before it reappeared from behind the Sun's disk, which is supposed to have a diameter of one million miles. (The drawing is from Mayer's *Structure of the World.*)

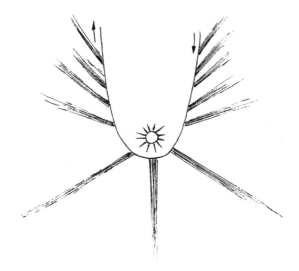

Figure 42

One sees that there are *facts,* such as the actual observation of the passage of the comet across the Sun, and yet one cannot come to terms with these facts if one tries to explain them with ordinary concepts. Rudolf Steiner in *The Relationship of the Diverse Branches of Natural Science to Astronomy*, [eighteen lectures, often referred to as the "*Astronomy Course*" — see Notes on the Text] spoke on this very point:

> If, for instance, one investigates the nature of a comet, one does not reach correct conclusions if one thinks of the body of a comet as one thinks of the planetary bodies.

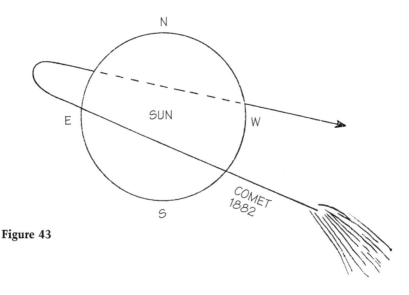

Figure 43

If you like, you may picture a planetary body as if it were a body complete in itself and would move forward, and you will not contradict the facts much. . . . [However] you will never understand a cometary body in its progress—its apparent progress—through space, if you look upon it as you are accustomed to look upon planetary bodies. But just try to consider it in the following way and to string all the empirical facts upon the thread of this method of consideration. Think that in this direction—toward the Sun— the comet is continually coming into being. It pushes its nucleus, its apparent nucleus, forward. To the rear something is lost, something vanishes. And so the comet pushes itself forward—always newly arising, but also passing away. It is not at all a body, in the same sense as a planet is a body. It is something that gradually arises and passes away, that in front adds on the new, and behind loses the old. It moves forward like a mere shining of light (although I am not saying that it is merely this.)

And further:

We must regard the comet as something completely transitory, a middle state—if we take the Sun and Earth into consideration between ponderable and imponderable matter, between matter that can be weighed and matter that cannot be weighed. It is an encounter between ponderable and imponderable matter, in which they do not immediately balance each other as they do when light is diffused in the air (another meeting of ponderable and imponderable matter). Rather they continuously spread out somewhat in a homogeneous way. They do not strike against each other. With comets we must have a one-sided striking, because they do not adjust themselves. Take air, for example. If there is a passage of light with a certain strength through the air, it spreads out homogeneously. But if the light does not adjust itself quickly enough to the air, then there occurs (but I beg of you not to take it in a mechanical sense, but as something inward), a kind of inner conflict between ponderable and imponderable matter. If you observe comets, there you find this friction between ponderable and imponderable matter continuing its way through space, something that is continually arising and passing away.

Figure 44

Scientists have concluded that the tail of the comet cannot be a permanent structure. It is regarded as a column of smoke or steam that is maintained by the gases that become freed from the otherwise solid nucleus through the great development of heat when it approaches the Sun. With such ideas one does not get beyond materialism, and riddle upon riddle piles up. But with comets, the weightiest riddles are anchored in the spirit. What they are as expressions and instruments of spiritual beings; what world-battles are fought around them; and what role the meteors play in this conflict—the whole mighty apocalyptic nature of the comet—this shall occupy us next time, after this more external introduction.

July 1929

Comets II

WE HAVE SEEN THAT COMETS represent something quite different in our solar system from what is represented by the planets. The planets are law-abiding inhabitants, whereas comets do not entirely follow the prevailing laws. They are more or less unpredictable entities, seeming to come into our solar system from another world. And even when a lawful relationship between comets and the solar system can actually be found it must at first seem odd. For example—at least in former times—an especially large number of comets appears at times when there are especially many sunspots, or they are brighter at such times. At first no reason for a connection between comets and sun-spots can be seen.

Rudolf Steiner in the Hague lectures of 1923 (*Supersensible Man*, lecture 3) lifted a corner of the veil from this mystery. There he speaks of a special connection of the Mars sphere with the present-day evolution of the Earth in the fifth post-Atlantean period, a connection that human beings experience when they pass through the Mars sphere in their descent to rebirth. The Mars sphere, however, is also interpenetrated by the Sun forces—which had the same significance for humanity in the fourth post-Atlantean period as the Mars forces have in our time. Thus a kind of co-working of the Mars and Sun spheres exists at the present time. What plays itself out between Mars and the Sun is a world war between good and bad spirits, and the Sun takes part in this battle in such a way that through the dark doorways of the sunspots solar substance is continuously cast out into the cosmos.

> And what is thus flung forth from the Sun as solar substance into the cosmos appears within our solar system as comets and meteors, as well as the well-known shooting stars. Those beings who guide the world from within the Sun send these things forth—especially

in our age—into our epoch of time. They have done this in former times; these phenomena are not appearing today for the first time. However, they now have a different meaning than previously. That is why I said: In earlier times what was principally at work was the spiritual impulse of the stars. Now those impulses that are contained in the dispersed iron begin to have a special meaning for human beings: they are employed in the cosmos in the service of the spiritual by a special spiritual being, who here again acquires a special significance and whom we call the Michael-spirit. In our age, therefore, something has entered the cosmos that was not there earlier in the same degree. The cosmic iron with its spiritual efficacy makes it possible for the Michael-spirit to mediate between the supersensible world and the sensory world of Earth.

There we look directly upon a battle, upon the mighty "war in heaven," in the destiny of which we human beings will be ever more involved. Later we will deal more fully with Rudolf Steiner's remarks relating to meteors and to Michael's role in the conflict. First we will consider more closely from an astronomical viewpoint the facts given us.

We already mentioned that after the passage of comets through the perihelion, after they have passed the Sun, they often display a surprising increase in brilliance. But what is most remarkable is that many comets have not been discovered until they have passed through the perihelion, so that there is no absolute certainty that they were even there before. Science assumes that the comet was so faint before that its approach had not been noticed, and that it could be seen for the first time only when—emerging again from the Sun's rays—it had received an incomparably stronger light. There is a series of such comets, among them those of 1843, 1861, and 1880. The middle one must even have passed through the Earth or, conversely, the Earth passed through the tail of the comet. This occurred, however, when the comet had not yet been discovered and its position was only hypothetically calculated. We need not wonder in that case that its passage had not been noticed!

The most remarkable case, however, is that of the 1843 comet. In Figure 42 of the previous Letter, we indicated its theoretical path in order to show the general principle regarding the direction taken by the tail of a comet. But it must be emphasized that in this case one half of

the comet's path (the right-hand one in the drawing) is absolutely hypothetical because the comet was not seen until the day after perihelion.
(The moment of perihelion, which must have taken place on February
27, was calculated after the fact from the further path of the comet.)
The comet, with its remarkable tail stretching as far as the orbit of
Mars, was so brilliant that one could see it in clear daylight, and two
days before there was nothing to be seen. There is no finer proof to
be found for the teachings of Dr. Steiner than this powerful comet of
the year 1843. It is noteworthy that the astronomer Flammarion, who
had a fine sense for the purely phenomenal in astronomy, described
this appearance in a way that almost coincides with the words of the
spiritual researcher:

> "We can even remark that if it (the comet) had been flung out from
> the Sun on February 27 at 10:29 with a velocity of about 400 miles
> [per second], its appearance and its path would be in agreement
> with all the observations actually made."

This is not to say that all comets come out from the Sun. In fact,
the majority are discovered before they reach the sphere of the Sun. But
in the Sun itself as well as in the Mars sphere we must seek important
forces that are involved with the generation of comets. One can look
upon a comet in physical terms as a "friction between ponderable and
imponderable matter traversing space," as Dr. Steiner called it in the
Astronomical Course. One can look upon it spiritually as an emissary
of the highest hierarchy. It pushes itself forward "as a mere appearance
of light" but it is not just this, nor does it remain so. Rather, what was
thrown out of the Sun into the universe permeates the Mars sphere
through its forces with the substance that constitutes the nucleus of the
comet. The Sun sphere works with its astral forces upon the tail of the
comet, and the strength of its light immensely increases. And between the
two, between the Sun sphere and the Mars sphere, the great conflict of
which we spoke briefly above plays itself out. One need only remember
that iron has been found in meteors, which are related to the comets,
and also in the cometary nucleus itself—and that iron forms the basic
substance of the Mars-sphere, in order to find the connection. In this
battle in the cosmos not only are the "good" spirits of the hierarchies,
such as Michael or the seraphim and cherubim, taking part, but also
spirits who have remained behind. What arises—what finally *comes*

into being out of the spiritual impulse to which the comets owe their existence—and then as a comet travels through space: that is the result of this warfare.

We know from *Spiritual Beings in the Heavenly Bodies and in the Kingdoms of Nature* that the thrones form the real group souls of the minerals. If, however, only the normally progressive thrones and the normal spirits of form were present, the minerals could never manifest the solid form in which we know them. That requires a countering force, the powerful opposition of the laggard spirits of will and spirits of form, who throw themselves against the other spirits. (Cf. Letter 1, Year One.) This conflict takes place in the region between Jupiter and Mars. That is the battlefield of the hierarchies, the cosmic "battlefield of Mars"! Out of the Sun sphere works the other reality, which will not tolerate this laggard principle, but casts it out through the sunspots. Both impulses connect themselves to the comets and the meteors. From the former is produced especially the solid, mineral part of the comet—its nucleus.

If we look at what Rudolf Steiner said about comets in the year 1910 and also in the Helsingfors lectures in 1912, we see that he drew a picture of the comets as having a "god-willed" mission. Their task is to carry out the purification of the astral realm and to bring a special impulse into human evolution. If in contrast we observe what interests science most about comets, we see again that it is really the backward, the abnormal that manifests in the phenomenal. This aspect of reality tends especially to the formation of matter, to minerals and also, as in the case of the outer envelope of the Sun, to gas formation—in other words, to the ponderable. Because one goes no further than this "ponderable" (which, since it is not on Earth cannot of course be weighed but only calculated) materialism enters in. If one regards the so-called ponderable as an expression of spiritual beings and of their battle with other beings, then deep riddles of world evolution unfold themselves.

From this point of view we will consider more closely the nature of the periodic comets that are actually observed fairly often upon the same path, whose reappearance, therefore, can be predicted with more or less exactitude. With these comets an impulse is sent into the universe that continuously repeats itself, although the comet itself, as we have seen, may be dissolved in the time between appearances. Now it is peculiar that the intervals of such comets lie within definite boundaries. There is one group in which all the members return in from three to seven years (one comes back after eight years). Others have periods of revolution around the Sun that are from thirteen to seventeen years, and a few from thirty-three to forty-six years. Some have a long period—from sixty-one to seventy-six years—Halley's comet being the last of these. (Only those comets whose return has been actually observed are enumerated here.)

If one constructs the orbits of these comets—naturally we are dealing here only with ellipses—one sees that they have a connection with certain planets in the solar system. Those with a short period (three to seven years) go around Jupiter in their orbits. The thirteen- to seventeen-year comets go around Saturn, those in the next group, Uranus, and the comets with the long periods, Neptune. Particularly the comets with short periods often have very broad ellipses. The shortest known orbit, that of Encke's comet, does not reach quite to the orbit of Jupiter. It returns promptly every three years, four months.

Astronomy regards these comets as "captured" by the planets in question. Thinking in terms of the common force of gravity in the universe, one assumes that the comet came at some time into the neighborhood of one of these outer, relatively very large planets and then was "attracted" by it, and forced to have its further path defined by the presence of the powerful planetary body. One therefore speaks of a "Jupiter family," a "Neptune family," and so on. Forty-one members of the comet family of Jupiter have been counted, but the majority do not return. In spite of the established elliptical orbit only twenty-two remain. Saturn and Uranus hold only a few comets in bondage, and Neptune but eight, among which are also a few whose return it has not been possible to establish.

Here we have a domain where, through calculations based on Newton's theory, much has been discovered that seems to support this theory and to establish comets almost as astronomical bodies that behave in a predictable fashion. The variations that the cometary orbits demonstrate through such attraction—what in astronomy one calls "disturbances"—can be calculated to a considerable extent. And yet the comets contradict the laws again and again. Whether a comet—even with its calculated elliptical path—is actually going to return is always a question. Sometimes it does, often it does not. The comets belonging to Jupiter pass quite near to it, although the planet with its gravitational force could bind comets at a much greater distance. The same pertains to the comets that are related to Saturn. Comets have come so near the Sun that astronomers honestly declare that it is incomprehensible that the comet should continue to exist afterward. It ought to have fallen into the Sun. When the periodicity of the 1682 comet prophesied by Halley and its return in 1759 was calculated, neither Uranus nor Neptune had been discovered. The comet was found solely through the "disturbances" of Jupiter and Saturn, although it belongs to the "Neptune family." (In connection with what was said in the last Letter, it is interesting to remark that the extremely tedious and complicated calculations necessary to establish the time of the return of Halley's comet, were worked out by a woman! This was Mme. Hortense Lepaute, a colleague of the astronomer Lalande. The plant hortensia was named after her, out of courtesy to astronomy. In almost every popular astronomy book, the comets of Jupiter are pictured as whirling around the planet. It is strange to consider these illustrations in connection with the results of spiritual scientific research.

There are yet other beings in the universe who have an "interest" in the comets, because with their help they hope to bring the planetary system out of its proper path. Rudolf Steiner, in connection with the Apocalypse, called them the "satanic" powers.

It is because the comets do not fit into the general laws that they are such desirable objects for those beings who do not wish to leave the future to the divine spiritual powers, but wish to claim it for themselves. Satan lies in wait in the cosmos for the comets, and he unites them in a troop, hoping to be able to gradually lead the planets out of their orbits. People who are bound to the usual scientific concepts could not begin to grasp such an idea, for they must consider the comets so weightless, so like spider webs in comparison with the powerful planetary masses, that they would never believe that the planets could be brought out of their orbit by the comets. Such people must think the reverse—that the planets bring the comets under their spell. That power who is named "Satan" in the Bible cherishes other expectations, however, and one gets a sense of his sinister cosmic ambush when one sees Jupiter and also the Sun as if caught in the net of the ubiquitous encircling cometary paths. Astronomical terms such as the "Jupiter family" of comets must in this connection give one a strange feeling. For these periodic comets encircling Jupiter are to be seen as confederates of a highwayman who pursues someone on his path with the intention of robbing him, rather than as a family group united through the peaceful tie of the "force of gravity."

We can also thus understand how the periodic comets can be gradually led away from the task given them by the gods and can become harmful beings in the universe. For an impulse that has once been given does not necessarily bring a corresponding effect to human evolution over centuries and thousands of years. In fact, Halley's comet is such an impulse. One can actually discern from the life history of the comets something of the conflict taking place around them. Halley's comet, which has a revolution period—or more correctly, a period of reappearance—of seventy-six years, can be traced back to the first or perhaps even the second century B.C. From then on one finds all the appearances, omitting none, recorded in Chinese star books, old chronicles, and elsewhere. It belongs to the retrograde comets; in other words, it moves in a direction opposite to that of the planets. We know that all planets revolve around the Sun, and the moons revolve in the same direction around their planets with the exception of the most recently discovered moon of Saturn, the four moons of Uranus (which move almost vertically in relation to the path of the planet), and the first discovered moon of Neptune. Rudolf Steiner has frequently referred to this fact to prove that Uranus and Neptune do not actually belong to our planetary system. They have "flown in" later, and so have become something like stationary comets. Even Saturn at the beginning of our Earth's evolution had the form of a comet, with a kind of nucleus situated in the orbit of Saturn and a kind of cometary tail caused by an external streaming from out of the universe (*Spiritual Beings in the Heavenly Bodies and in the Kingdoms of Nature,* lecture 10, April 14, 1914). The spirits of will, the thrones, who at the same time form the group soul of the minerals, directed this tail until at a later time the planetary system was closed off and the "tail" formed itself into the Saturn rings. "To occult sight the rings of Saturn have exactly the same appearance as a comet's tail." In a peculiar way even today we find an indication of the cometary nature of Saturn, in its tenth moon, Phoebe, discovered in 1898. It moves in a retrograde direction, and is far removed from the other nine, and even now reaches into the cometary region of Saturn's former cometary tail.

Halley's comet comes here as a spiritual impulse just out of that region depicted in Figure 40. Rudolf Steiner has plainly set forth on various occasions what kind of impulse that is:

Now the appearance of Halley's comet, or what it signifies spiritually for the further evolution of humanity, is connected with what humanity had to absorb out of the cosmos at the various periods of Kali Yuga so that thought should descend more and more into materiality. With every new appearance of this comet a new impulse was born, to drive the ego away from a spiritual conception of the cosmos to understand the world in a more materialistic way. (*The Christ Impulse and the Development of Ego-Consciousness,* lecture 5, March 9, 1910.)

And also:

Halley's comet—and we are speaking of its spiritual dimension—has the mission of so impressing its own nature into the whole nature of humankind that whenever the comet comes into the special sphere of the Earth, approaches the Earth, human nature then makes a step forward in the evolution of the ego, leading it forward in its conception of the physical plane. (Lecture, March 5, 1910)

The latter quotation relates more to the task of Halley's comet in general, the former especially to its appearances since 1759. We can well understand that just in that time when we encounter the earliest reports about the "terrible comet," an impulse was necessary that would take hold of the human ego and lead it into the physical sense world. For in this sensory world the Christ was to appear in order to give a meaning to the Earth, and the ego of the human being must unite itself upon Earth with the Christ impulse. (The last appearance of Halley's comet before the Mystery of Golgotha was in the year 12 B.C.) That at first an unspiritual concept of the world, that is, materialism, came about through this impulse has to do with the destiny of the Kali Yuga. Through the appearance of the comet, organs were created in the human physical and etheric bodies:

. . . fine organs, that are suited to the progressive evolution of the ego, of this ego that has developed itself as consciousness-soul especially since the time of the coming to Earth of the Christ impulse. Since that time the appearances of the comet signify that the ego . . . acquires such physical and etheric organs as this progressed ego can make use of. (*Loc. cit.*)

Humanity of old stands appalled before this cosmic impulse to materialism. It appears to them as a veritable "divine rod of punishment." In 837 A.D. the comet appears and prepares for the removal of the spirit [from the church's doctrine about human nature – Trans.] at the Council of Constantinople. In 1066 it shines before the Normans who cross over to conquer England. It appears in 1456 three years after the conquest of Constantinople by the Turks, and the Pope tries to turn aside the scourge of God by the pealing of bells—the origin of the "angelus." In 1682 the comet fulfilled its mission, inasmuch as it brought Halley to the discovery of its periodicity after Newton, two years before, in studying the comet of 1680 had recognized the parabolic form of the orbit and had proved it according to his system. One sees that there were then still great tasks to perform, heroic impulses. It was different from the eighteenth century on. The last appearances brought in fact only a shallow materialism. In 1759 came the impulse that led to the "Enlightenment" preceding the French Revolution, and out of the appearance in 1835 was born the scientific materialism of the nineteenth century. One has the feeling: There has been enough of materialism now. Therefore Rudolf Steiner warned us in 1910, two months before the perihelion of the appearance in that year, that humanity should now really look upon the comet as a rod the loving good God displays so that humanity should not fall into materialism. Otherwise forms of materialism will arise that are much worse than those of the nineteenth century. Almost two decades have passed since then, and already one can get a picture of what the comet has brought about in humanity, a humanity that no longer fears the comet but has abandoned itself to it without a care. The last three appearances of the comet are in their effect quite different from the former ones. For the necessity of "plunging into matter" with our thinking has not been present with the same intensity since the eighteenth century, and has completely disappeared with the end of the Dark Ages. Only the satanic power, one might say, still has an interest in preserving Halley's comet, and letting it appear again and again.

The archangel Michael, however, fights against the cometary being that might help the unrighteous spirits to victory in the world conflict. There is much to relate, too, of this conflict. That shall be our concern next month, in August, when the cosmic iron falls to Earth in the August meteor showers.

August 1929

Comets III

Shooting Stars and Meteors

AT DIFFERENT POINTS IN HISTORY very different interpretations of comets have been put forth, and these throw light upon the particular understanding of the nature of the cosmos that existed at the time and within the circle in question. Aristotle, who observed the comet of the year 372 B.C. and who divided comets into the two classes of "bearded" and "tailed," held the view that comets are exhalations of the Earth, gases that rise out of the ground and ignite in the higher strata of the atmosphere. It was inevitable that he should ascribe a terrestrial origin to comets, since according to his views the heavens are the archetype of the immutable, and comets therefore could not originate in the heavens. We have here to some degree an astral concept of the comets, which may well have its source in ancient mystery wisdom. For if the comets actually come near the Earth in order to purify the astral atmosphere, what requires purification in this atmosphere is certainly of earthly origin: everything that ascends into the astral world from the sins and passions of humankind. The astral world has its representative in the gaseous or aerial, just as the etheric is represented in the fluidic. Thus in a certain sense the comet actually does ignite itself on the exhalations that rise from the Earth. Aristotle's theory only became a barrier to the advance of human knowledge during the Renaissance, when scientists wished to adopt a purely spatial concept of the universe and yet did not wish to abandon the fundamentally spiritual concept of Aristotle. For, since variability and transience can only exist in the "sub-lunar sphere" (as Aristotle was understood), comets must have a sub-lunar nature and must evoke great unrest, war, disease, and epidemic in the elemental world "beneath the Moon." Newton was the first to determine the cosmic origin of comets through his calculation of the path of the 1680 comet. Thus over time comets went from being an astral, then an elementary, and finally a purely physical reality, and human beings tried to understand them more and more in this way. One hoped gradually to understand the abnormality of the comets' movements and of their physical behavior through the increasing application of celestial mechanics and celestial physics.

The author of the Apocalypse [The Book of Revelation], who was able to penetrate deeply into the secrets behind the veil of nature, held other, deeply spiritual views. In the same document that deals with the war in heaven and Michael's fight with the dragon, he describes the seven-headed beast that arises from the sea and has ten horns, and he describes the two-horned beast that desires to do humanity evil and whose number is 666 (Revelation 18).

We know from Rudolf Steiner that these images depict events in the other world that also play themselves out in our time. And the battle of Michael today is as exalted and "apocalyptic" as it was in the time when the Apocalyptist directly observed it. The evil powers are cast upon the Earth and their place is no more found in heaven. Comets become an expression of evil, of the satanic power. Their often multiple tails are the "horns" of the "beasts." Here is a rendering (Figure 45) of the comet of 1744. Its five tails may indeed give the appearance of the ten gigantic horns of a monster rising up at the seashore. [See Notes on the Text.]

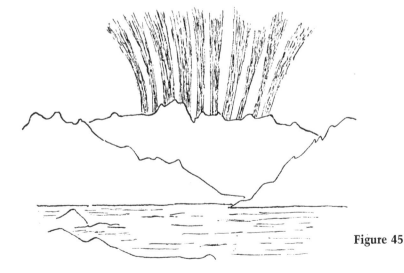

Figure 45

Oddly enough, there is another picture of this comet (Figure 46) dating from that time (by Klinkenberg) in which the comet has seven tails.

Figure 46

Since the 1840s Michael has been fighting the dragon again. The battle is the same as the one depicted in the Apocalypse. Again the dragon is cast down to Earth, only now he is turned to another use than in the time of the Apocalypse. The two-horned beast has also shown itself, until it was cast down to Earth and is no longer to be found in heaven. This is the remarkable history of the Biela comet, which in the popular scientific literature has always received preferential treatment, yet has a deeper spiritual-scientific meaning that has been revealed for us by Rudolf Steiner.

The comet was first seen in 1772 and at that time did not seem to be particularly impressive. And yet even then it seems to have inspired the terror that was later to spread abroad. For in the following year the astronomer Lalande intended to give a lecture in the Paris Academy, which he also brought out as a treatise: "Consideration of Comets That Can Come Near the Earth." Here he occupies himself more with the results of a possible collision than with the probability of an actual occurrence of the catastrophe. However, the rumor spread that Lalande intended to predict such a collision for May 12, 1773. In that time of the Enlightenment this new, scientific end of the world evoked no less terror than the earlier, more religious fear at the scourge of God. The comet was one whose path intersects the orbit of the Earth. This however, is far from being the same as colliding with the Earth. When the comet (in the Copernican sense) approaches the orbit of the Earth, the planet is not necessarily at that point where the comet will intersect the Earth's orbit, will have its node. The panic that this caused, over the supposed end of the world, was so great that the police had to step in. The beautiful poem by Albert Steffen in *Das Goetheanum* (February 27, 1927, "The War in Heaven") relates to this event. It also depicts the further destiny of the comet and the participation of the astronomer from the spiritual world.

The comet, a periodic one, was seen again in 1805, and then again on February 27, 1826, by the Austrian officer Biela, who calculated its orbit at that time. The time of revolution was about six and two-thirds years, and it should therefore reappear at the end of 1832. Again, there was great popular excitement, for the astronomer Olbers had calculated the meeting of the comet with the Earth's orbit for October 29. Again, however, Earth was not at the point of intersection when the comet's orbit crossed its own. The astronomer Littrow now calculated ("Concerning the Dreaded Comet of the Present Year 1832, and Concerning Comets in General") that a meeting of the comet with Earth itself could only occur in a year when the comet passes near the Sun in the last days of December. According to his calculations, this will happen for the first time in 1933.

Rudolf Steiner has pointed to the gravity of this prospect, stating that the comet will encounter the Earth just at the time when great possibilities in spiritual life will lie open to humanity. We owe to the deed of Michael the fact that the comet will not collide with Earth, since its power has already been taken away. This deed manifests itself in the remarkable destiny of the comet.

After it had spread the terror in 1832, which was quite out of place at that time, the comet could not be observed during its next return, in 1839. However, it was seen again in 1845. In the last days of December it was discovered to have a second comet near it. At first this traveled quite close to the main comet in the same orbit, but then distanced itself more and more, and at the same time became ever brighter. When the comet was seen once more in 1852—again in an unfavorable position—the two parts had separated still further, but they looked quite similar and followed a common path. There was the "beast with the two-horns" ready to do harm to the Earth and its humanity! But it did not come again. It was not seen in 1859 or in 1866, and was thought to be dissolved. What had become of the two-horned beast?

In 1872 occurred the miracle that, exactly at the time when the Earth was near the former intersection point with the path of the comet, part of the heavens seemed to

Figure 47

be covered with fire due to a colossal shower of shooting stars. Thousands upon thousands of shooting stars shot through the air. Rudolf Steiner has related how he himself as a little boy at that time experienced the wonderful display.

> It was as if a nocturnal fire fell down from heaven in many tiny dazzling sparks upon Earth below. The comet first split into myriads of tiny particles that could be taken up by the Earth's atmosphere, be united with the Earth. . . . The comet had chosen to be absorbed by the Earth.

The comet had broken up into meteors, whose substance penetrated into the Earth. These meteors and shooting stars now followed the path of the former comet. In 1879 they could not be observed, for Earth was not at the intersection of the orbits, though it was not far distant. It was just before the time when Michael was again to assume his rulership. And with this cometary shower that had become a shower of light—so said Rudolf Steiner—the rulership of Michael reached Earth. The meteor shower was seen again in its full glory in 1885 and in partial display in 1892. Since then only an insignificant swarm remains, which every year in the last days of November provides a few shooting stars, as the shower of Bielids or Andromedids. (These are not to be confused with the Leonids that appear in the middle of November and are far more numerous.)

The dividing of cometary nuclei has been observed fairly often in the comet of 1882 and in other comets. And in a remarkable way still other comets have entirely disappeared, although not under such dramatic circumstances as the Biela comet during the time of the cosmic battle of Michael. The comet Bvorsen, discovered in 1846—in the same year, therefore, that the dissolution of the Biela comet began, and having a period of about five and one-half years—failed to appear once and then after 1879 disappeared entirely. So, too, has Tempel's comet [Tempel I, with a period of about six years] disappeared after 1879. Another comet (Holmes), first appearing in 1892 with a revolution of seven years, seemed to dissolve after returning twice and has not been seen since 1913. It really seems—as has also been remarked by astronomers—as if the time of the really large comets is over since Michael began his reign. In the early 1880s some very important comets were seen, although by no means comparable with those of 1811, 1843, and 1858. The largest comet of the nineteenth century, that of September 1882, quickly went into a kind of dissolution. The twentieth century brought, at least to the Northern Hemisphere, scarcely any noteworthy comets (from the standpoint of the ordinary observer), with the exception of the More-house comet in 1908. Halley's comet, too, did not fulfill expectations. The generation that grew up in the early part of the twentieth century scarcely knows a single comet through direct observation.

The opposite is true in regard to shooting stars, and especially to meteors, if one understands by that term the stones that fall to Earth— meteorites, uranolites, aerolites, and so on. [See Notes on the Text.] In these bodies in which the cosmic iron comes to Earth we have a different world trend, which one might say is on the ascent. They are the "falling stars," already known in antiquity. However, the idea that stones could really fall "from heaven" came very late to scien-tific consciousness. Up until the turn of the eighteenth and nineteenth centuries, news of such an event met with disbelief among the learned scientists, even in academies. Ancient chronicles tell of human beings being injured and of buildings damaged by stones falling from the sky, but right into the nineteenth century these reports were taken to be fairy tales. At best people believed them to be products of volcanic activity, and thus of earthly origin. The Aristotelian concept that in shooting stars one has to do with atmospheric phenomena played a role here far longer than in the case of the comets. (The word "meteorology" is actually derived from meteor.) The empirical proof that they are cos-mic bodies was first furnished at the end of the eighteenth century. Yet Littrow's *Wonders of the Sky,* which appeared around 1835 and was much esteemed by Rudolf Steiner, omits shooting stars entirely, while it deals with comets in great detail.

In the nineteenth century, the development of the means of dissemi-nating information through the telegraph and so on has greatly increased the possibility of receiving news of the fall of meteoric stones and has thereby facilitated their study. Yet we shall not go far wrong if we accept the fact that both shooting stars and meteors have become much more numerous since the beginning of the nineteenth century. They play a role in human evolution today which, as a matter of fact, they did not play earlier. That was indeed clearly expressed in the passage from the Hague lecture cycle quoted in the last letter. Therefore we would like to observe these bodies somewhat more closely.

The differentiation between shooting stars on the one hand and meteors on the other is in part a purely quantitative one. It is probable that for every shooting star that bursts into radiance and is immediately extinguished, very fine substance in the form of dust or powder falls to Earth—as is to be found, for instance, on glaciers or on polar ice, spread out over extended areas. By meteorites one understands stones of various sizes, the smallest of which may be the tiny particles of cosmic dust mentioned above. But what one understands generally by meteors differs from the shooting stars in their mode of appearance. Meteors move more slowly and stay brilliant longer. Then they burst asunder, sometimes with explosions like that of a fireworks rocket. They differ particularly, however, by appearing at any time and at any place in the sky. Shooting stars, however, also appear in swarms that return year after year at a definite time. There are also isolated shooting stars that are to be observed at any time of the day or of the year. Generally speaking, shooting stars are an extraordinarily common phenomenon in comparison with the distinctly rare meteors, and the still rarer meteor whose fall has been properly authenticated. Anywhere in our latitudes, four to six shooting stars may be seen every hour. This rate, applied to the whole surface of the Earth, yields an enormous number. It is calculated that each day there are 15–20 million shooting stars visible to the naked eye. (We cannot deal further here with the distribution of their appearances in the course of the year, in the hours of day and night, in the different quarters of the sky, and so on. Shooting stars in general are a domain extraordinarily rich in phenomena; one may read about them in a detailed astronomical work.)

The mass that comes to Earth as a result of these bodies is also considerable, although it may seem trifling in comparison with the whole Earth. It is obvious that one can give no exact amount, but it certainly comes to several thousand tons yearly, the little dust particles of the shooting stars as well as the large stones of the actual meteorites both contributing. It may be supposed that several thousand meteorites fall to Earth every year. The number is naturally very uncertain, and is only mentioned as a contrast to the number of shooting stars. Meteorites consist for the most part of a stone mixture that, almost without exception, contains iron in the form of iron sulphide and similar compounds. There are also meteorites of pure iron—often mixed with some nickel— though these are not the rule. Among the many substances contained in the aerolites are tin, copper, silica, and carbon in the forms of diamonds. Neither quartz nor lead are ever found.

When the meteorite bursts in the air it falls to Earth as a veritable shower of stones. Up to 100,000 pieces of one meteorite have been found. The weight of a single meteoric body can be tens of thousands of pounds, and in this case is always an iron meteor. In 1929, there was a report in the press about the discovery of an unimaginably large meteoric stone that fell in central Siberia in 1908, but was not studied until a short time ago. An interesting article about it appeared in the July 1929 issue of the German magazine, *The Coral*.

The shooting stars that appear in showers are undoubtedly the most interesting. The best known shower is the Perseids, which takes place from the middle of July to the middle of August and reaches its peak on August 10. The Perseid shower takes its name, as do the other showers, from the constellation in which the so-called "radiant" of their apparent path lies. The radiant is the point from which all the shooting stars—if one follows their glowing paths in a reverse direction—seem to issue in the form of rays. The radiant, however, is not really a single point. Calculations indicate that the radiant for the shooting stars of a particular shower is actually a small surface area of the firmament.

The meteor shower that occurs in July and August therefore has its radiant in Perseus; the first one in November in Leo (Leonids), the other in Andromeda, and so on. In addition, there are the Lyrids from April 18–24 (radiant in the Lyre), while in the first half of August, at the same time as the Perseids, still another radiant shower comes out of Aquarius.

To an objective observer, it must seem totally accidental and inconsequential that the radiant is in, or rather, in front of one or another constellation. For even if one thinks of the shooting stars as coming from outside the atmosphere and penetrating into it, one imagines them, and indeed rightly, as traveling within the solar system just like the comets. The fact that the radiant of the July-August shower appears in Perseus would thus be just as "illusory" as the fact, for instance, that Saturn stands before Sagittarius. From a spiritual perspective that cannot, of course, apply—our anthroposophical cosmology assumes to the highest degree the reality of just these directions in space. Thus to us it is very meaningful that in late summer when autumn is approaching, the shooting stars that bring down the cosmic iron that overpowers the sulphurous dragon appear from the direction in which stands Perseus, understood in all traditions as the constellation of the archangel Michael.

It may be quite sufficient here merely to point to Rudolf Steiner's lectures about cosmic iron in connection with the mission of Michael. (It was printed in the weekly *Newssheet* of Michaelmas 1925.) The whole connection between comets and meteors on the one hand and the work of Michael on the other shall continue to occupy us next time.

YEAR THREE

September 1929–August 1930

September 1929

Comets IV

Shooting Stars and Meteors—Cosmic Iron

IT MAY SEEM STRANGE that the subject of comets and shooting stars is treated in these letters in such detail, relatively speaking. But it will become increasingly clear that in these heavenly bodies we have something that is strongly connected with the spiritual destiny of just this present time and of the future.

It is well known how human beings reacted to the appearance of comets in the past. The comets excited fear, and fear is never an expression of understanding. People could not fully comprehend the task of the comets in the universe. To be sure, they knew they were connected with the anger of God at human sinfulness, and feared them on this account. This knowledge, however, was not based on insight, but on superstition. There was a marked difference in early humanity between the way the soul regarded the comets and the way it regarded the workings of the starry and planetary world. For the human being of the Grecian age, and even still of the Middle Ages, had very definite—and in a certain sense very profound—views about astrology. (That was naturally still more the case with the Babylonians and the Egyptians, whom we do not cite here only because nothing is known of a contrasting fear of comets among these peoples.) One knew in detail how the orbits of the planets, their various aspects in relation to each other, and so on are connected with the rule of destiny in human life and in the life of a people. We have already often spoken of the fact that today a human being can no longer have the relation to the active star forces that was possible in the time when the sentient soul or even the intellectual soul was being perfected. Human beings have already become too free for that, too independent of these forces, and have emancipated themselves too strongly from the cosmos through the intellect. To begin with, we have before us only a calculated model of the celestial phenomena. On this the "astrologers" then formulated their prophecies, which are very often not in harmony with the facts. Thus in astrology we have a branch of knowledge that has been regressing since ancient times and whose reality for humanity is constantly decreasing. Today we can attain a new relation to the starry world only through the development of new spiritual faculties.

Comets on the other hand have had the peculiar destiny in human evolution to be feared at first, and then to be understood scientifically to a certain degree, but without being understood spiritually at all. Enlightened humanity stopped fearing them at a time when spiritual beings of the most strong opposing forces set about conquering the comets for themselves. Moreover, the mission of comets must change when human beings become more and more responsible for their acts. They are now becoming the focus in a cosmic war. In the course of this warfare something increasingly emerges that to an extent seems to be their polar opposite, but is linked to the fleeting coma—the cloud around the nucleus of the comet. This is the stone traveling around in space, the hard iron that then falls to Earth as meteorites.

This is what Rudolf Steiner referred to as cited in Letter 11, Year One. The substance of the comets and of the shooting stars that is cast out of the Sun existed in former times, but now, especially as meteors, the cosmic iron, it has another significance. In earlier times those spiritual impulses which come from the stars—the object of astrological research—were active and had an effect. Today those impulses are chiefly working through the expelled iron. Thus:

> . . . for our age something has entered the cosmos that in earlier times was not there to the same extent: the cosmic iron in its spiritual significance gives to the Michael-spirit the possibility of mediating between the supersensible world and the sense-perceptible world of Earth.

A firm, steadfast directive meets the human being with the cosmic iron, and it is important to turn our gaze away for once from the eternal dependence upon the star forces and turn it toward the directing gesture of Michael.

The passage just quoted makes it understandable that it was reserved for the nineteenth century to discover the cosmic origin of meteors and their connection with the comets, naturally without any idea of the spiritual foundation. Anthroposophically, too, we can at first only point to these relations. The future assuredly will reveal its deeper meaning.

In the past century there were several extraordinarily heavy showers of shooting stars like the one we described in connection with the Biela comet. The first was in November 1833. It belonged to the already well-known Leonid shower (radiant point in Leo), but in that year, and also in the previous year, it was unusually powerful—a real rain. This occurred again [in 1866] and research into shooting stars in general, until then in a deplorable condition, now came upon a number of remarkable laws. (Figure 48 shows the shower of shooting stars of November 1866, and in it one can plainly see the radiant in the head of the Lion.)

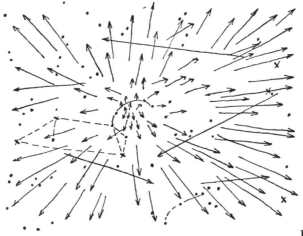

Figure 48

It came to light that in 1799, Alexander von Humboldt had already observed a similar outburst of meteors in the November showers that according to certain traditions had also been seen in 1766 in Central America. The Leonids, which still appear each year in November, give a maximum display every thirty-three to thirty-four years. In a remarkable way they divide the century into three parts and thus seem to follow a historic law. It was then assumed that the meteors of the Leonid shower are spread over an elongated, elliptical path, upon which they complete a circuit around the Sun in $33 \frac{1}{4}$ years. This orbit would be to an extent filled with meteors along its entire length, and at a certain point there is supposed to be a cloudlike clustering of meteoric bodies. Every year in November the Earth arrives at the same point in their orbit and the whole unbroken mass passes by. Every thirty-three years, though, it meets the point at which the meteorites are most dense, and the unusually thick shower of stars must then follow.

One sees that this description in essence applies for a cometary orbit and for the assumed intersection of a comet with the orbit of the Earth. The comet, though, is found at a single point on its path, while the meteors are strewn over the orbit's whole length, with a concentration at a particular place.

Now the surprising thing that was found by the excellent astronomer Schiaparelli (not, however, for the November shower, but for the August shower, the Perseids), stimulated by the great star showers of 1866, was that the orbit of the August shower coincided almost exactly with the path of the comet that had appeared in 1862. Immediately following this the identity of the orbit calculated for the Leonids with that of the comet of 1866 was established. This comet [Tempel-Tuttle] also has a period of revolution of 33.2 years, and the direction of its path corresponds to the paths followed, according to calculations, by the meteors or shooting stars that each year in November shoot out of the constellation of Leo. One can picture to oneself the orbit of Halley's comet, as depicted in figure 40, as being approximately also the orbit of the August meteors and of the comet of 1862, if one keeps in mind only the form and the elongation of the orbit. One should think of the meteoric stones as spread along the whole length of the ellipse, so that the Earth encounters a portion of the swarm every time it crosses its path in August. The single shooting stars on the orbit are splinters, products of the disintegration of the comet—principally from its nucleus, which in the course of long periods of time had always stayed on the cometary orbit and had gradually filled it up.

These views, which were put forward in 1867 by astronomers, received a significant confirmation in the shower of shooting stars of 1872 which we saw was produced by the extinguished and transformed Biela comet. In earlier times, too, always at the same time—the end of November—a slighter shower had appeared. It was known that twice, in 1798 and 1838, this had occasioned an important shower of meteorites. These had coincided with returns of the Biela comet. After the comet had failed to appear in the year 1866, its appearance was replaced in 1872 and also in 1885 by a powerful rain of fire, as we have already described in Letter 12, and thereafter only a moderate-sized shower was left. Thus, here we see a comet disappear but a meteor shower continue to exist.

The comet of 1862, which corresponds to the Perseid shower, has been observed only once up to the present time, its period of revolution being calculated at about 120 years. The same holds good for the comet of 1861 (1) whose orbit would coincide with that of the Lyrids (the April shower in the Lyre), which must have a period of several centuries—in other words, in fact, a quite uncertain one. The 1866 comet, corresponding in its orbit to the Leonid shower (as discussed in the last Letters), was last seen in 1899 and then disappeared, became extinct. . . . [See Letter 10, Year Two, on comets dissolving and returning—also, Notes on the Text.] So we are here led to a connection between comets and meteors that at least in some cases seems to be definitely established.

It is peculiar to notice what a great role the years 1861–1863 played in these extraordinarily important appearances—that is, the close of the second third of the nineteenth century. In 1863, when the Lyrid shower produced a sudden maximum of shooting stars, the astronomer H.A. Newton set to work to calculate for the first time the orbit of the meteoric swarms, not as the single meteors appear lighting up in the atmosphere, but as the whole swarm describes an orbit in space, corresponding to a definite period of revolution around the Sun. In 1866, Schiaparelli and others, prompted by the heavy shower of stars in that year, compared these orbits with those of comets, and found for the well-known swarms of the year a correspondence with three comets that had appeared respectively in 1861, 1862, and 1866. Then the year 1872 helped confirm this point of view when the Biela comet of 1866 failed to reappear. In this way, the year 1866 became just as much a crucial point for the existence and the understanding of meteors and comets as formerly the year 1833 had been. (The "much-feared comet of 1832"; the shower of shooting stars in 1833 with a thirty-three-year period, which was the first to cause astronomers to seriously consider the problem of shooting stars; a cometary appearance in 1834; and Halley's comet of 1835.)

When we come, on the other hand, to the year 1899, the close of the last third of the nineteenth century, the end of the Kali Yuga and of the first twenty years of Michael's rulership, we see a different picture.

In this year the November Leonid shower was to be at its thirty-three-year maximum. For the first time this was consciously awaited, but it brilliantly stayed away! At the same time a special revival of the Biela swarm was expected at the end of November, because of the six-to-seven-year period of the former Biela comet. This swarm, which in 1872 and 1885 had produced glorious meteoric showers, ought to have given us another beautiful display in November 1899. However, the heavens also denied us this. What should confront us in the year 1933 but whose nature has already been turned to good, we have already seen.

With the exception of those mentioned above, scarcely any instances of coincidence of cometary orbits with the orbits of meteoric swarms have been found. However, with the four examples given, we have in fact exhausted the principal showers of the year. A certain agreement was discovered for the orbit of Halley's comet with that of the May Aquarids, but this did not seem to be verified. When the comet then appeared in 1910 and had its conjunction with the Sun in May, extraordinarily this shower, which comes in May and has its radiant in Aquarius, showed a sudden increase in its activity as if the presence of the comet had also worked upon it with a stimulating effect.

Here in quite an elementary way we have some insight into the historical effects of comets and meteors. It cannot be denied that great

riddles are still bound up with these effects and with the relation between comets and meteors. For astronomical science, too, shooting stars today present the most remarkable riddles, whose solution probably can only be supplied by a much deeper spiritual understanding of the phenomena than is customary at the present time. One has only to remember the problem of the so-called "stationary radiants" that still confronts the Copernican world-view as a complete riddle.

We have explained that the shooting stars that appear in showers all indicate, from the paths they traverse during their brief illumination,

Figure 49

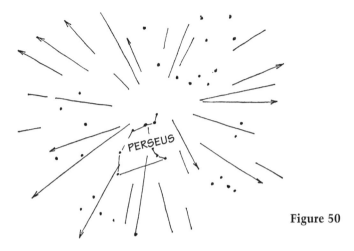

Figure 50

one point, or a small surface, from which they seem to emerge. Figure 48 clearly shows this point—the radiant of the November Leonid shower. For the August meteors it lies in the constellation of Perseus. The meteor shower lasts several weeks, and during this time, Earth because of its movement around the Sun changes position relative to the constellation. Thus, in the course of the shower the radiant should change position in relation to the stars, if indeed the meteors that shoot out of the constellation are independent of Earth and its movement. In the case of the Perseid stream this has actually been observed. The radiant remains, indeed, in Perseus, but moves along over a distance of about 45 degrees, which corresponds to the six weeks of the duration of the meteoric fall. It passes through the upper part of the constellation and, as one sees in Figure 49 (from Bode's *Star Atlas*) passes right through the sword and the arm of Perseus! We must therefore imagine that the shooting stars that come from this region in the summer weeks of July and August have a kind of radiant point just where Perseus-Michael swings his sword to vanquish the sea-monster that threatens Andromeda. If one fixes one's gaze upon the cluster of stars in Perseus—plainly recognizable to the naked eye—one has exactly the point (lying in the hand that holds the hilt of the sword) from which the shooting stars emerge at the height of the shower.

This shift of the radiant—which theoretically ought to take place in all showers of long duration—has, however, been established only for the Perseids. In the case of other showers that go on for a long time—and there are a good many in the course of the year, less numerous than the August shower, but of considerably longer duration—the radiants remain unchanged. They do not move in relation to the stars that appear as their background, but the radiant seems in each case to be fixed in one definite place in the heavens, while in the August shower the radiant seems to pass in front of the background formed by the constellation of Perseus. These astronomical matters—still in dispute—are mentioned here only because they seem to point to a significant inner difference between the August meteors (by which are always meant the Perseids) and those at other times of the year. The Perseid showers because of their frequency and regularity, their short, quick illuminations, their appearance in the hot summer nights, are for us the quintessential shooting stars. Thus it must strike us as significant that just this shower— which Rudolf Steiner brought into a special relationship with the archangel Michael—distinguishes itself even by its physical laws from the other showers.

We are thus led over from the more or less historical meaning of shooting stars to what they mean for human life. The lecture about Michael and the cosmic iron spoke of this latter issue. When in summertime the human being is subjected to the sulphurizing process, and in soul and spirit becomes luminous for the beings in the cosmos, when Ahriman then creeps near, desiring to make the human being his prey through dreaminess, through a diminished consciousness, then the cosmic iron comes to humanity through the shooting stars. Then in miniature there sparkles in human blood just such a shower of shooting stars as is to be seen on a grander scale in the firmament. Then the formation of iron streams down from the head into the blood, while the sulfuric leaves, passing upward from below.

> And so as the gods with their meteoric stones fight against the spirit, who would ray out fear over the whole Earth through his serpentine form, by causing iron to ray out into this dread-atmosphere of fear, which is most intense when autumn approaches, when summer comes to an end—the same thing as the gods do takes place within the human being when the blood is permeated with iron.

And the setting for this event is the conflict of Michael with the dragon.

But we only represent rightly, we only paint rightly, when we let the atmosphere or space in which Michael unfolds his glory, his power against the dragon, when we let the space be filled, not with indifferent clouds, but with descending meteor showers of iron. These meteor showers form themselves through the power that streams from the heart of Michael, are melted together for the iron sword of Michael, who overcomes the dragon with his iron sword formed of meteors. [Lecture 1 in Steiner's *The Four Seasons and the Archangels*]

Thus it is in summertime that then leads into Michaelmas [September 29]. But the same thing is going on in an uninterrupted stream the whole year through. Incessantly the iron (born from a cosmic warfare, as we tried to describe in Letter 11, Year One) falls to Earth, and must now be turned to the service of healing. It forms in a similar way the physiological foundation of human freedom, in that it continually brings the forces of iron into the blood.

In the lectures of 1923 given by Rudolf Steiner in The Hague (*Supersensible Man*) the facts are described as follows:

Backstage, behind the "stage curtains" of existence, there is strife and warfare in the spiritual world. And that which is cast by the Sun spirits into the cosmos as iron—even to the degree of being physically visible—becomes in the most comprehensive sense the cosmic armor of Michael. Michael now has his task in this cosmic warfare—confronted by these powers of battle and conflict behind the veil of civilization, to help humanity forward in the right way. Thus on the one hand one is met by strife and battle, on the other by the interventions of Michael.

But all this again is connected with the development of human freedom. For as earthly human beings we have iron in our blood. If we were beings who had no iron in the blood, the feeling of freedom, the impulse to freedom, could quite well arise in our souls, but we would never have a body that we could use to realize this impulse of freedom. That we not only can grasp the idea, the impulse of freedom, but that we can also feel in our body the strength to make this body into the bearer of the impulse of freedom, arises from the fact that in our era we can learn how Michael was able to mold to his service the cosmic iron that in former times

had also been released. It arises too from the fact that if we more
and more understand the impulse of Michael, we can learn how to
place the inner iron into the service of the impulse of freedom.

The human being needs iron in the blood in order to become a bearer
of the impulse of freedom, and meteors have become the instigators of
this process just as comets had to build up certain organs in the human
being. These things are not present for the first time. One finds the Perseids mentioned in old records that go back to the year 830 A.D.; the
Leonids in records dating to 902. The thought may suggest itself that the
eighth and ninth centuries coincided with the epoch in which the cosmic
intelligence gradually fell away from the Michael-spirit. Rudolf Steiner
used the expression that in earlier times cosmic intelligence "rained
down" upon Earth. The first great showers of shooting stars (single
meteors and shooting stars have naturally been known from far earlier times) may have been a Michaelic stimulus to human non-cosmic
thought power, just as now, working in the blood, they make it possible
for the human will to realize the impulse of freedom.

But something else as well comes to Earth with the shooting stars. As
we have seen, they are related in some way to comets. When in 1872 the
stream of fire of the former Biela comet came down from the heavens,
it brought with it to Earth, to some extent, the spiritualized remains
of the comet. And so it is in other cases also. The shooting stars carry
with them in a similar way pieces of disintegrated comet substance, and
indeed we know that since the last century comets have often dissolved
or have broken up.

To these cometary remnants also adhere nitrogen and cyanide that
descends with the iron or with the other types of stone that comprise
the meteorites. This passes into the Earth, is absorbed by it and again
ascends out of it; passes through the plants that one eats, through the
air that one breathes, into the human being; and works intensely, in
an extremely dilute form, upon the human astral body. The effects
differ according to the nature of the impulse that was bound to the
original comet. Many comets—according to Rudolf Steiner—"unchain
turbulent astral forces when they rise again after having been absorbed
by the Earth." But there are others that—because of the extremely
small amounts of nitrogen they contain—work in a purifying, healing,
and strengthening way upon the human astral body. The human being

needs this especially since the nineteenth century because of the great stress laid upon the nervous system—in other words, upon the astral body—from the advent of railroads and the technological developments that followed. "An extraordinarily important cosmic physician is active in the cosmos, who is more or less continuously making use of such therapy."

The "beast" of the Apocalypse comes out of the Earth. For the present time it can be evil, as it was seen by the apocalyptist [St. John of Patmos, who wrote the Book of Revelation]. But it can also affect human beings so that their nervousness is balanced therapeutically; it can give him strength by way of the astral body to withstand the stresses of modern civilization.

In this way we can understand the appearance of many significant comets in the nineteenth century and their tendency to split up and break apart, and also the mighty showers of shooting stars and falling meteors in the last decades. We can begin to understand that a meteor of such immense size as that described in the last Letter had to fall in the most distant region of Siberia where it remained unobserved for twenty years and gradually sank in the swamps of that region before it could be utilized for commercial purposes. [See Notes on the Text.]

We see how human beings receive what they need from the cosmos in order to become self-reliant and independent. The Michael-spirit himself desires this freedom, this cosmic independence, for he leads the human being, who has become spiritually free, to the Christ who bears within himself as law the new cosmos and the new Jerusalem. In relation to the existing cosmos, the modern human being does not only need to develop feelings of dependence, of no matter how grateful a nature, but needs above all to develop a feeling of shared responsibility. What will become of the planetary system under the assault of Satan, what the still-awaited comets of the twentieth century will accomplish in human life (Halley's comet returning in 1986, and other well-known periodic ones in 1954, 1972, 1984)—that is given into the hands of humanity to an ever-increasing degree. In the coming decades the human soul will stand in a time of the most weighty decisions and trials, but through the cosmic iron and above all through the Michael-spirit, it will be granted the power to prevail.

October 1929

The World of the Stars I
Planets and Fixed Stars

WE WILL NOW CONSIDER the actual stellar universe that in the spectacle of its brilliance and the arrangement of its points of light reveals itself so majestically to human sight. Quite a different kind of observation is necessary when the stars appear, shining in their abundance and their sublime quietude, and when the planets or even the comets, the roving, wandering stars, pass before us. Indeed, one speaks of these in contrast to the world of the fixed stars. In the modern sense this term is actually misleading, for in modern astronomy one recognizes in the stars so many movements and such variability that they can hardly be called "fixed" in the traditional sense of immobility and invariability. Nevertheless, when we speak from the occult point of view, we must see in the world of stars, especially that pertaining to the zodiac, something that belongs to the "realm of duration." Their forces, their effects are subject to duration. The planetary world, in contrast, is one of "changeableness." The fixed stars, especially those that do not belong to the zodiac, have a "relative duration." They certainly change, but only over long, long periods of time, or else their variability is an enduring, rhythmic one, which is clearly distinguishable from the mobility of the planets with their orbits and loops. We shall often have to speak of this variability within the world of the fixed stars.

First of all, we must be clear that in the planets together with Earth, the Moon, and the Sun we have what we call the "solar system," or even "our planetary system," which is intimately linked with our whole evolution. We need merely look at Rudolf Steiner's *An Outline of Esoteric Science*, in which the history of our solar system is described, in order to learn about the origin of the individual planets of this system. They are stages upon the path of evolution which our Earth has passed through in its earlier and present embodiments. The planets surround us and penetrate us with their spheres, which are our dwelling places in the life after death. The planets themselves at the very beginning of Earth evolution separated themselves one by one from the original common substance, because "all the bodies of this [solar] system have arisen through the different stages of maturity of the beings inhabiting them." (*An Outline of Esoteric Science,* chapter titled "The Evolution of the World and the Human Being.") They were then, like Earth itself, drawn into circular movement by causes that also lie in the spiritual. (See Letter 6, Year Two.)

Already during the Old Moon stage of evolution a series of planets was at one time formed, and even the Old Sun saw a Saturn planet arise as a rebirth of the Old Saturn (*An Outline of Esoteric Science,* same reference). The Sun at the time of the Old Sun stage of evolution was already a kind of fixed star, a "world-sun that is a Sun, so to speak, through its own power" (Steiner's *The Spiritual Hierarchies,* lecture 5). It was a fixed star also in the sense that we find described in the "Akashic record" (*Lucifer-Gnosis,* 1904–1906): "In the sense of occult science a fixed star is one that sends life-forces to one or more planets separated from itself." It was the same during the Old Moon period, when the Moon and Sun separated for the first time and during the Earth stage of evolution, when the Sun separated itself from Earth. The Sun then went through a still further evolution because the Christ being is connected to it, and will in a distant future be united once more with Earth and will ascend to a yet loftier existence. We will consider this later. First we will distinguish the concept of fixed stars from that of the planets.

In the planets, and likewise in the Moon and the Sun as former planets, we have thus a piece of our own history as humanity, as inhabitants of the Earth. They are the various signposts or boundary stones on this path. Saturn indicates with its orbit the approximate extent of the whole system during the Old Saturn period, Jupiter that of the Old Sun period, Mars that of the Moon period. They are for the physical eye the only visible spots, so to speak, in the sphere to which they belong, a "hole", in fact, on the periphery of the sphere. (See Steiner's *The Spiritual Beings in the Heavenly Bodies,* lecture 6.) In these spheres is contained the activity of the etheric formative forces that especially affect the human being. We carry within us their activity as organ-building forces. The positions of the planets in relation to each other at our birth depict our destiny. Just as Earth is, they too, are linked with the Sun, although in a different way. Moreover, each planet is linked to the Sun in a unique way different from that of the other planets.

The planets are relatively few in number. The ancients named seven of them: Moon, Mercury, Venus, Sun, Mars, Jupiter, Saturn. Present-day astronomy counts as planets: Mercury, Venus, Earth, Mars, Jupiter, Saturn, Uranus, Neptune, and the host of little planets, the planetoids or asteroids between Mars and Jupiter—of which more are being con-tinually discovered. The smallest are supposed to be only a few miles in diameter, and thus are about the same size as the largest meteor.. At the present time [1929] over 1,000 have been discovered. [Note: By the year 2000 over 65,000 planetoids were known.]

If one follows the planets with the naked eye, they distinguish them-selves from the fixed stars through their circular movement (which is in the opposite direction to the daily revolution), through their retrograde motion, loops, and so on. It is a steady movement that can be calculated, but gives the possibility of constantly new combinations. (It would be a good exercise in the coming months to observe Jupiter. It is now rising in the early evening, and since the beginning of October is describing its loop. It lies at present almost midway between the two brightest stars in Taurus, Aldebaran and the "Horn" of the Bull, and will move between Aldebaran and the Pleiades backward and upward until January 23, 1930, and only in May will return to its present position.)

Seen through the telescope the planets appear as little disks. Most of them have moons, and these revolve around the planet at what is often a very high speed. The stars, though, even through a strong telescope appear only as little sharp points of light. To ordinary sight the planets certainly appear also as stars, but they are distinguished from the stars by their quiet light that lacks the twinkling which the stars, especially on cold winter nights, can so plainly show. This characteristic can help one distinguish a planet from a star in case one isn't sure what one is observing. Only Mars can sometimes cause one some doubt, for under certain conditions, especially when it is lying low down on the horizon, it can twinkle quite noticeably. On the other hand, its red color is immediately noticeable.

In Letters 7 and 8 of Year One we described the planetary motions as actual phenomena, in other words as they can be seen on the firmament. There they all move, Sun, Moon, and planets as if on the inner side of the hollow sphere of the celestial vault. One cannot conceive of a successive order based on distance, only at the most a sequence based on time, that is, according to the duration of the revolutions. (This was dealt with also in the letters mentioned). The spatial element arises to a certain degree with the theory of the spheres that was held in ancient times. In that theory it remains uncertain in what way the spheres lie within each other. In any case, the stars have a sphere for themselves—the sphere of the fixed stars, which in the Middle Ages became the "crystal heavens"—which is the outermost, most distant sphere. The spheres of the planets lie closer to us. Through spiritual science we understand that this feeling of the spatial proximity of the planets stems from the intimate connection between humankind and the planets, of which we have already said various things. How little "spatial" this system was we can see from the Pythagorean view of the harmony of the spheres. The music of the spheres was believed to be produced by the gliding of the spheres over one another, and thus for this the spheres must have been in direct contact with each other.

The development continues in that one more and more considered the planets in terms of space, thinking that they moved in circles and that there was space between these circles. One can say that out of the vast throng of stars in the firmament, the planets were brought to the fore, and arranged spatially. Until Copernicus, the stars remained attached to the dome of the heavens with no differences in terms of distance. In the Middle Ages one imagined that behind this world of the stars lay the spiritual world, the sphere of the blessed ones.

The first attempts to determine the distances of the Sun and the Moon from Earth in terms of pure measurement began quite early in ancient times, in that scientific stream that was less concerned with the teachings of the spheres that had come out of the Chaldean mysteries than with the inflexible concepts of Egypt and the epicycle theory. Aristarchus of Samos, who held a heliocentric world view and was thus the forerunner of Copernicus, tried first to establish the relationship of the distance of the Sun and of the Moon from Earth. Hipparchus, proceeding from this, first gave definite numbers for the distances—which, however, are far too small according to present-day scientific concepts. Thus, following upon the concern with the spherical element there is an interest in the radial. This is appropriate for the Earth and involves the effort to calculate the distances of the planets from Earth or the Sun in stadia, miles, or kilometers, and to conceive the whole of space in a terrestrial, three-dimensional way. One arrives then at numbers which for instance in the case of Saturn are far more than a billion miles.

We are not now concerned with asking whether these numbers are right or not. They are at all events the correctly calculated results of certain hypotheses. And to formulate these hypotheses was appropriate for human consciousness in a certain epoch as a necessity of world history. For us it is more the question what ideas shall replace the ones given by history. And it is anthroposophical spiritual science that should supply the foundation for this.

It can be clear to us that each theory of planetary motion, whether Ptolemaic or Copernican, deviates from what is seen by the eye—that is, from the purely phenomenal, from what appears in the heavens. Each imagines events in some sort of space which it depicts as existing between Earth and the starry heavens. With Ptolemy the essentials of this space remain more or less undefined. With Copernicus they are already formed more after the pattern of our known earthly space, and his successors have brought entirely terrestrial concepts into those spatial processes. Through anthroposophy, first of all the concept of space itself will have to be newly formed, so that it may correctly separate and correctly combine the worlds of the planets and of the fixed stars.

The stars remained until the time of Copernicus in the sphere of the fixed stars, which is located at an indeterminate distance. The Copernican system, however, in its consequences, led to moving the stars almost immeasurably far away, but at the same time to different distances just like the planets, but in a way, to the other side. With this, the crystal heaven, the sphere of the fixed stars, was finally destroyed and the "blue firmament" reduced to an illusion, a maya. It is not possible now—but it may perhaps be done later—to show how the Copernican theory in its concrete historical development has led to the "light years" of modern astronomy. (One can read about it in Dr. W. Kaiser's book *Geometrical Concepts in Astronomy*.) A "light year" is the space that light is said to pass through in one year, a sort of wave-like spreading-out of light being suggested. The rate is accepted to be 300,000 kilometers (186,330 miles) per second. One sees that even for the smallest distance of a star that has been calculated until now according to this method—about four light years—a number is reached that greatly surpasses the distance of even the farthest planet of our system. For in the case of Saturn, for example, the distance would be only a bit more than one "light-hour." Since this view has been reached, according to scientific thinking an immense gulf yawns between the solar system and the stellar universe. In the ancient teachings about the spheres the sphere of the fixed stars directly adjoined that of Saturn. One can often find in old atlases beautiful depictions expressing in a pictorial way this intimate connection felt between stellar and planetary worlds. The idea of the present day, however, is that each fixed star with its attendant planetary system floats like a little forlorn island in an endlessly great, cold, empty cosmic space that contains only abstract physical "ether." Yet the stars' light rays penetrate to us. Although these rays travel for years, hundreds of years, even millions of years with the incomprehensible speed of light, unaltered and undimmed, crossing each other in a thousand ways and yet not influencing each other, at length they reach the human eye on the little Earth planet.

If one contrasts with this concept the teachings of spiritual science that bear upon the life between death and rebirth as, for instance, they were presented in the astrological letters of last year, then one sees that for the reality of the life after death, human beings enter the sphere of the stars beyond the Saturn sphere, and within it go through most important experiences connected with the preparation of their new incarnation. There we experience the stars "from the other side." We are united with the beings who comprise the soul and spirit of the stars. In a word, we experience a reality that cannot at all coincide with the spatially abstract worldview of modern astronomy.

We shall come to an insight into these things only by dealing with the stellar world as the planetary system was dealt with in *An Outline of Esoteric Science,* by describing its origin from divine spiritual beings. We must therefore go beyond the evolutionary stage of Old Saturn to that which was the basis for this Saturn period. In *The Spiritual Hierarchies and the Physical World* (lecture 5), we find it described how still another "solar system" must have existed prior to Saturn—although such indications of time actually lose their relevance here. Then the beings of the highest hierarchy, who come over from this earlier system, those who "enjoy the direct sight of the godhead," receive from the divine trinity the plans of the new world system.

They now seek for themselves, according to the inspiration they received from the highest trinity, a globular space within universal space, and say to themselves: "Here we want to begin." (And the actualization of this begins by the thrones) letting their own substance, the substance of the primeval world-fire, flow into the space that has been marked out, so to speak, for a new world system. (April 14, 1909)

These thrones together with the cherubim and seraphim represent the grade that in occultism is called the zodiac. They have brought with them from the foregoing stage of evolution the faculty of creation. Out of only a small part of their own forces they cause to arise the fire-matter of Old Saturn and the first rudiments of the human physical body. They themselves stand like a mass of fiery streaks around this Old Saturn, as the metamorphosed essence of the whole foregoing stage of evolution, ascended to duration (cf. lecture January 27, and February 8, 1908). They have trodden the path of evolution that our Sun, together with Earth, will also tread, so that one day at the periphery of a new epoch the Sun too will shine forth as a zodiac. "When a Sun has progressed so far that it unites again with its planets, then it becomes a periphery, a zodiac."

We see here the spiritual concept of evolution applied on a mighty and cosmic scale—from planets that stand in some kind of cosmic dependence, to the fixed star existence, and from this to existence as a zodiac. The evolutionary ideas of modern science, applied to the celestial world in such a pathetic way, seem petty and insignificant in contrast to this. Yet we must be thankful that the idea of evolution first arose in the nineteenth century. It has opened the way for a spiritual teaching of evolution such as forms the basis for the whole work of Rudolf Steiner.

The concept of the zodiac existence—indeed of the zodiac itself—is only to be grasped in a spiritual sense. A zodiac cannot be conceived as something physical. For modern astronomy the word merely represents an outmoded superstition of antiquity. For modern astronomy it means only a belt of constellations containing the ecliptic as a central line. The planets are always found within this belt because their orbits never move further away from the ecliptic than the width of the belt itself. Moreover, these orbits, as also the ecliptic (the Sun's orbit), are only the "apparent" orbits, and must be distinguished from the "real" orbits, which are thought of as going around the Sun as circles or ellipses.

We here meet with that undervaluing of the "picture" the senses perceive of the world that is manifest in the heavenly spheres, which is such an intrinsic part of modern consciousness. Yet it is precisely this picture from which the old atavistic clairvoyance drew its deepest wisdom, the nonspatial, one might say, imaginative picture. The surface of a globe—and the firmament presents itself to us as the inner surface of a globe—is mathematically a two-dimensional form, and as such is suited to pictures, to imaginations. One will not come nearer to the understanding of this sensory imagination of the zodiac and the constellations if one changes it into a spatial three-dimensional concept. But we will now return to that primeval time of which spiritual science speaks.

In those far-off times the zodiac was not a spatial ordering of stars, but a flaming belt. During the Sun evolution this became a belt of light, then nebulous masses of clouds. During Earth evolution these gradually became the stars of the zodiac that group themselves into the familiar constellations. And since our Earth and all the planets of the present solar system have ultimately come into existence out of Old Saturn, it has likewise come into existence out of the zodiac—that is, out of the beings of the first hierarchy. These beings are of such lofty spirituality that they do not confine their forces to a single fixed star, but they spread themselves over a group of fixed stars, and are a kind of bed in which the stars of a single zodiacal configuration rest. Each of the twelve zodiacal constellations is therefore an outer expression of a working together of thrones, seraphim, and cherubim. (Perhaps someone will prove someday in terms of astrophysics that the stars of the zodiac are differently constituted than those of the rest of the fixed-star world.)

In the other stars, those outside of the zodiac—we see in addition to the beings of the first hierarchy those beings who had not yet, at the beginning of the Saturn evolution, risen completely to the creative state: the spirits of wisdom. They represent the stage of evolution of the fixed star in contrast to that of the zodiac. In the whole mighty host of fixed stars above live the spirits of wisdom. Whereas out of the zodiac forces continually "rain" down upon Earth and then rise again to the zodiac, the other stars evoke a kind of mirroring, but an actual, substantial mirroring of their being on Earth. We will go into this in detail later.

This description only gives in quite broad general outlines the spiritual origin of the world of the stars. But it nevertheless establishes a spiritual reality that is in contrast to the unreal materialistic concept of the present day. It does this in the same way that the description of Earth's origin in *An Outline of Esoteric Science* stands in contrast to what the Kant-Laplace theory says about it. The history of planet Earth is interspersed with the interventions of the most diverse beings, among them the luciferic beings, but among them also the Christ. Through this, Earth's evolution has in many ways taken a different course from what it otherwise would have taken. We must keep in mind what has come to pass in the celestial world on the one hand through the entry of backward beings and on the other hand through the "eminent fixed star" that we call our Sun, because for long periods of time the Sun was the dwelling place of the Christ. We shall be able only gradually to come to those ideas that are necessary if the planetary world and the world of the stars, the being of the human being, and the being of the gods are not to be rent asunder in a complete estrangement.

The World of the Stars II

The Spiritual Beings in the Stars

IN OUR LAST OBSERVATIONS we tried to build a bridge between the world of the planets and the world of the stars by deriving the origin of our solar system from the stellar world and particularly from the zodiac. In mainstream science, in contrast, the Kant-Laplace theory explains the origin of the universe by a primal nebula, which actually is applicable only to our planetary system. A special world nebula must be conceived for the arising of every single star. Because of the immense distances imagined to lie between the fixed stars, these primal nebulae and the stars arising from them can have nothing to do with each other nor with our planetary system. We will not concern ourselves with this materialistic picture of the world any further. The stars directly invite us to ask about what is completely lacking in the materialistic world-conception: to ask about the spiritual foundation, the spiritual beings from which the stars take their origin, and through which they are connected with our solar system, with Earth, and humanity.

We need only quote what was given in the Helsingfors [Helsinki] cycle, *Spiritual Beings in the Heavenly Bodies and in the Kingdoms of Nature* (which was briefly recapitulated in the first letter of the first year) in order to see the interrelationship. The spirits of wisdom, the highest stage of the beings of the second hierarchy, are those who live in the stars. We also find them as the spirits who regulate the consciousness of the planets (the lowest general consciousness), the spirits whose dwelling place is the Sun. From this point of view the Sun and the fixed stars have the same level of being. Among the fixed stars exists a mutual under-standing that is brought about by the seraphim. The spirits of will or thrones, for their part, give the impulse to the movements of the planets in space. The cherubim regulate the total movement of the system, so that each planet aligns to be in harmony with the whole system:

As order is brought, let us say, into a group of human beings from which one has gone out here, another there, and they begin to strive together toward a common goal, so are the movements of the planets guided until they harmonize. This harmony of the movements of one planet with the other, this fact that in the movements of one planet regard is paid to the movements of the others, corresponds to the activity of the cherubim. (April 7, 1912)

We need not merely think in this way about the planets of our solar system. The stars, too, can have planets around them, and modern astronomy assumes the existence of planets that revolve around stars. However, these planets are not visible to us because of their proximity to the fixed stars, which predominate and give the planets light and life. As explained last time the stars have progressed from the stage of planet to that of fixed star, in exactly the same way as it came about that our Sun had to separate itself from Earth, because Earth could not evolve at the same speed.

A fixed star is an evolved planet, and it has cast out what could not evolve forward with it. The higher beings have established an existence for themselves on the fixed stars. Each fixed star has arisen from a planet. Together with the Earth we are changing ourselves into beings of a higher order who will be able to tolerate a fixed-star existence. (Lecture by Steiner, February 8, 1908)

And every planetary system with its fixed star—which in a certain way stands there as chief guide under the direction of the cherubim—has also a relationship to the other planetary systems belonging to other fixed stars and has come to a clear understanding about its place in space, and about its significance in relationships to its neighboring systems, just as individual persons come to an understanding and discuss with one another their common goal. As human beings establish a social system through having mutual interests, so also do the planetary systems have mutual interests. Between one fixed star and another there is a reciprocal understanding. Through this alone has the cosmos come into existence. What the planetary systems speak to one another throughout universal space in order to become a cosmos, is ruled over by those spirits whom we call the seraphim. (Lecture, April 7, 1912)

We are here led to an almost inconceivable height of spiritual activity. We are reminded of the sublime lines the divinely inspired poet Christian Morgenstern wrote to Rudolf Steiner about this cycle of lectures at Helsingfors.

Your work leads to beauty!
For beauty streams
Through every revelation
Which it brings to us.   —from *We Have Found a Path*

A feeling of nearness, of safety, even of the cosmos itself comes over us, completely opposite to those sensations the worldview of modern astronomy tends to call forth.

So the stars become for us what Rudolf Steiner always mentioned when he wished to point beyond the maya of external appearance to reality. The stars become for us colonies of spiritual beings. Rudolf Steiner also pointed out that the Earth, if it were observed clairvoyantly "from outside," could also be seen as such a colony. Group souls of the plants and of the animals, the individual souls of human beings, the folk souls, and so on, would make up its population. The physical in this way would come but little into consideration. Thus each star also shows us the direction in which a colony, although of far more sublime beings, is to be found.

We must take very seriously the term "direction" as indicating the gathering place of spiritual beings. We will not meet the spiritual beings themselves in the star we see shining in the heavens. They are no longer directly united with the star itself. In fact, the star, in a certain sense, is only there, is only visible for us because it is no longer the body or the dwelling place of a spiritual colony. There we meet anew with the mystery of divine evolution, the development of spiritual beings, which leads them upward in the course of time from stage to stage. We see how a planet can become a fixed star, and progress further from a fixed-star existence to a zodiacal one. The fixed star, however, also goes through changes when the beings united with it take further steps forward in their development. And so it happened at one time during the period of earthly evolution that the spiritual beings no longer needed to make use of their star bodies and left them, just as a human being leaves the physical body at death. Rudolf Steiner often said that stars are forsaken bodies of the gods.

What has gone forth into space from the body of the gods has become a star. They (the spiritual beings) passed through an evolution. When they had reached the point that for the human being during earthly existence signifies physical death, the moment had come for these gods when their physical substance parted from them and became a star. Stars are the bodies of gods whose souls carry on their activities in a new manner in the world, independently of these bodies. (Lecture, August 21, 1911)

It is not the seraphim, cherubim, and thrones who are united with the zodiac, and the spirits of wisdom who have reached the fixed-star existence, whom we see in a star. The star merely points to the place where the beings have their impulse of activity and their abode in the universe. If this were all there were, we would certainly be unable to see anything of the world of the stars with our modern consciousness and sense organs. At most there might be a brief, lightning-like illumination. This is because the thrones penetrate into our world through lightning, using the sudden rending of space as their physical manifestation. But the stars shine upon us with an enduring light that is visible to the physical eye and that in spite of its radiance is restful. That this is the case, that we can enjoy the sight of the starry sky at all, we have to thank the luciferic spirits. We also find an explanation of this point in the lectures on the spiritual beings in the heavenly bodies.

The nature of the luciferic spirits is first described so that we can understand their connection with the world of the stars. They differ according to the hierarchy to which they actually belong but within which, on account of having stayed behind in evolution, they no longer hold their actual rank. In the case of the stars it is for the most part the luciferic spirits out of the third hierarchy, angels and archangels, who have stayed behind. It is the peculiarity of the beings of the third hierarchy:

> . . . that they actually perceive what they reveal from themselves, and that when they turn to their own inner being, they do not have something that is so independent and enclosed within itself as in the case of the human being. Rather they become luminous in their inner being and feel springing up within them the powers and beings of the hierarchies that are above them. . . . These beings can therefore hide nothing within themselves that is a product of

their own thinking and willing. Everything they achieve in their inner being reveals itself outwardly.

This is the state of things for the normally progressed angels, archangels, and spirits of time. If, however, they deny their nature and have the desire:

> . . . to experience something in their inner life that is not immediately externally manifest they would have to assume another nature. This . . . has really taken place in the course of time. . . . They wanted to get over this being spiritually filled with the substance of the higher hierarchies. They wanted to be filled with their own being, not only to be filled with the beings of a higher hierarchy. They could achieve this only by detaching themselves, by separating themselves from the beings of the higher hierarchies and thus procure for themselves their own being out of the substance of the higher hierarchies. (Lecture, April 8, 1912)

This condition was then depicted in the symbolic drawing reproduced here.

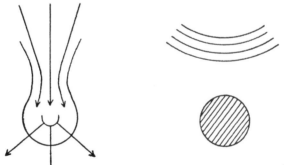

Figure 51

On the left are the normal beings of the third hierarchy, who take the nature of the higher hierarchies completely into themselves and bring it to revelation. On the right are those who wish to keep the spiritual life for themselves. Thereby they split themselves off as independent beings:

> . . . retaining the light in their inner being. Thus they steal what should only have filled them, and which they then should have returned to the higher hierarchies. . . . This concept can provide an

explanation of events in the cosmos. Were it not for these events, we human beings, with our physical consciousness, would be quite unable to grasp the stellar system or the continued existence of the stars in general.

In Figure 51 we see the star form itself out of the radiant light that the luciferic spirits have stolen from the beings of the spiritual colony ruling above them. Since the lucerific spirits let this appear as their own light, it becomes a physically visible star. Without luciferic angels and archangels there would be no visible starry heaven! The body that was abandoned by the gods does not disintegrate as does the human body after death, but it streams in light externally perceptible to the senses.

> Whenever we direct our occult vision to a fixed star we first encounter the normal spirits of wisdom. The whole heavens would be invisible to physical sight and only visible to clairvoyant consciousness if none but these normal spirits of wisdom were active. But everywhere luciferic spirits are mingled with the normal spirits of wisdom and bring their own physical light into the world of the fixed stars. When at night the starry heaven is illuminated, phosphorus actually works down upon us from countless points. . . . Because of the normal spirits of wisdom, the starry world is invisible to physical eyes but visible to spiritual sight. It becomes luminous to physical eyes, it is revealed in maya through Lucifer or through the luciferic spirits who are and must be active every-where. (April 14, 1912)

So in the whole stellar world we must distinguish between two elements. There is the sublime divine spiritual that is present but remains invisible not merely because it has withdrawn itself from the stars, but because the truly spiritual can never be visible for physical eyes. There is also the rebellious spiritual, the luciferic, which makes the starry heavens accessible to our eyes, because it was Lucifer who actually "opened our eyes." If we feel disappointed that the divine does not speak directly out of the stars, we would be in error. The divine works in the starry worlds through something other than mere light. It works through something which—again with the aid of Lucifer—is quite plainly perceived, namely, through the "configurations" of the separate constellations, through the gathering of stars into definite groups and shapes. Let us look at such characteristic constellations as the Great Bear, Orion, and Leo.

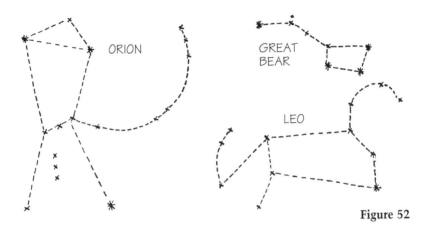

Figure 52

That these configurations are just so and not otherwise, that the stars are in just this relationship to each other, and that they pursue their way in a definite curved path over the vault of heaven by night—and naturally also by day—is the result, the enduring remnant, of the working together of divine spiritual beings. They are the deeds of the highest hierarchies that have become visible. The constellations have a deep spiritual meaning. Their forms are the actual archetypes of all forms and shapes upon Earth. (We will consider this later more concretely.)

There is naturally no validity, from the spiritual point of view, in the objection that these stars are grouped together "by chance, that in reality they need have nothing to do with each other." This objection might be made from the point of view of modern science. If the stars are looked upon as incalculably distant from each other, the juxtaposition of the seven principal stars of the Great Bear can only be an illusion created on the likewise illusory firmament of the nocturnal sky. Nevertheless since the last century astronomers have observed to their astonishment that most of the stars of the Great Bear, of the Pleiades, of the Hyades, and so on, (this is the case in many of the most noticeable constellations) are—in terms of certain characteristics and of direction of movement—in fact related to one another. Thus one may ask if there may be a certain validity after all in the traditional constellations.

To spiritual understanding, the seven stars of the Great Bear—if we keep to this constellation—are the traces left by seven lofty spirits, called by the ancient Indians the seven Rishis. Their working together was carried out in the very form we still see today in the heavens. We may bear in mind here that, because of the recently discovered "proper movement" of the stars, these seven stars of the Great Bear can actually take up quite different positions with regard to each other in the course of thousands of years.

Ancient humanity, not led astray by modern astronomical theories, beheld these constellations as "imaginative forms" and could never have considered them to be accidental groupings. And today as well, one can get a full impression of the interrelated whole by following, with eyes for such phenomena made somewhat more acute through spiritual science, the constellation Orion, for example. One can see how the hunter comes up obliquely on the horizon, then raises himself upright in the south and again sinks slanting in the west. Better yet, one can observe a circumpolar constellation, such as the Great Bear or the Little Bear or the Dragon, and see how in their entirely fixed, invariable form they complete the circuit of the celestial pole in twenty-four hours or in the course of a year. And this impression, which is given us by Lucifer—for were it not for him, we should see nothing of the starry heavens—has a certain significance for the incarnated human being, Rudolf Steiner pointed this out in the so-called "karma lectures" when he spoke of the influence upon the next earthly life of the attention or interest a human being brings to bear upon certain things in life—or fails to bring. He says:

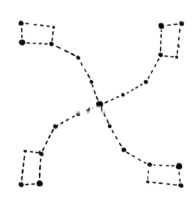

Figure 53

There are human beings who during their whole life—this was also the case in former times—never look upon the stars, do not know where the Lion or the Ram or the Bull is, who have no interest at all in these matters. These persons will be born in their next Earth life with a body that is in some way weak. If through the vigor of their parents they receive a constitution that spares them this, they will become feeble and listless in the body they build up for themselves. (March 1, 1924)

Here Rudolf Steiner indicates what a human being can gain in a life, must gain from gazing upon the world of the stars—what in the next life will bestow a firm bony skeleton, a taut bodily structure. We must acquire this by observing the constellations with their characteristic forms. This does not mean just a mere undiscriminating enthusiasm for the stars. In fact, a sentimental enthusiasm that pays no attention to the strongly configured constellations, that perhaps is not even aware of them, that only wishes to luxuriate in the brilliance of the thousands of sparkling, glittering stars, such an enthusiasm for the most part stands under the influence of the luciferic, which in the starry heavens is the opposite pole of the divine-spiritual. Moreover, such an attitude of soul has certain results, brings certain dangers with it. We find the karmic source of this in the Dornach lecture of January 29, 1921:

> We have the spectacle of the Milky Way[1] and the rest of the starry heavens, because they are a revelation of the luciferic element in the world. What to a certain degree surrounds us, radiant and luminous, is the revelation of the luciferic nature of the world. It is what it is because it has stayed behind at an earlier stage of its existence. Hence there is the possibility that we too should give ourselves up to the sense world by gazing upon the heavens and make ourselves more and more luciferic. Thus if in the conscious life between birth and death we wish to surrender ourselves to contemplation of the heavens, it signifies that something remains with us as an instinct from the time we spent in the spiritual world before birth or conception, when we lived with the stars. There we have entered into too close a relation with the cosmic worlds. We have become too similar to those cosmic worlds, and therefore retain an inclination from those worlds—not that this inclination is very noticeable—to contemplate and consider them chiefly through sense perception. We develop this inclination if, through our karma—which we always carry with us between birth and death—we sleep away too deeply the time between death and a rebirth; if we develop too little an inclination to have full consciousness there.

---

1. It may be noted here how it is the Milky Way that is spoken of, that is to say, a part of the sky that is most thickly set with stars, but has the least configuration, whereas in the foregoing example just the most noticeably characteristic constellations were brought forward—Aries, Taurus, and Leo. Again and again one can marvel at the wonderful exactitude, the detailed facts presented by Rudolf Steiner.

So there mingle for us in the vision of the starry heavens the true divine, which speaks through the revelation of light, and the luciferic, which has stayed behind. The world of the stars is the manifestation of the astral—as the word itself implies—and the astral world is the revelation of the Holy Spirit, and also the dwelling place of the luciferic spirits. Thus as the etheric becomes visible in the blue sky, so does the astral body of the cosmos become visible in the stars.

Please realize that in reality every star we see glittering in the heavens is a gate of entry for the astral. Thus, wherever the stars are twinkling and glittering toward us, there the astral is also shining in. Look at the starry heavens in their manifold variety. In one place the stars are clustered together, in another they are scattered far apart. Then you must say to yourself: In this wonderful configuration of radiant light, the invisible, supersensible astral body of the cosmos makes itself visible.

For this reason we may not understand the world of the stars in a nonspiritual way. To look up to the world of stars and speak of masses of burning gas is just as though (forgive the apparent absurdity of the comparison, but it is absolutely appropriate) you were gently stroking someone whom you loved, holding your fingers a little apart as you did so, and the other person were to say that what he or she feels in being stroked is so many little ribbons being laid across their cheek. To the same degree that tiny ribbons are laid across your cheek when someone strokes you, to that same degree do there exist in the heavens those material entities of which modern physics speaks. Rather it is the astral body of the universe that is continuously exerting its influence—like the gentle stroking fingers—on the etheric organism of the cosmos. This cosmic astral body is organized to last a very long time. Thus a star, which is always an influencing of the cosmic ether by the astral universe, endures longer than the stroking. A human being could not stand being stroked for quite so long! But in the cosmos things last longer, for in the cosmos we are dealing with gigantic measures. Thus in the starry heavens we perceive a manifestation of the soul-life of the cosmic-astral world.

In this way at the same time, an immense soul life—truly, a soul life—is brought into the cosmos. Think just once about how dead the cosmos is when we look into the far spaces and see nothing but burning gaseous bodies. Think how alive it all becomes when we know that the stars are an expression of the love with which the astral cosmos works upon the etheric cosmos. This is a perfectly correct way to express it. (Whitsuntide lecture, June 4, 1924)

One sees again that the stars must be grasped as expressions of the moral and spiritual life. If we are to grasp the true nature of the stars we must continually put aside the belief that one can comprehend the world of the stars on the basis of purely physical assumptions or of mere mathematical calculations.

Human beings calculate, calculate, calculate. It is just as if a spider spins her web and then imagines that it is spun throughout the whole world. The reason is that these laws according to which human beings calculate here, are not valid out there. At most, one can make use of the moral element that is in us to acquire a sense of what exists out there. Out there in the starry heavens we meet moral confronts, and sometimes also the unmoral, the ahrimanic, the luciferic, and so on. But if I take the moral as a generic concept, the cosmos is an expression of moral, not of physical nature. (July 28, 1923)

Here there opens the vast crevice between the modern scientific and the anthroposophical-spiritual world views. The phenomena that have been investigated so wonderfully by astronomy certainly need not be denied. The discoveries of science doubtless will receive recognition in the right place and within the proper limits. This is true even of those discoveries (for example, those concerning the phenomena of spectroanalysis) which in view of the way in which they were made already are seen as very one-sided. But these phenomena are given a meaning by astronomers that belongs to the worst materialism of the nineteenth century. The evolutionary theory as it is applied to the world of stars—not only by popular authors, but by serious scientists—stands approximately at the level of the crassest Darwinism with the "struggle for existence" and so on.

Biological sciences have at present somewhat departed from this crass Darwinism simply because experiments have been made that have disproved many of the early orthodox Darwinian ideas. It has not until now been possible for science to conduct such experiments regarding the stars. People consider them out of reach and therefore can not possibly contemplate a "working of the stars in earthly substances," much less expect a conclusion concerning the nature of the stars themselves derived by experimental methods. In this realm, because no means of correction is available, theory is much more catastrophic than in the "earthly" branches of science.

Thus today, people still luxuriate in fantasies about cosmic worlds being born out of nebulae; the coming into being, arising, and fading away of stars; and about their destruction through gradual cooling down or through collision with other heavenly bodies or through bursting into flame as a result of friction with masses of cosmic dust. The same picture unfolds as has been presented for Earth by nineteenth century science—evolution progressing between the two poles of the "primal nebula" and the death of warmth; the whole moral life of soul and spirit sinking down as into an abyss. For the world of the stars though, the picture is enlarged a thousand, a millionfold.

This world-picture has likewise entered a thousand- and million-fold into the hearts of human beings through the popularization of science. In order to place another view of the world against this picture, we have dealt in such detail with the anthroposophical foundations of a spiritual theory of evolution that proceeds from beings and their moral stages of existence. The importance of this presentation may also justify our having included so many quotations from Rudolf Steiner's lectures. The intention was to unfold a picture of such sublime spiritual activity that only the words of the spiritual investigator himself could be considered fitting. What remains to be said about this branch of astrosophy must be reserved for the Christmas Letter that is to follow.

December 1929

The World of the Stars III

The Human Being and the Stars

> *The spirits sent by God shine as stars*
> *In the heavens of eternal being.*
> *May every human soul*
> *In the realm of earthly existence*
> *Behold their flaming light.*

THESE WELL-KNOWN WORDS of Rudolf Steiner, which he spoke for the first time at the close of a lecture on Zarathustra (January 19, 1911) need not be merely a simile presented in connection with Zarathustra as guide of humanity. The belief that stars are human souls, that they have to do with human beings, is a very ancient one. With the rise of the new astronomical picture of the world this belief had to withdraw more and more into the background and finally became an absurdity. Spiritual science alone will be able to again throw light upon this relationship without any superstition. The understanding that the name "Zoroaster" means "golden star" does not in any spiritual-scientific sense contradict the ancient belief, but rather confirms it. Zarathustra—or Zoroaster—was indeed a "star of brilliance." The name-giving of earlier times, for human beings and for stars, was not something arbitrary, but of deep significance. Rudolf Steiner once remarked in a humorous way that all that people today know about the stars are the names, and therefore they have only an astronomy, no longer an astrology or an astrosophy! These names, and especially those of the planets, of Saturn, Jupiter, and so on, that have come to us from the ancient past, are composed of consonants and vowels in such a way that in them the essential nature of the star or planet is manifest in sound, as in a cosmic language. One must of course disregard "the little urchins," the planetoids, all discovered at the beginning of the nineteenth century. These have been given quite arbitrarily the names of gods and human beings until there were no more left, and finally, like the stars, they were given numbers. In the same way Neptune, discovered by calculation in 1846, has little to do in its essence with the god of the sea. Uranus, however, whose discovery by Herschel with the help of the telescope occurred in the eighteenth century, expresses something in its name which, if the planet is brought into relation with the ancient Uranos, the husband of Gaia, is still correct.

We find the connection between human beings and stars expressed very directly in Steiner's third lecture of the cycle "The Karmic Relationships of the Anthroposophical Movement." We are there reminded of the link that the human being has with the starry world between death and rebirth. One can say that the human being who is descending from cosmic space to an earthly existence always comes down from a definite star. Thus the ancient concepts, independent of tradition, emerge again in modern spiritual research. One can indicate a direction from which the human being comes who is descending to birth. This points to a definite star, a fixed star that is the spiritual home of the person. And again the facts are described with the extraordinary exactness of the spiritual investigator:

> If we take what is experienced beyond all space and time between death and a new birth and translate this into a spatial image, we can say: all human beings have their individual star, which determines what they work on between death and a new birth, and each comes from the particular direction of a particular star. . . . We cannot, however, speak of the midnight hour of existence between death and a new birth without thinking of some star where the human being dwells between death and a new life—although we must always bear in mind what I have said about the beings of the stars.

Only the souls of those who have just died and of those about to be born are to be found in the region of the planets. For the others, the stars are the cosmic symbols from which the soul life of the human souls not incarnated on Earth shines toward us.

Of course, every human being living on Earth has such a star, and we must figure on—we get into numbers in an apparently trivial way— about 1.8 billion stars just for the human souls that are now incarnated.

For those not incarnated the number would be many times greater. Modern astronomy, which except for the star names handed down by tradition and those arrived at by some other means, understands everything in a purely mathematical way, has determined that with the help of the telescope and the photographic plate up to 600 million stars have been registered. Whether this number will perhaps be doubled or multiplied many times simply depends upon technological progress. In mathematical terms, however, the number of stars is already of the same order of magnitude as the number of human beings living on Earth, being about one-third of that number. On the other hand, the number of stars visible to the naked eye is very much smaller—about 7,000 for the entire heavens. These are classified according to their brilliance as stars of the first, second, up to the sixth magnitude. (Today [1929] light-sensitive plates show stars up to the twenty-first magnitude.) The great majority of the 600 million stars belong to the Milky Way, which consists of a swarm of tiny and very tiny stars. There are only twenty stars of the first magnitude, fifty-two of the second magnitude, and so on.

These statistics are given here because they relate to what was said above. If the stars represent all human souls, incarnated and not incarnated, then about twenty of them would be of the "first magnitude" and in the course of their incarnations these souls must lift themselves out of the ranks of the other human beings as leaders, as "God-sent spirits." The "stars of the second magnitude" would stand out a little less, and with the sixth magnitude, visibility, in a historical sense, would cease.

To avoid misunderstandings, we refer to that very important passage in the lecture quoted before. There, the relation of the Sun to the star of a human being during the time when the person is living on Earth is described. Rudolf Steiner states that at birth the Sun obscures the star, but then by degrees falls behind it. After seventy-two years, when the difference amounts to a full day, the Sun leaves the star more or less free, so that the human being can find the way back to it. Therefore, seventy-two years is considered as the normal length of a human life. We deal here with a deciphering of the "writing of the stars" with, as is expressly stated, an imaginative, inspired comprehension of cosmic facts. This passage therefore cannot be understood as meaning that the Sun on its path along the ecliptic meets with a particular star on each of the 365 days of the year, and that this star only becomes free when the Sun because of the precession has fallen one degree behind. For the star that can be regarded as the home star of a human being must indeed be able to lie also outside the ecliptic, the direct path of the Sun. Also, the Sun in its annual movement would already on the second day of a person's life be moving away from the star in the opposite direction. But, also—it is not necessary for a human being to live exactly seventy-two years! One sees clearly that it is a matter of deciphering the star script, not of seeking materialistic interpretations. The star script clearly indicates the falling behind of the Sun in relation to the stars in the course of the Platonic year, and of the connection of this falling behind to human life (one degree in seventy-two years: Letter 2, Year One). We should remember that at the moment of a human being's birth the configuration of the starry heavens is impressed upon his or her brain, and that the Sun has a certain position in relation to this configuration. Now the whole starry heaven has somewhat revolved, and has moved away from this Sun engraved in the brain. Through this we can get a feeling for the "setting-free" of the star by the Sun after seventy-two years. The imaginative speech of the spiritual investigator expresses it in these words:

> During the time when the Sun can remain in the region of his or her star, a human being can live on Earth. Then, under normal conditions, when the Sun is no longer there to reassure a person's star regarding his or her life on Earth, when the Sun no longer says to a person's star: "The person is down there, and I am giving you from myself what this human being has to give to you; for the time being, as I cover you, I am doing for this person what you do for him or her between death and a new birth." When the Sun can no longer speak thus to the star, the star summons the person back again. . . .
>
> These things cannot be understood in any other way than with reverence—with that deep reverence that was called in the ancient mysteries "the reverence for what is above." For this reverence leads us ever and again to see what happens here on Earth in connection with what is unfolded in the sublime, majestic writing of the stars. [See *Karmic Relationships* lecture above.]

A particular human being, however, is connected not only to one star, which can be looked upon as that person's star. This star, as the genius of the language so beautifully expresses it, can be regarded as "rising" or as "setting." ("I could behold your star. It shone in fullest strength," says Maria to Johannes in *The Portal of Initiation*). In fact, at the beginning of the life between death and a new birth the person has a connection with another group of stars, just as on Earth a group of human beings lives closely connected and in a sense forms constellations. These star groupings provide human beings with the individualization they have on Earth through their physical and etheric bodies. The astral body of the human being always has an inclination to flow together with those of other persons. This happens also to a certain extent during sleep. But during the day the astral bodies and also the individual egos of the various persons are separated from one another because of their connection with the physical and etheric bodies. After death the possibility of this separation ceases. During life a person, because of his or her feelings, worldview, impulses of will, and so on has had relationships with certain angelic and archangelic beings. Now these relationships begin to play a role. They connect a person with a particular formation of stars. Human beings are then differentiated according to regions of stars, so that different human souls have a number of stars in common. (Cf. *Earthly Death and Cosmic Life*, lecture 7, from which the following diagram is taken.) A human being can belong to thousands of angels and archangels, soul-beings that in a sense embody his or her feelings, ideas, and concepts in the astral world.

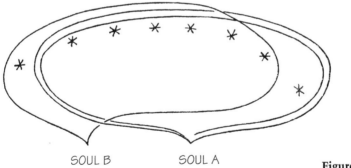

SOUL B   SOUL A   **Figure 54**

These are more or less luciferic beings, since even these exist in the world of the stars. On Earth such feelings, social concepts, ideas of justice, and so on are held in common by many people who, for instance, inhabit a definite territory. After death, these people have stars in common in their star-groupings. However, no two souls have exactly the

same stars. This grouping holds good so long as the human being still has
an astral body—in other words, during the passage through the spheres
of Moon, Mercury, and Venus. There one experiences what, on a large
and a small scale, is connected with social relations. (Cf. Letter 5, Year
Two.) Then, when human beings enter the Sun sphere and also leave the
astral body behind as a corpse, the Sun releases them again to their star,
and the coalescing and at the same time the individualizing according to
star groups comes to an end. The human being as ego being spends the
midnight hour of existence as the inhabitant of a certain star.

So we get a sense of the great multiplicity of connections that bind
human beings and the stars together. We only find our way in this
complexity if we do not let ourselves be misled by the materialistic
prejudices of modern science. Nor may we resort to dogmatic question-
ing that obstructs our outlook. Rudolf Steiner often intimated that such
a question as "Is the world finite or infinite?" cannot be answered in
terms of ordinary Earth consciousness. Both answers allow themselves
to be proven with equal validity. After death, however, the human being
actually comes to the border of the physical, sensory world and then
experiences this cosmos "from the outside." He or she also experiences
the world of stars from outside, insofar as it belongs to the physical,
sensory world.

Here we touch another problematic question often stated and discussed among our friends, but which is destined to remain fruitless as
long as it is decided only by abstract reasoning. This is the question of
whether or not the stars are to be conceived as material bodies in the
earthly sense. That this question cannot be answered in such a simple
way emerges from the fact that in Rudolf Steiner's lectures, there are
countless references to the nature of the stars. Some represent the stars
as not at all physical and material and strongly reject the idea that they
are material bodies. Other references just as plainly speak of the mineral, physical nature of the stars or of the gaseous nature of the Sun.
Precisely in this domain we must avoid becoming dogmatic by the way
we ask our questions.

In the Hague lectures of 1923, *Supersensible Man,* Rudolf Steiner
gives an approach that can help us with this problem. He speaks there
of the different worlds in which the human being takes part. The first is
the perceptible, physical world of our earthly environment. Then there is
a second, an imperceptible, superphysical world—the etheric, elementary

world, into which the human being at death disappears from earthly sight. There is, however, a third world that is also super-physical but is at the same time perceptible. This is the world of sunlight, and of the light of stars and the Moon. The nature of the stars is super-physical, but they are visible (we know that this came about through Lucifer). In this visible light the dead reveal themselves to us. It is the garment of the souls in the spiritual world who, after they have disappeared into the second, imperceptible invisible world, actually become perceptible again for us in this cosmic light. It is the world of the second hierarchy, as that previously mentioned is that of the third hierarchy. We find the highest beings of the second hierarchy, the spirits of wisdom, in the stars as well as in the Sun. It is their nature that conceals itself as the super-physical factor behind the light of the Sun and of the stars.

There is then a fourth world that is also physical but imperceptible. It exists in such phenomena as physical "gravity," which allows us to walk upon the Earth, but which in itself is imperceptible. In this clearly physical world, which is not material, are active the first hierarchy—the thrones, cherubim, and seraphim. Within it live the human souls who are removed from visibility a second time during that period called the midnight hour of existence. There the attributes of the physical body of the future earthly life are already being built up spiritually, in a way imperceptible to the ordinary Earth consciousness. This activity is played out right in the world of stars, in the zodiac itself, to which the beings of the first hierarchy belong. Here, however, zodiac does not mean the visible belt of stars—since that must be seen as part of the third world—but as a spiritually active being that even has the ability to work directly into the physical realm. Thus, what in the star world can be called "physical" is not visible, and the visible in it is not physical but "super-physical"!

Only through such reflections can one come to a fruitful way of posing questions in these matters. Only in this way, too, can one come to the interrelation between the macrocosm and the microcosm. When, for example, here on Earth a human being uses the larynx, there emerges as sound what live as forces in the constellation Taurus, in the Bull. These physical but imperceptible forces built up the larynx while, on the way to being born, the human being passed through the spiritual-invisible Taurus constellation that is under the beings of the first hierarchy. But this cosmic world-stream becomes in a way invisible for the human being when it flows down out of the cosmos at the time when the Moon shines from near the Pleiades (cf. lecture, December 29, 1917). There is a relation between the moonlight that comes from Taurus (to which the Pleiades belong) and what comes out of human beings when they use their larynx. That is in a sense the third world, the astral, which is perceptible to the human being, but which in its nature is actually super-physical.

We can make this "astral" world clear through another description from the lectures of Rudolf Steiner:

> Let us think about what we actually see, when for example, we look at a distant planet or a fixed star out there in the cosmic spaces. What do we actually see? What we see around us here on Earth—a covering of plants, cloud formations, the brown-green of the ground, and so on, we do not see when we gaze into the universe and behold the stars. The stars, even the Moon, are too far off for that. But whatever lives there on the other cosmic bodies has everywhere an inner dimension, has processes that metamorphose substance. When we direct our telescope upon a star we see what is living there as processes of substance in the highest beings present. Thus, if someone of another celestial body, let us say the Moon, were to direct a telescope upon Earth, would they see our plants, animals, and so on? No, our Earth is too far away from the Moon for that. But if he or she directs the telescope down toward Earth, then they are looking within you, within the stomach, the heart, and so on. That is what shines out into the universe. Since the human being belongs to the highest kingdom upon Earth, the beholder from afar sees what is going on within the human skin. (July 25, 1920)

So we see that just as what would be seen of Earth viewed from other worlds is only what goes on in the human organism, so we only perceive in the stars the inner processes of the metamorphosis of substance in the highest beings of those celestial bodies. One can ask oneself about the nature of these "substantial processes" that these beings, the luciferic ones also, have within themselves, but the term "super-physical" certainly applies.

On the other hand this lecture also describes how "matter" is not actually to be found in external nature, but only in the human being, in our organic processes. In a similar way we could find "matter" in the stars if we could grasp the inner processes in the beings of the stars. Here there opens a field for far-reaching anthroposophic-astronomical research.

We can remember another explanation Rudolf Steiner once gave of a phenomenon that has only become known to us through the telescope—the so-called "canals of Mars." The astronomer Schiaparelli, who had an extraordinary gift of observation, in the 1870s observed straight, crisscrossing, interconnected dark lines upon Mars. These were then taken to be canals constructed by the inhabitants of Mars for irrigation and other purposes. The "canals" revealed themselves in the course of time to be structures on the surface of Mars that are more or less unchanging.

To a related question, Rudolf Steiner answered that Mars must be conceived as being in an earlier stage of evolution than Earth. Mars is going through the stage that one finds described for Earth in the Germanic-Nordic mythology: At that time there were twelve streams coming from frigid Niflheim that flowed into the human being and became the twelve nerves of the human brain. Out of the warm stream from Muspelheim in the south came the sparks of fire. These processes exist in our modern environment as irregular phenomena, as currents of air and sea. Formerly, they occurred quite regularly, so that the Earth could have been seen as permeated by such "canals" that passed in and out of human beings and that then gradually coalesced and materialized in the human head. (Something similar was the case in the evolutionary stage of Old Moon. See lecture 10 in *The Theosophy of the Rosicrucian.*)

In the canals of Mars one is observing processes in the Mars beings that have not yet become entirely inner, organic processes, as is the case with human beings now on Earth, but which are spread out over the whole planet and thence penetrate into the beings on it. Such singular phenomena as the canals of Mars and the streaks on Jupiter, are naturally not to be seen on the stars. It is only through their phenomena of the light-ether and the chemical-ether that they offer us the possibility of gaining knowledge about the activities of their beings. Indeed, Rudolf Steiner called what can be studied in just this way through spectral analysis and so on "an outer shining that is rather unessential for the heavenly body."

Not essential on the other hand, but significant in the highest degree, is what streams into the cosmos from inside of the human being. In the first of the archangel lectures Rudolf Steiner describes how the human being in midsummer is permeated by an inner sulfuric fire, a sulphur process, and how this process streams out and shines in the cosmos:

> Much is happening in the cosmos when in the summer the human being is inwardly illuminated with sulphur. It is not only the glow worm that shines for the physical eye of the human being around St. John's Day [June 24]. Seen from the other planets, the interior of the human being around midsummer day, shining for the etheric eye of other planetary beings, becomes a being of light. (October 5, 1923)

And then toward autumn, iron streams into the blood of human beings. Just as the meteors appear in the outer world, so the insides of the human being become then to cosmic sight a meteoric shower.

Then in the depth of winter Earth becomes a self-enclosed cosmic body. Its soul has withdrawn into an inner realm and spiritualizes itself with the cosmic forces through its saline nature. Earth becomes vivified through the ashes of the plant seeds that have rained down upon it. Inwardly the Earth becomes moon-like, but at the same time has the greatest possibility of taking up the forces of the Sun. And beyond the Sun, Earth reaches into the heavenly, the stellar realms.

> Then, going into the expanses of the cosmos, one would see what appears there above, what the human being rays out into the cosmos, what I would describe as a heavenly earth-star radiance that Earth sends into the wide spaces . . . For if one looked from the cosmos at Earth, it would so appear that one were looking through the shining of the stars on to Earth itself, as if Earth under its surface were glittering within, in rainbow colors. (October 6, 1923)

Earth shines like a star into the universe, and the universe beholds the body of Earth thus enlivened, shining like a rainbow. Never are Earth and the universe nearer to each other in freedom and full consciousness than at Christmas time.

Upon this Earth spiritual beings fix their gaze. One of their number, the highest, the Sun being himself, will descend upon this Earth. The birth of the Christ-bearer must precede this, and also the rebirth of the messenger of the Sun, Zarathustra. The wise men from the East see his star rising and they draw near to the place of his birth. His name Zoroaster means, as we know, "golden star" and we are told that the wise men of the East, who were among his disciples, saw in him the "star of humanity" itself, an image of the Sun. We remember that the Sun too is a fixed star and that Zarathustra was initiated by Ahura Mazdao, by the Sun himself. However, the Sun is more than a fixed star. Up to the time of Zarathustra, the being who is higher than the thrones, cherubim, and seraphim—the Son of God, the Christ—was still united with it. And as the Christ united himself with Jesus of Nazareth, whose body had been destined to become the bearer of the Christ, not only a star, not only a reflection of the Sun, but the Sun himself had come down to Earth. The spiritual Sun became flesh and lived among human beings. Then he was taken away at first through death into the invisible world, and overcame death and lives and works in human hearts. But the time is coming when the Christ, even though he lives in the super-physical world, will become visible, not merely in sunlight and moonlight, but in the "clouds" in the etheric world. And from human hearts and the human countenance the Christ-force will stream out into the universe at Christmas time as the seed of the Sun-world.

The World of the Stars IV
Plants and Stars

A PICTURE OF THE WORLD OF THE STARS has emerged from what we have been considering thus far. It depicts on the one hand divine-spiritual beings standing behind the stars as members of a "spiritual colony" that, although invisible, works directly into the material realm. We have found human souls to be fellow members in this community of spirits in the life between death and rebirth. On the other hand, the visible stars are the revelation to us of this divine-spiritual reality in the sparkling points of light that work as "super-physical" creations in the world of being through their configuration, their actual form and shape. We shall experience this starry heaven not as removed to distant realms but as working today in every point in space where forms arise. It only reveals itself at the boundaries of space through the starry points of light, by which Lucifer-Phosphorus in his own way allows us to partake of the revelation of love in the cosmos. There the spatial way of looking at things must become a qualitative one. In the sphere that lies beyond the stars space actually ceases to exist. It has become something qualitative. But this spatial, non-spatial realm forms itself into images and from these images proceed the astral forces that here on Earth create whatever has form and shape. On the other hand the planetary world creates all that is formative, etheric, force and that brings about growth, metamorphosis, and transformation. Finally, Earth contributes, according to its nature, the material aspect and the assimilation of matter. According to the different worlds from which these forces come and the different domains in which they work, the different kingdoms of nature arise.

This view, which underlies the whole of anthroposophical-scientific work, requires astronomy also to proceed from quite different basic assumptions from those customary in the science of today. It leads us to see that a simplistic, materialistic astronomy is as little valid as any other science that concerns itself only with the earthly. The starry heavens, if one takes it in its full and also its spiritual meaning, and includes the planets, must be understood as the archetype and cosmic womb of all that exists on Earth. But it is comprehensible only on the basis of everything that is to be found on Earth. One will always come to merely hypothetical or relativistic theories of planetary movements and so on if one tries to explain these movements or the other stellar phenomena only through the phenomena themselves. To use the oft-cited simile given by Rudolf Steiner: one cannot explain the magnetic needle in its alignment with the magnetic pole on the basis of the needle itself, but only on the basis of the whole Earth. Similarly, one cannot explain the phenomena of life on Earth or the astronomical phenomena in the widest sense from themselves but only mutually, each in terms of the other. On August 20, 1916, Rudolf Steiner for the first time indicated very definitely facts that sound very strange to modern science, which he summarized in these words:

> Astronomers will found biology by means of their own science, and the biologists will by means of their science found astronomy. And a biology founded on the true essence of astrology will be a spiritual science, and an astrology founded on the essence of a genuine embryology will be a spiritual knowledge of the heavens.

From this viewpoint we will consider something of this connection between the world of the fixed stars and the world of the plants. In the Torquay lectures *True and False Paths in Spiritual Investigation,* lecture 2, Rudolf Steiner points out a connection between the stars and the plants that speaks deeply to human feeling—even of the ordinary consciousness: Earth is a mirror of the cosmos, with a mirroring surface that does not just reflect outer forms as do the mirrors made by human beings, but reflects so that the mirrored image lives and grows and develops. That is the plant world here upon Earth; it is the living mirrored image of the heavens. It reflects the star world, the world of the fixed stars. And for the initiated consciousness described there, the stars also become like organic entities, growing and weaving, and take on the most manifold forms. And the single stars reveal themselves as the actual plant beings. They are like the pearls of dew that sparkle here on Earth in flowers and on leaves. In the actual spiritual world that, as we have tried to show, transcends the world of the stars the plants are ego-beings as are human beings; they are beings with self-consciousness. And just as the pearls of dew rest in the blossoms, so the visible stars rest like pearls of dew within the world of mighty spirit-beings, a living, weaving world that is invisible to ordinary consciousness. We need only remember that the spirits of wisdom represent the hierarchy common to all the fixed stars and that the group souls of the plants stand as the offspring of the spirits of wisdom (see Steiner's *The Spiritual Beings in the Heavenly Bodies and in the Kingdoms of Nature* for insight into the real connection between the stars and the plants.)

The stars are bound to particular constellations, and as mentioned earlier, are not fortuitous combinations. Rather, the constellations are a visible manifestation in the star world of the interrelationships of the spiritual beings working behind them.

In these rigid, unchanging forms lie the archetypes of all fixed forms on Earth. When we stop looking at the plant world as a whole, but consider the single plants and their principles of form, we must seek out the archetypes for the individual plants.

If, however, we consider the plant covering of Earth, this must be seen as a whole, just as the starry world is also a whole. The plants belong to the whole Earth. Rudolf Steiner often used the simile that the plants in relation to Earth are as human hair is in relation to the whole human being: it grows out of human beings, and can only be considered in connection with them. So in the multifarious plant covering of Earth we can see the image of the starry heavens. The plant world covers the body of the Earth with its many different trees, vegetables, and grasses, just as above the stars are strewn over the entire heavens. And we find the instinctive expression of this connection again in our language. How many plant names express a relation with the starry worlds, and how often are flowers compared with stars? One can sometimes find beautiful old drawings that represent this in a naïve, imaginative picture. Above are the stars, five- or six-pointed, and below on Earth are the flowers of the plant world, disproportionately large, looking like stars, just as the stars resemble the blossoms of Earth. Or one looks at the dandelion, which in its whole development so marvelously brings the universe to expression: the enormously long, straight root, symbolizing Earth's radius; the sun-like blossom expressing the planetary workings, and then finally, when the flowering time has passed over and the fruit is to begin to develop, the little universe of the sphere set with tiny stars that is left over from the plant that has finished flowering.

Thus the plant world as a whole is a mirrored image of the starry heavens. The mirroring is not quite adequate, however, as was said in the Torquay lecture. It emerges to a certain extent as a reflection of color in the colored yellow, red, and even green plant covering of Earth. We know that out of the plants' world of color the activities of the planets speak, placing themselves in a way before the workings of the stars and modifying them. The forces of growth as well, the tendency to movement in the spiralic placement of the leaves, and so on, these formative forces arise from the planets. But what comes from the stars are the forms, the configurations. As was expressly stated in Steiner's lecture of July 22, 1922, these come from the fixed stars that lie outside the zodiac, such as Ursa Major, Ursa Minor, Pegasus, Orion, and so on. The zodiac itself has to do with the forces of the animal organism, as its name plainly implies. So we come to the scheme given in the lecture:

The plant world receives its forms from the starry heavens, and the animal world its form from the zodiac. Human beings receive their form from the whole sphere of the heavens, not from the single constellations, just as we also bear in our head an image of the entire stellar universe. Again we find the human being as the synthesis, the perfect embodiment of the entire cosmos. In the other kingdoms of nature, we find in contrast one-sided expressions of one or another part of the whole.

We find in the plant also an image of the universe, namely in the cell, which is spherical and thus replicates Earth. In its inner configuration, however, it reflects the cosmos with its planetary connections and so on. The cell becomes in the whole plant only visible through the earthly matter that is imbedded in it. But as etheric form the plant is an imagination. (Cf. lecture July 28, 1922.) As such it would be visible only to imaginative consciousness. Through the filling-out with earthly matter it becomes visible to the physical eye in a physical way.

But the constellations are also imaginations, fixed, immovable imaginations of the living, changing, working spiritual beings behind them. They correspond to the imaginations that are the plants. The plant imaginations in reference to their spiritual origin are only modified in another way—namely through their appearance in the physical realm, through their being subject to terrestrial laws, through their being built up out of little cell bodies, and so forth. There is a connection between the two kinds of imaginations and it is to be found in the forms of the plants.

Rudolf Steiner, in the above-mentioned lecture (July 22, 1922) describes how, if a human being becomes clairvoyant through his or her will, he or she can with this expanding will behold the cosmos "from outside." (See Figure 55.) He or she can also behold the stars from outside, just as the souls that are not incarnated have this perspective:

> . . . from there, where already there are no longer any stars, not from the realm of the etheric, but from the realm of the astral, about which one can say there is still space, and about which one can also say, there is no longer space. There is no point in speaking of what I have indicated outside the circle as if it were still space. One feels, however, as if one has space within one. But then, you see no stars. You look upon the stars, but you do not see any stars. Rather you see pictures. You actually see pictures everywhere within the realm of the stars. It will now be immediately clear to you why in ancient times when people depicted the celestial spheres, they did not paint only stars, but pictures.

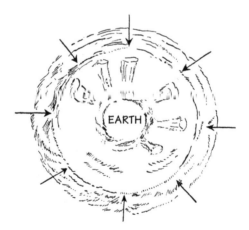

Figure 55

Regarding these pictures or images it is then said: If a person who is in the position described looks through these images onto Earth, he or she notices how forces, effects of light and of force, proceed from these images and stream down upon Earth. There they actually create the forms of the plants. Into these forces that emanate from the motionless constellations, there mingle the forces of the movement of the planets that stand nearer to Earth—Saturn, Jupiter, and Mars. These forces draw the plant out of the root, cause it to grow, and so on. If we disregard these planetary forces, just the star forces remain. These bring the forms of the constellations with them into the plant world. We will consider this connection between constellations and plant forms more closely.

At first, it may not be appealing to look away from the growth and development of the plants and seek for bare rigid forms, the "skeleton" that is present but invisible in every plant. We shall recognize these forms in the plant world with a certain effort, for they are continually overcome and metamorphosed during the life of the plant. We must employ a certain concentration that involves abstracting what is living and changing in order to see the underlying forms of the constellations. These no longer represent the real weaving imaginations, but, bereft of life and substantiality, have also become motionless structures. This also applies, although to a lesser degree, to the old pictorial representations of the constellations, which are a final, traditional, but often very exactly preserved relic of the former imaginations. For example, the Bull springing forward and charging with long horns has only its front half depicted. Andromeda is chained to the rock in propitiation for the arrogance of her mother, Cassiopeia, who, seated on a throne, displays the attributes of her vanity. Meanwhile, Perseus as the winged divine messenger, with his sword in one hand, the severed head of Medusa in the other, hastens to her rescue, and so on.

If one looks at the starry heavens in this way, there emerges the peculiar fact that the traditional pictures are those of "gods, beasts, and men," and of objects, such as a chalice, a crown, and so on, but not of plants. In the whole sky one finds no single constellation that has the name of a plant. Only Virgo, the Virgin—who, however, belongs to the zodiac—carries an ear of corn: Spica, a star of the first magnitude. Another star in Virgo, Vindemiatrix, the "vintager," or "vinegatherer," is supposed to derive her name from the connection between her early rising with the beginning of the vintage time in the ages when this name was given to the star. Today these conditions are considerably altered because of precession. Virgo, however, is that constellation which preserves in itself the power of multiplication, of the "shooting into number," and the ear of corn and indeed the grape too are to be looked on as images of this Virgo impulse. So the constellations reveal no imaginations that have to do with plants. They send down to Earth the forces that give shape to the plant, but not what must have appeared to human beings of old as the real being of the plants, the life, the formative forces. These belong to the etheric world.

In the same lecture Rudolf Steiner refers emphatically to a concrete case:

> Whoever sees imaginatively says: the lily, that is a plant form to be found on Earth that in form and structure is created out of one group of stars. Another, the tulip form, is created out of another group of stars.

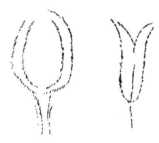

Figure 56

The forms of the tulip and the lily—both fundamentally southern or oriental plants that have been introduced into our regions—are often thought of as the archetypes of blossom formation. They represent two different gestures—the calyx that opens itself, and the calyx that closes itself. In *Spiritual Beings in the Heavenly Bodies and in the Kingdoms of Nature* we also find (lecture 4) reference to these two basic forms, along with a reference to the pointed and the broad leaf forms, as to those [See Figure 56.]:

> . . . of a blossom that grows upward in this way, and one that opens outward. There is a world of difference in inner experience if one looks with occult vision of the second stage upon a tulip blossom or upon a lily blossom.

If we look up to the starry heavens keeping in mind what has been said, we find an archetype of the tulip form in the constellation of the Northern Crown (Corona Borealis). We can very well picture to ourselves that from this constellation, which becomes so clearly visible in our regions in the spring, emanate the forces that shape the tulip and tulip-like blossoms.

The lily, on the other hand, corresponds in shape to the constellation of the Lyre, the typical summer star-picture of our zone. This correspondence is partly discernible in the arrangement of the stars, and more clear in the traditional images of the constellation Lyra. [See Figure 57.]

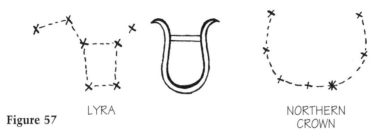

Figure 57

LYRA

NORTHERN
CROWN

We have spoken here of spring and summer. But we must consider
the entire course of the year since the constellations gradually rise and
set earlier, so that the winter constellations, such as Orion, Canis Major,
Taurus, and Gemini, are different from those of summer. This single revolution of the starry heavens in the course of one year is only a reflection
of the path of the Sun through the zodiac. Also, the geographical position
of a place or even more of a whole zone comes into consideration. That
this plays a role in plant growth is self-evident. The tropical flora are
different from those of the temperate zone and again from those of the
arctic zone. Naturally the position of the Sun as regards Earth, with its
flattened or steeply ascending daily arc, plays a role, as does the stronger
influence of the cosmic forces in the polar regions (insofar as a vegetation can develop there at all) and of the stronger effect of the terrestrial
forces at the equator. For the form and structure of plants—our primary
concern here—we must consider which constellations shine over a region
and at what time of year. That was plainly stated in the lecture referred
to. One can only grasp the plants when one can say to oneself:

> Here I walk over a district, let us say, of central Europe. For
> central Europe these particular constellations have quite a special
> significance in the time of blossoming. Therefore the plants of this
> region grow here, because the heavens cause plants to grow upon
> Earth in a definite region. [July, 22, 1922]

Let us picture vividly to ourselves how differently the stars appear in
the arctic zone where their paths always lie nearly parallel to the horizon
and the same constellations are visible almost all the time. In our region
because of the obliquely ascending orbits a noticeable alteration takes
place in the course of the year. At the equator the stars rise and set at
right angles to the horizon, and every six months there is a completely
different set of constellations visible at the same time of night. (One can

best get a sense of these relationships from *An Introduction to the Phenomena of the Skies* by Dr. von Baravalle, which is being published in *Die Drei* starting last month.) At the equator one does not have the so-called circumpolar constellations, which never set, for there the pole star itself lies on the horizon. In our regions, just those constellations must be looked upon as important for the plant world that are circumpolar that always, summer and winter, are visible at night because they move close to the north pole of the heavens. In the polar zone, where a remarkably luxuriant flora blooms in the short summertime, nearly all the constellations are circumpolar; there is long duration and little change.

In this description there is already a picture of the differences that one finds in the forms and structures of the plant world as one goes from south to north. From east to west this difference disappears, because the same stars shine over all the countries that lie on the same geographical degree of latitude. The differences we find in the plant world as we move from east to west must be sought in terrestrial causes—soil, altitude (and the consequent climate), and so on.

We may here perhaps interpolate the interesting observation that the ancients (according to tradition it was Hipparchus, the noted astronomer) employed the expressions longitude and latitude in geography because they experienced the following: Going north or south one experiences rapid changes. The constellations relative to the horizon rise or sink, and a permanent increase of cold or warmth is noticeable. As one travels east to west, however, these differences are absent. The stars remain exactly the same, and the climate changes only over great distances. So people felt the Earth to be long and extended from east to west, and as more pressed together from north to south. They spoke therefore of longitude and latitude. The geographical latitude corresponds to the altitude of the pole, so that for example Dornach lies at 47 $\frac{1}{2}$ degrees north latitude, and the pole star is 47 $\frac{1}{2}$ degrees above the horizon. In astronomy these terms mean something different than in geography, because in astronomy one [also] calculates them from the ecliptic, but in geography from Earth's equator.

If we now look at the circumpolar stars, which are the most important for our zone, and which through their constant presence must deeply influence the archetype of our vegetation, twice we see—in the Great Bear and in the Little Bear—the same characteristic configuration of stars— seven stars arranged so that four form a square and three a tail.

We find the same design on a yet larger scale if we consider the principal stars of Andromeda and Pegasus, constellations that shine in our night sky for most of the year. If we bear in mind all that we have said about the principle of form in the stars and in the plants we can see there the archetype of the twig with the foliage leaf. In the temperate zones trees with leaves are typical, or annual plants with the leaf on a stalk. Only in the temperate zone of the Northern Hemisphere is the thrice-repeated form present in the heavens in such a dominating way. Toward the pole Andromeda and Perseus lose their influence and toward the equator, the Great and Little Bear. In the temperate zone of the Southern Hemisphere the vegetation is again of quite a different character from that in the Northern Hemisphere. Entirely different stars are shining there.

Whoever observes the constellations and the plant world with a discriminating eye will discover the most remarkable principles of form realized in both. In addition to the pattern of the stiff rounded-off leaf stalk, there is the twisted, bent form that one can see, for example, in the branches of old trees or in their roots. Old oaks and apple trees, in their hardened trunks and twigs, in the knotted windings of their roots (just where the fixed principle of form is most plainly revealed, since that is where the weaving life is least present) show those shapes that stand out in the starry skies as the various dragon and serpent forms (Draco, Ophiuchus with the serpent, and the serpents in the hand of Hercules). Rose hedges too sometimes present a pattern like the water serpent (Hydra) with their many intertwinings.

Figure 58

Hydra is a prominent spring and summer constellation for us. In southern regions where tropical vegetation presents an image of manifold interlacing and entwining, this constellation stands out much more strongly, as does also the serpent-bearer, Ophiuchus [Figure 58]. In general, the skies of the Southern Hemisphere are noticeably far more thickly set with stars, but have far fewer clear configurations than the northern. A similar contrast may hold good between the vegetation of those regions and of our own.

One can also reflect that because of the precession of the vernal equinox, by which the axis of the Earth revolves in 25,920 years around the axis of the ecliptic, in the course of time new stars rise over a certain region, while others set for thousands of years. The precession, the Platonic year, has a similar effect with regard to the stars as a single day has—stars rise and set. The difference is that the movement takes place around the pole of the ecliptic instead of around the pole of Earth. (See Letters 11 and 12, Year One.) Therefore as the millennia pass, the precession brings with it stars and constellations that are different from those that the day and the year bring with their movements.

Thus in Europe several thousand years ago, the Southern Cross must have been visible, and in several thousand years Sirius will disappear from view. A different star will gradually become the pole star, and other constellations will become circumpolar. The equator, which now passes through the uppermost of the three stars in Orion's Belt (the "three Kings"), will gradually descend. Orion has been raising itself above the equator for a long time. Aratus (third century B.C.) wrote the first popular book about the stars, a work that was one of the most widely distributed of ancient times—even St. Paul quoted it (Acts 17–18). If one reads Aratus's detailed description of the heavens one finds a significant difference in the position of the lines of the tropics—which run parallel to the equator above and below it each at a latitude of 23 $\frac{1}{2}$ degrees— compared with their present position. This clarifies the effect of the precession on the constellations. Aratus for example thus describes the Tropic of Cancer:

> Upon the tropic are the heads of both the Twins. Upon it lie the knees of the neighboring Wagoner. Perseus rests on it with his left shoulder and leg. It grasps Andromeda's right arm just at the elbow . . . the palm of the hand is higher, farther to the north, while the elbow is toward the south. Then come the hooves of the

Steed (Pegasus), the lower part of the neck and also the head of the Swan; of the Serpent-bearer the shoulder. . . ." (Rendered from the German translation of Manitius.)

If one compares this graphic description with a modern representation —in which the constellations are reproduced in pictures—one sees the whole movement that the tropic—following the equator, to which it always remains parallel—has completed in the last 2000 years. Today this tropic—the Tropic of Cancer—no longer passes through the heads, but through the shoulder of the one, and the knees of the other, of the Twins; through the foot of the Wagoner and the left arm of Andromeda; while Perseus lies quite above it. All this expresses the same fact as the words: at that time the vernal point lay in Aries and now it lies in Pisces.

Through all these changes, new forces of the stars—that is, form-giving forces—gradually shape the plant world of a wide region. We experience anew that the great Platonic world year bestows something that transforms all the conditions of human civilization from age to age, because these conditions are obviously related to the vegetation of a definite period of time. In general, because of the precession those constellations located near the vernal point are gaining influence and those near the autumnal point are losing influence. Vegetation must change accordingly.

Thus we seek to regard heaven and Earth together so as to free ourselves from what Rudolf Steiner called the mole-like existence of modern human beings, who stay under the Earth and do not look up to the stars, or if they do, only project onto the heavens what they can find, mole-like, within themselves: mathematical relationships! Certainly that had to come about, so that the human being could attain freedom. But now we can get beyond this point and still preserve our freedom. We can close with a last quotation from the lecture that is fundamental for the connection between the plant world and the world of the stars:

> The world-conception arose that no longer asks: What is out there that enables a lily blossom to arise upon the Earth? What is it out there that enables a tulip blossom to arise? In the new age human beings have lost the possibility of looking out from the blossom of the lily, from the blossom of the tulip into the starry heavens, just as the mole has no possibility of looking out beyond the darkness

of the Earth. . . . One can indeed say: The human being could only reach an experience of freedom by going through this mole-like existence for a time, by looking upon the lily and no longer knowing that an image of the heavens is reflected in the lily's blossom, by looking upon the tulip and not knowing that in the tulip an image of the heavens reflects itself. In this way human beings have turned their forces more inward and have acquired the experience of freedom. But today we have reached the point where of necessity we must grasp again the spiritual universe with the eye of the soul. What for centuries has appeared merely as a mathematical mechanical framework of space, must reappear before the eye of the soul as a universe interpenetrated by spirit.

The World of the Stars V
Nebulae

WE HAVE YET TO CONSIDER those regions of the heavens that for the most part are not visible to the naked eye—that can be perceived either through long observation or only through a telescope. This is the world of cosmic nebulae and star clusters, and the world, too, of variable stars and new stars. Prior to the seventeenth century, almost nothing was known about these worlds. Except for the ancient Chinese masters of astronomy, Hipparchus was the first to notice a new star or "nova." Some variable stars can be seen with the naked eye, but they were not recognized as variable stars before the seventeenth century. There are a few nebulae and star clusters visible to the naked eye, but investigation of such heavenly bodies began only in 1610 when Galileo observed the heavens with the first [astronomically effective] telescope. (He had built this himself after learning of the discovery of [a telescopic arrangement of] magnifying glasses in Holland.) Besides, Galileo's discoveries lay more in the realm of the planets: the moons of Jupiter, the rings of Saturn, and the phases of Venus. The actual world of the stars was not investigated until later.

With the telescope we can have the same experience we have with the microscope. Both mislead the healthy human senses, as Goethe said. They bring excessively into consciousness certain details that previously had merged into a harmonious whole. (Cf. *Wilhelm Meister's Travels,* book 1, chapter 10.) We know in any case that the telescope shows us something quite different from what one would in a superficial sense expect. It is not the "outer nature" of the heavenly bodies that the telescope reveals to us, but rather the inner processes of the beings dwelling there. (See Letter 4.)

But the world that was opened to the human senses through the telescope is so extensive, complex, and revealing that it has added an entirely new domain to the one already known. In this there is a certain similarity with the world of the microscope, which in the same way has made countless contributions to our knowledge of the human body and of the other kingdoms of nature. The origin of both instruments lies in the same epoch, since both are based fundamentally on the same principle. The microscope has led to the important understanding of the cell as primal building block of organic forms, and thus has brought to light a great deal about the formation of human organs and about metabolism.

The telescope, especially the reflecting telescope in its present technical perfection, shows pictures of the starry firmament that exhibit a quite remarkable relationship to the pictures that the microscope conjures up for us. To correctly assess what the microscope offers us we must enlarge our view from the tiny section to the whole world—or at least to the organ from which the tiny section was taken. Then the microscope and its images will be able to reveal to us not something one-sided and partial, but something deeply significant. So, too, what the telescope shows to us is like a world behind the stars. It is something that can be understood or at least sensed, if one relates it to the nature of the human being, to what works in the human physical body and lives in the human soul.

The whole human being is born out of the cosmos. He or she builds himself or herself up from the forces of Sun, Moon, planets and stars. The planets bestow as their contribution what human beings carry within them as the seven "organs of life"—the spleen, liver, heart, and so on. This is in the realm of the rhythmic system, in which the metabolic system also takes part. In a different way the outer planets are manifest in the system of the head.

In the Hague lectures of 1923, *Supersensible Man*, Rudolf Steiner further develops the connection of the human being with the planetary world. The formative forces of the planets produce the skin, including the sense organs, and the third hierarchy is at work there. The movements in the planetary system reflect themselves in the human being as the nerves and as the glands of secretion. The blood vessels originate in the cosmic rhythm, the cosmic music—the "harmony of the spheres" as it was formerly called. With all this we are in the realm of the second hierarchy. Through the highest beings of the second hierarchy we reach into the world of stars. And out of the stars, out of the single scattered stars that form the great host of the starry skies, are created the muscles, the "flesh" that is not differentiated into particular organs and that through the formative forces of the planets is covered with the contoured surface of the skin. Here we are in the realm of cosmic speech. And from the first hierarchy, the cosmic word sounds toward us. This lives physically in the human being as the system of bones. Only through the earthly substances of lime, magnesium, and so on does the world Word become our hard skeleton, which is the symbol of death. Here we no longer have the stars as a whole but the active forces of the zodiac of the first hierarchy. The twelvefoldedness of the zodiacal forces divides the human physical body in a threefold way into seven parts. (See *Man in the Light of Occultism, Theosophy and Philosophy,* lectures 5 and 6.) This involves the physical body, whose initial spiritual foundation is formed from the zodiac and the star world as a whole.

The physical body has three major parts. It consists of a sense system, a rhythmic system, and a metabolic system. We should be able to find this complete human being in the starry heavens, since he builds himself up there as "spirit germ." From the foregoing description we know that many parts of the human being, organs and their forces, are related to the planetary world. However, their basic structure, their "skeleton," must be found in the actual world of stars, just as the skeleton of the plant kingdom is found there.

Human beings build themselves up from the whole sphere of the heavens, and the head in particular is an expression of this sphere. In the variable stars we shall find the origin of a rhythmic system, the primal principle that is then metamorphosed by the planetary forces and elevated into life. In the nebulae of various kinds and in the Milky Way the archetypes of the human metabolic system reveal themselves to us. The human head is here also, insofar as the head, containing a physical brain with convolutions, is something like a human organ, only sluggishly sustained from below by the metabolism. In contrast, the metabolic system itself is to be conceived as always creating and recreating.

Let us consider nebulae first as phenomena, as they reveal themselves to the telescope and then are reflected onto a photographic plate. In our hemisphere only the nebulae of Andromeda and Orion are visible to the naked eye. Other little clouds that seem similar are star clusters, collections of stars, as that in Perseus. One can also include among them the "Seven Stars," the Pleiades, though with a telescope many more than seven stars are visible, as well as remarkable torn nebulous veils

around individual stars. That the remaining nebulae are all invisible has
nothing to do with size. They are the largest of all the heavenly bodies,
extending over surfaces into which the disk of the full Moon would fit
several dozen times. They are extraordinarily varied in structure, ranging from the little, faint, round "gas nebulae" and the more disk-shaped
so-called "planetary nebulae," to the annular (ring-shaped) and spiral
nebulae formed with almost mathematical exactitude. Still more spread
out, extending sometimes over several constellations, are the nebulous
veils, cloud-like structures without configuration, which seem to have
in part their own light, in part a reflected light. Moreover, quite dark
clouds suddenly arise and place themselves like an impenetrable wall in
the night sky, which is never quite dark, since it is always pervaded by a
faint reflected sunlight. These too are only perceptible with a telescope,
for example, right in the neighborhood of the Orion nebula or near the
so-called "cave nebula" in the Milky Way. Each of these nebulae is at
the end of a dark starless tract in the midst of the star-rich Milky Way,
as if it had passed along this dark streak and had extinguished all the
stars in its path. There are great dark stretches in the Milky Way visible
to the naked eye in the neighborhood of the Swan, and in the southern
hemisphere in what is called, very unpoetically, the "Coal Sack," in the
constellation of the Centaur.

   We have reproduced here some of the best-known nebulae because
of their representative forms. Unfortunately, we can't depict more details

The Andromeda Nebula

A Spiral Nebula in Canes Venatici
– the hunting dogs (after a sketch
by Lord Rosse)

Figure 59   **Figure 60**

of the whole starry surroundings of the nebulae or the Milky Way, with its structure reminiscent of microscope slides. However, one can easily find more detailed representations in any astronomical book or atlas, or even in the illustrated magazines that of late often have such reproductions. These are made possible by the marvelous photographs taken with the new giant telescopes in the American observatories or in Heidelberg. That the text attached to such reproductions springs

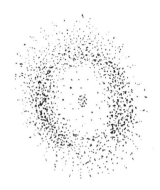

Annular Nebula in Lyra (the Lyre)

Figure 61

for the most part from a gross materialism need not be emphasized. Besides, one must keep in mind when viewing such photographs that in spite of the long exposure time they are after all only "snapshots." This is not because the star nebulae are more or less variable heavenly bodies, and do not have a full share in the immensely long duration of the fixed-star skies. Rather it is because each exposure varies according to the instrument with which it is taken. The magnitude of the instrument; its being a refracting or a reflecting telescope; and its recording exactly what is seen in the eyepiece or a somewhat smaller or large area; all are factors. The researcher also affects the end result. Different investigators

The Orion Nebula

Figure 62

using the same instrument under only slightly varying light-conditions will always produce radically different pictures.

Indeed nebulae cannot be depicted. They are something like visions, like dreams in the world of the stars. They can just as little be reproduced in definite forms as a human being can describe his or her dreams in sharp outlines. Rather, just as a person can only describe dreams using his or her imagination, so every person and every instrument creates a unique, individual imaginative picture of the cosmic nebulae. Consider, for example, the classic drawings Lord Rosse produced with the aid of his famous reflector telescope in the 1860s. These have a multitude of details—shades of light and dark, interspersed stars, openings, concentrations, convolutions, and so on. Compare, for example, his drawing of the Orion nebula with photographs of the same nebula, one taken through a middle-sized medium, and one through a large telescope! In the photographs most of the details disappear; the images are more indistinct, are milky-looking. But when the powerful modern reflectors are used, quite new parts emerge that formerly had not been reflected because of their faint light. The nebula greatly increases in size and takes on new forms. In this way the Orion nebula goes from the well-known heart-shaped structure in which the middle star of Orion's sword is as a star of the sixth magnitude, to a mighty two-winged spiral nebula. It has also been compared to a signet ring, in which the part that was first known and is perceptible to the naked eye represents the signet stone, and the ring the part that was discovered later. Even before photography had reached its present-day perfection, Dr. Steiner stated (February 16, 1907): "If you could see the Orion nebula in its entirety, you would perceive two intertwined vortices. We see here one world that is passing away and one that is coming into being."

So, too, in Steiner's *At the Gates of Spiritual Science*: "The sign of this stage of development—when one culture is ending and another beginning—is the vortex. There are such vortices everywhere in nature; in star-nebulae as, for example, the Orion nebula. There too, one world is falling into ruin and a new one is coming forth."

The sign of the occult script, the Cancer or vortex sign used here, shows that this is not a case of merely physical events. Since every event in the physical realm is the expression of a spiritual act, here too, spirits destroy worlds and build worlds up. Precisely in the world "behind the stars," in the world of the star nebulae that conceals itself almost completely from human sight and whose feeble light can leave an impression with the help of special means, we have a world out of which Lucifer speaks less than out of the actual world of the stars. The vortex sign of Cancer—if it is carried over from the living human organism to the mighty tranquillity of the cosmos—points to the rise and fall of worlds and at the same time to all the creative and disintegrative processes in the human being. In spite of their appearance—which makes one think of whirling, whizzing fireworks—and in spite of their changing in the course of time, these spiral nebulae are something permanent. They are in fact a token of the occult script. Several of them very clearly have the form of the human embryo. We are again reminded of the "head human being," which we have connected with the spiral nebulae, and as which the human being actually first appears in the embryonic state.

The nebulae divide themselves in a remarkable way over the whole sky in relation to the Milky Way. The Milky Way itself should be understood as a giant star cluster. In other words, in spite of its sometimes nebulous appearance, it is actually a concentration of stars and is that band in the heavens richest in stars. The spiral nebulae—and among these one includes today nearly all the clearly configured nebulae, such as that of Andromeda—have the tendency to congregate where the stars are least numerous, for example near the poles of the Milky Way, as removed from that dense belt of stars as possible. In the northern hemisphere one of the poles of the Milky Way is located in the constellation Coma Berenices (the "hair of

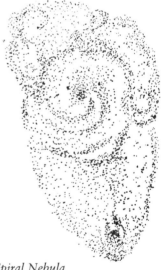

Spiral Nebula
from a photograph   **Figure 63**

Berenice"), not far from Virgo, where the Sun stands at the autumnal equinox. If one imagines a circle that passes right through the poles of the plane of the Milky Way and crosses the latter perpendicularly (in our hemisphere that would be near Cassiopeia), one would find most of the star nebulae on this circle, with a particular

concentration in the neighborhood of Virgo. In general, more such nebulae are found in the northern than in the southern half of this circle.

In the Milky Way we can see something like the process of metabolic
life, fixed in a state of rest, and embedded in it the gas nebulae representing the lymph system, which in the metabolic human being has the most
astrality. The spiral nebulae, which are as far distant as possible from
the Milky Way, on the contrary symbolize an astrality pertaining more
to the head-system. One also finds them near the pole of the equator
and the pole of the ecliptic. In the Great Bear and in the Hunting Dogs
are the most beautiful spiral nebulae. Just as one can say of a human
being: the more he or she is metabolic-person, the less is he or she head-
person, one can make the general statement: the more stars there are in
any region, the fewer spiral nebulae there are.

The spiral nebulae, however, indicate a connection with the variable
stars in that they have a striking number of such stars in their neighborhood. They are thus also linked to the rhythmic system. Moreover, in
these nebulae appear new stars, mostly only small ones, and a rather
large number of these are constantly being discovered. We must look
for the larger ones, in contrast, in the Milky Way itself. There the other
kind of nebula, so-called "gas nebulae" are mostly found. Their name is
not derived so much from their appearance as from the spectroanalytical
analysis of these bodies. These, too, seek out the regions in the Milky
Way in which there are few stars. The statement: the more nebulae, the
fewer stars, and vice versa, is even more true of the gas nebulae than of
the spiral-shaped nebulae.

Examples of a gathering of nebulae are the Greater and Lesser
Magellanic Clouds. These are situated outside the Milky Way in the
neighborhood of the South Pole, and look like little bits of the Milky
Way cut adrift. Each is in fact a little universe. The Great Cloud
contains 291 nebulae, 46 star clusters, and 582 stars, the Lesser cor-
respondingly smaller numbers.

We have here symbolically all the substances and processes that
play a part in the human metabolic system. If one looks at representations of large stretches of the Milky Way or of the bordering regions
with their nebulae, star-clusters, star-nebulae, nebulae-veils, and so on,
one sees on a macrocosmic scale something similar to the retina of the
human eye or to the abdominal membrane. There a world is surging,
gushing forth, and whirling. It lacks actual movement—manifesting the

immutability that generally characterizes the starry world when judged
by human standards. But it reveals to us the archetype of the physical
human being in a pictorial form.

The number of nebulae is immensely great, supposedly about a million. Most are thought to be spiral nebulae, but we must point out
that there is a tendency today to consider every possible nebula to be
spiralic, even if it looks like a long, drawn-out disk, as for example, the
Andromeda nebula. The idea is that the system is observed "sideways,"
in perspective, and therefore appears flat, but that in the interior the
coils of the spiral are nevertheless to be found. This is the view of the
new astronomy, which is connected to that science's whole conception
of space. It assumes various world systems, and sees the system to which
our Sun belongs as just one of these. This system is enclosed on all sides
by the Milky Way. Behind this ring of the Milky Way are assumed to be
galactic systems, that make themselves manifest to us through their stars
or star nebulae. According to this view, there are thus stars and nebulae
that belong to "our" system and lie within the ring of the Milky Way,
and others outside it that belong to "other" systems. One sees that it is
a strictly spatially conceived universe. People think that this viewpoint
is substantiated by what is revealed through the telescope and camera.

This three-dimensional space, however, is certainly not visible to
the naked eye. The eye sees the stars, despite their varying degrees of
brightness, not spatially one behind another, but all upon the spherical
inner surface of a single firmament. Nor do the visible nebulae such as
the one in Andromeda give the impression of being further away than,
for example, the stars in the Milky Way. That through the telescope and
still more in photographs there is apparent three-dimensional perspective of before and behind, with some stars being closer and others farther
away, may very well be occasioned by the nature of these instruments
themselves. It was through these instruments that the impression of
depth was first evoked.

I might point, as a comparison, to the well-known stereoscopic
pictures. These ordinary two-dimensional photographs create an impression of three-dimensionality with graphically real forms. That these
stereoscope pictures give us an impression of a greater (and also more
corporeal) reality than the mere photograph is no doubt connected with
the fact that the photograph is a reproduction of an actual three-dimensional space, which through the stereoscope is artificially reproduced.

But the stereoscopic pictures always give the impression of being artificial. The figures seem to stand in actual space and seem to be alive, but they do not move, nor are they statues. The telescope in a similar way evokes a sense of three-dimensional space, and when combined with the photographic plate, does this yet more strongly. Because of our daily experience of space, we believe that we must experience this impression of space as real, just as we do with stereoscopic pictures.

It is also believed that there is apparent proof in other phenomena of these entirely spatial concepts. In the planetary world we see at times the Moon place itself before the Sun, the satellites of Jupiter before their home planet, and from time to time stars are occulted by the Moon or by planets. These phenomena are also to a great extent visible to the naked eye. There one indeed encounters a spatial element. In the actual world of the stars, however, there is no corresponding phenomenon of perspective positioning, of one object lying behind the other. All that one thinks one knows of a dimensional depth in the world of stars is obtained by another kind of phenomenon, namely from certain linear distortions in the spectrum of the stars—the Doppler effect. The laws of nature discovered for the Earth are then extrapolated to apply to these phenomena. But the truth of these natural laws, just as the truth of earthly gravity, diminishes "according to the square of the distance." To these laws of nature one must also include the fact that our earthly space is a three-dimensional one. This three-dimensionality ceases just where the stars show themselves to us. There another lawfulness begins to be increasingly valid. We know it to be the law of morality, of human soul-life.

Our destiny is written in the stars. Our destiny is an outpouring of what in the human being surpasses even the starry worlds. It is an outpouring of the human ego, our eternal being. In the starry worlds the human being builds up the foundations of the physical body, not according to the laws of nature, but according to moral laws, in keeping with his or her destiny. But just as destiny is related to the stars, so are our dreams related to that which is to be found in this world of the stars as nebulae, nebulous veils—those things that in a sense represent the purest "astrality" of the star world. Rudolf Steiner referred to this in the important lecture of September 22, 1923, printed in *Das Goetheanum* 1927 (no. 3436). It is incumbent upon us now to approach this significant aspect. We will begin with it next time.

March 1930

The World of the Stars VI
Nebulae and Variable Stars

AT THE END OF THE LAST LETTER we brought the star nebulae and human dreams into connection with each other. Before that we tried to depict the dreamlike appearance of cosmic nebulae, the dreamlike mutability of the revelation of their being. If we are to bring this world into relation with human metabolism and also with the physical brain, we find it related to what arises from the human being as dreams. Dreams arise from the fact that the astral body and the ego—which in sleep are outside the physical and etheric bodies—have a slight connection to these two aspects of the human being or they merge completely with them at the moment of waking. In the nebulae something is faintly visible that is related to the brilliance of the star world as the dream consciousness of the human being is related to waking consciousness. They stand between the invisible "spirit colonies"—that to clairvoyant sight are behind the stars—and the visible stars. Naturally, the expressions "behind" and "between" are not to be understood quantitatively and spatially, but in terms of quality and being.

In his lecture of September 22, 1923, Rudolf Steiner points out the connection between dreams and star-nebulae. Both protest in a sense against the laws of nature. A dream is not concerned with the laws of nature; it has its own set of laws. This is little known to humankind at present. The human being perceives in his or her world, in his or her dream fantasies, in a merely fantastical way. This however, "originates only from people not having the faculty to recognize the connections that confront them there. It is the person him or herself who carries the fantastic element into the dream. But what lives and weaves there is entirely another world-sphere, which the human being enters in dream . . ."

There is today no real science of dreams, except for some modest beginnings in anthroposophical research. To explain the world of dreams one either employs fantasy (psychoanalysis) or accepts the results of purely physical experiments.

It is basically the same in the case of the nebulae. Their extraordinary formations indicate that they have many more and very different things to reveal to us than what we discover by applying terrestrial natural laws. There is only a lack of knowledge of the laws that pertain there, which one must imagine for oneself. This happened at times to the student of nature, Johannes Muller, in his experiments:

> And, rightly considered, it must be assumed that if one did as Johannes Muller did—if one did not think about the Orion nebula as people do in observatories and astronomical institutions, but rather dreamed about it, then one would actually discover more about it than one does by thinking and pondering. I would like to say that this is connected with the fact that in pastoral times, when shepherds used to sleep at night in the fields, they actually dreamt about the stars, and therefore they knew more than those who came later. It is really true, it is so indeed.

This world of dreams and nebulae is characterized in another way:

> In short, whether we enter the inner life of the human being and draw near to the world of dreams, or whether we go out into the wide universe beyond the zodiac, we enter, as the ancients said, a world of dreams. And now we are at the point where we can understand what was meant by the Greeks—who still had some knowledge of such things, when they used the expression "chaos."
> . . . What did the Greeks mean when they spoke of chaos? They meant the prevailing lawfulness of which one gets an idea if one immerses oneself in dreams, or which one must assume in the farthest periphery of this universe. For the Greeks the world is born out of chaos—out of a condition that does not as yet follow natural laws, but is like a dream or like the cosmic expanses that still exist today in the constellation of Orion, the Hunting Dogs, and so on. There one enters above all a world that still announces itself to humankind in the fantastic but living world of dream pictures. [Lecture, September 22, 1923]

The world is born out of chaos and also will continuously be maintained by chaos. Chaos, the Tohu-wa-bohu of the Hebrews, is what was there before the appearance of the world. In concrete terms, we can say that the spirits of will brought forth the world substance of Saturn out of chaos—which was their own substance. This substance, through the evolutionary stages of Sun, Moon, and Earth, has become what underlies the laws of nature that pertain today. The spirits of will, however, only let a part of their being flow into this substance. All the rest, one might say, remains in the condition of chaos and continues to work—forming, transforming, dissolving, and creating.

In an important lecture on October 19, 1907, Steiner related that the word "gas," which we use for a steam- or air-like condition, was deliberately coined by the Rosicrucian Van Helmont from the word "chaos." Van Helmont said "I name this spirit (or breath) 'gas.' It is not far removed from the 'chaos' of the ancients." Out of it the world has formed itself. Gas, moreover, is a dim version of the original foundation of the world-chaos. At the same time there is present in it, so Rudolf Steiner said, a concept of space quite different from that of today. It is a concept of space not as an endless emptiness, but as an infinite realm of seed-germs, out of which the visible world has been condensed.

> Chaos works, however, not only in the beginning of world-evolution, but continues. . . . It is the first, original creation. Then it condenses; the seed-germs form themselves; worlds come into being. Everything—every stone, every being—is still permeated by chaos. And not only are the beings in the outer world permeated by chaos, but also your soul and your spirit. Because a human being is here on Earth, that person's soul and spirit partake of what has remained of chaos.

Then Rudolf Steiner explained how chaos works concretely, for example in the products of animal excretion, which become manure, which gives fertility to the fields and draws forth the crops. The manure was perhaps first a beautiful, exquisitely formed plant that, itself having once arisen from chaos and having passed through the animal organism, returns again to chaos.

> Chaos works in manure, in everything that is thrown off, and unless you mix chaos in with the cosmos at some time or other,

progress is never possible. No human being could continue to exist if only the cosmos worked upon them. And what is the cosmos? The cosmos is nothing more than what has formed itself from pre-existent causes and formative forces. Not only all physical things, but also all moral and intellectual teachings, arise from causes that have been laid down before.

So genius works out of chaos as a new spark that springs from the marriage of chaos and cosmos. And so arises all that is new in the world, even new worlds themselves. For the creation of these new worlds science can give only external natural causes. But with some justification it relates these to the cosmic nebulae formations. Indeed, science even calls some of these "gas nebulae."

Chaos works into the microcosm of nature that immediately surrounds us. But we also find signs of it in the activity of the mysterious nebulae and nebulae veils that withhold themselves from direct human sight. Macrocosmic fertility may rule in these formations. They are closely connected to the nature of the divine-spiritual. They differ from the luciferic radiance of the star world and from the ahrimanic threatening cold of the dark cosmic cloud nebulae, the study of which is so eagerly carried on today. It has become known (strangely enough) largely through several decades of work at the Vatican observatory that such dark nebulae—whose existence in the region of the Milky Way has long been known—really stretch over the whole sky and that they are most extended in the region of the pole of the Milky Way, where most of the luminous nebulae also lie. The Vatican observer (J. G. Hagen) considers the dark nebulae to be the original form of the stellar matter out of which those stars evolve which, judged by their spectroscopic constitution, are at the beginning of their development. As an anthroposophist one is not bound to agree with these views, and other investigators have denied the existence of dark nebulae of the size assumed by the ecclesiastical researchers. One can perhaps rather think of the words of Rudolf Steiner already quoted:

> Out there in the starry heavens it is the moral that is real and that rules. Sometimes also it is the immoral, the luciferic, the ahrimanic. . . . There, it is the moral, not the physical, that is real and that rules. (See Letter 3, Year Three.)

We can perhaps also sense that the mighty realities that stand before us can only be adequately described in a new mythology. The Greeks had their magnificent mythology of the arising of successive worlds through Uranus and Gaia, and through Chronos and Zeus. They knew chaos and also its antithesis, "a-chaos"—which lives on in the Indian word akasha, the "ether." The age of natural science brought the dreary, impoverished Copernican mythology of balls rolling in universal space (see Steiner's *The Spiritual Hierarchies and the Physical World,* lecture 5). Our age has added to that a cosmogony of invisible, dark nebulae, and of stars, which at first glow white, gradually cool down to a dark red, and at length—through a total equalization of temperature, the so-called "death of warmth"—come to an end. Thus in the not-so-distant future—when the new faculties slumbering in human beings awake—a new and true mythology should be created, one that presents in mighty images what has been revealed by the telescope, camera, and spectroscope but has not been fully grasped by the materialistic consciousness. The Godhead between Lucifer and Ahriman—that is the theme of all mythology of the new age and of the future.

Such a mythology—different from the Copernican—would have its roots in the spiritual. But it could be based upon what has been learned through the research of materialistic science, for this materialistic science has discovered many facts. The mythology of the future naturally could not arise merely through something that corresponds to the forms of the ancient constellations, being arbitrarily attached to the cosmic creation. These ancient constellations—the Great Bear, Leo, and so on, were not added to the external stars in ancient times by arbitrary fantasy, but were living imaginations of the beings standing behind them. A new mythology would have to deal with the relation of the visible heavenly bodies to those that are invisible but are accessible with modern instruments; with the relationship between chaos and cosmos and between the divine creation and the creating gods; and with the role of the adversarial powers. In other words, it could not be born out of a mere astronomy, nor out of astrology, but out of astrosophy. And it must take into consideration human beings who experience the star world in their perception and thought, and for whom the nebulae are a world of dreams.

Just as dreams are a second stream into which human beings dive
when they leave the physical, natural world, so they reach—as was
mentioned in the lecture that deals with the nebula of Orion—yet a
third stream that is "beyond the world of dreams and has no connection whatsoever to the laws of nature. The world of dreams, in its
pictorial quality, rebels against the laws of nature. It would be nonsense
to think that this third world operates according to the laws of nature.
It contradicts boldly and completely the laws of nature because it also
intrudes upon the human being. When a dream appears in the living
world of pictures, this third world becomes manifest most of all through
the voice of conscience in the moral world view." [Steiner's lecture of
September 22, 1923.]

This third world also belongs to cosmic mythology. It is the world
in which the gods speak to human beings when they are in the spiritual
world during the night. We do not experience this consciously because
we are in deep sleep, but we experience this in waking as the voice of
conscience. That is the world beyond the zodiac, completely beyond
the stars, the world of the gods behind the stars into which the human
being, in contrast to the animals, can enter. There, above all, only moral
lawfulness is active, and not a single sense-perceptible indication ever
exists.

What the true cosmic mythology today cannot yet fully provide can
(if we go by Rudolf Steiner's words) be found embodied in miniature in
an important scene in his Rosicrucian mystery drama *The Portal of Initiation.* In the final scene, in the Sun temple, twelve individualities stand
around Johannes Thomasius. They are linked to him by "the threads
that karma spins in the becoming of worlds," and these threads form
a knot in the middle of which Johannes Thomasius stands. The twelve
are bound to him not only karmically, they stand there in such a way
that in them the aspects of the being of Johannes are expressed in the
way that the twelve parts of the zodiac are united in the incarnation of
a human being. Johannes Thomasius's experience and knowledge of self
are divided among these individual persons, and the particular qualities
of the one man are divided among them all. "Everything plays itself out
twice—in the macrocosm and in the microcosm of the soul of Johannes.
That is his initiation."

There we have the zodiac, for it is expressly stated that there are
exactly twelve persons around Johannes Thomasius, and they, together

with him, comprise a unity. The rest of the world outside the Sun temple, with its many, many souls and with their lives straying into the luciferic and ahrimanic, represents the rest of the star world. But the hierophant, Benedictus, is also there: "And thus we have the whole, because one human individuality stands above all these persons. This is the hierophant, who intervenes, guiding the threads, just as the sun of this Sun temple, the Sun-hero, who follows his path through the zodiac." We see here the world of initiation with its relation to waking consciousness. In the later dramas, that enigmatic spirit, the "other Philia," also plays a role, introducing Johannes to the dream world. She says to him:

> *And waking dreams*
> *Reveal unto souls*
> *The hidden weaving*
> *Of their own being.*

Dream figures meet Johannes on his path of initiation, nebulous forms like the spirit of his own youth. This being, because of his guilt, cannot return to chaos and must lead a dreadful, enchanted existence. These figures with their "chaos character" are like hints of the cosmic world of the nebulae.

Then the voice of spirit—which is the voice of conscience—resounds, invisible but audible, into the drama in moments that are decisive for the soul life. It comes from a being who cannot yet appear in an embodied form on the stage. We can imagine a future in which human beings will experience the being—which they feel as the voice of conscience—in a form that is connected with the world of deep sleep, just as today we have in the world of nebulae the cosmic expression of the dream world. Thus we find the whole macrocosm portrayed microcosmically in the mystery plays of Rudolf Steiner.

After this general survey we will briefly consider the *variable stars,* so that next time we can conclude with a description of the new stars.

With variable stars there is a kind of rhythmic element in the otherwise unchanging starry heavens. Since ancient times the world of the stars had been understood—largely because of Aristotle's definition—as a world of duration, of eternal unchangingness. This on the whole does represent its nature. Without this generally accepted view, humankind perhaps would have noticed earlier that variable stars exist, since some are visible to the naked eye. In fact, the new consciousness that arose

with the age of natural science following Copernicus, and in particular
the appearance of a brightly shining new star (discovered by Tycho
Brahe in 1572) were necessary to draw enough attention to the starry
skies that these variable stars were actually also found. It was still
before the discovery of the telescope, at the end of the sixteenth century,
that a star, the famous "Mira Ceti"—"the Wonder in the Whale" as it
was then called—attracted attention through its disappearance and re-
illumination. This observation was forgotten for decades, in spite of its
occasional mention by Kepler. People were still too strongly impressed
by the "new stars" appearing on the scene at that time. Their appearance kindled the whole dispute between the adherents of the new natural
science and the conservative "Aristotelians" who, still swearing by their
master's word after two thousand years, denied the possibility that such
"novae" could really be *stars*. We shall return to this when dealing with
new stars. It was only in the last third of the seventeenth century that
the star in the Whale was recognized as a variable star with a period
of eleven months. It faded from about the third magnitude to such a
faint radiance that at that time it remained invisible for several months.
Around 1800 the variability of Algol, a star in Perseus, was remarked.
This is the star that represents the severed head of Medusa in the left
hand of Perseus. It has a much shorter period [about sixty-nine hours]
than the one in the Whale, and remains visible to the naked eye even at
its minimum brightness. However, its variability is much less striking
than in the case of Mira. It was only at this time that people began to
study variability in a systematic way.

Today new stars are thought of as simply a special class of variable
stars. We shall, however, abide by the older distinction between variable or periodic and new or temporary stars. It is precisely in the single
illumination of the so-called new stars that we must see something different from what is seen in the regular—and also irregular—repetition
of fluctuations of light. (Spectroscopically, too, the new stars are quite
different from variable stars.)

Variable stars show great differences among themselves in their fluctuations of light, both in duration and intensity. If one represents the
periods graphically, according to these two functions, one obtains different curves of oscillation, similar in nature, although not in form, to
those of the human heartbeat.

The length of the period during which such a star increases in brilliance can vary from about two years to a few hours, and the fluctuations in magnitude can extend to nine degrees of magnitude. (It may be recalled that the visible stars are divided into six degrees of magnitude according to their brilliance. The telescopic stars, invisible to the naked eye, can go up to the tenth, twelfth, fifteenth magnitude [today up to the thirtieth magnitude using electronic detectors with the best modern telescopes]. Variations from one to five degrees of magnitude are the most usual. As regards the duration of the light fluctuation, these stars are divided in terms of short and long periods, and the dividing line, which is of course not very rigid, is about seventy-five days. In the first group, those with a period of one day or less are the most numerous. In the second group, the most numerous are those whose period lies between 200 and 350 days. Among several classes of variables the periods are not consistent or can be determined only with difficulty.

In order to call forth at least an idea of the working of these stars, we give here the diagram for some of the most characteristic groups (after Carl Schiller: *Introduction to the Study of Variable Stars,* 1923).

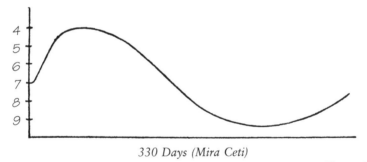

330 Days (Mira Ceti)

Figure 64

On the left, vertical side of the graph, the degrees of magnitude are given, and below, on the horizontal, the duration of the entire period. Mira Ceti here represents the group of variable stars with long periods. Today [1929] these number over 600. [Today around 10,000 are known.]

In figure 65 is an example of the stars with changeable periods. The numbers given pertain to a particular, representative star of this group—*U Geminorum.* They are not the same for other stars of the

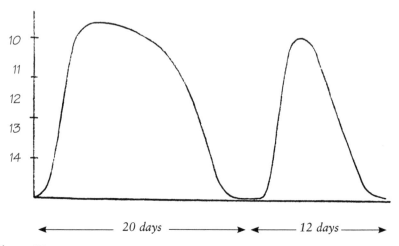

Figure 65

group, although in fact not different. Only that period in which the outbursts of light take place is shown, the entire period of this star being about eighty-six days. However, none of the numbers shown is constant. In the case of this group there are continually changes in the duration, intensity, and sequence of the maximum illuminations. Only a very few stars belong to this class.

There is also a group of quite irregular variables, whose fluctuations are very small. Their variation in light cannot be calculated at all. Figure 66 gives a concrete example of a star with a very great variation.

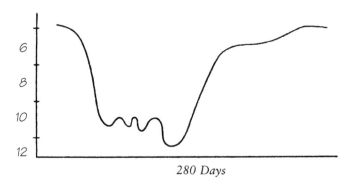

Figure 66

The stars with a short period are the most regular, and one of the prime examples of this group is shown next.

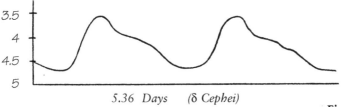

5.36 Days   (δ Cephei)

Figure 67

In a somewhat metamorphosed form this type is to be found most frequently among variable stars in general and especially in star clusters. They bear the most resemblance in their pattern to the human pulse-beat, as evidenced by the so-called sphygmogram reproduced below.

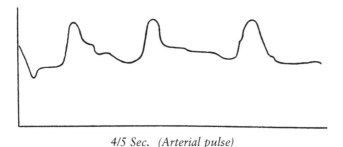

4/5 Sec. (Arterial pulse)

Figure 68

One assumes of Algol and the other stars of its type that from time to time they are partially eclipsed by a satellite that revolves around the chief star—in the same way that the Sun is darkened for us by the Moon at a partial eclipse of the Sun. Therefore there is change that begins suddenly, lasts a short time, and involves a minimum of light intensity. In the case of Algol, one can observe this with the naked eye if one knows when to look. The whole change takes place in only a few hours.

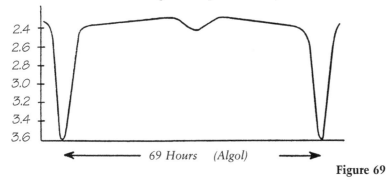

69 Hours   (Algol)

Figure 69

To the approximately 130 stars of the Algol type there must be added as eclipsing variables the 21 stars of the Beta-Lyrae type. These are continuously undergoing variations of their light. It has been found that the period in this case is increasing by two-thirds of a second every time. One sees from this that even in the world of the stars one must sometimes deal with very short periods of time.

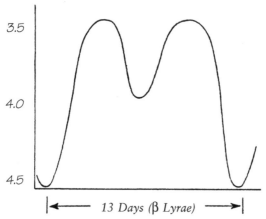

Figure 70

The Algol stars are to be found overwhelmingly in the region of the Milky Way (Perseus, too, to which Algol belongs, is crossed by the Milky Way). Here also are the short-period stars belonging to the same group as Delta-Cephei. This is not the case with the remaining short-period stars. The star-clusters in which they chiefly occur are not situated exactly in the Milky Way. The irregular variables and the stars with long periods have no connection with the Milky Way. In these and similar patterns there is no doubt concealed something significant about the nature of variable stars. We have still however to consider the question: What is the cause of variability in general?

For the Algol stars, the so-called eclipsing variables, astronomical science gives an exact theory, holding that the eclipse occurs because of a satellite. For the others a whole series of hypotheses is set up, all based on the application of terrestrial law to the celestial world. We will here only mention by name some of these hypotheses: the flood hypothesis, the cinder theory, the formation of spots (as with our Sun), mutual influence of two bodies without eclipse (pulsing stars), and so on.

If we observe variable stars from the standpoint of spiritual science, we are reminded of the description of the ancient Sun-condition, which is to be found in Rudolf Steiner's *The Spiritual Hierarchies,* lecture 3. What is described there as the Old Sun with its breathing process, with its inflowing and outflowing of light and smoke and gas, presents a condition of change that corresponds to what we experience of the different variable stars.

A ball, shining on the surface, within filled with streaming gas, currents flowing in all directions:

> One is fully justified in calling it a sun, and what are suns today are now passing though this same process. They are inwardly masses of streaming gas. On the other hand, they cause that gas to turn into light, and broadcast light into the universe.

This gas and light also represent processes going on within the beings who inhabit this sun. The archangels, who were going through their human stage, had a body of light, gas, or smoke, and fire that was separate from the general substance of the Sun itself. But they could also take into themselves their whole environment, which consisted of smoke and gas:

> We have now a process of real breathing! On the Old Sun you would have perceived those currents of gas as a process of breathing. You would have found there certain conditions when there was an absolute stillness, and you would have said to yourselves "Now the archangels have breathed in all the gas." But then the archangels began to breathe it out again. Inner currents began to flow and at the same time light came forth. (You have here also a description of the difference between the Old Sun and the Sun of today. Our present Sun is always shining and darkness is produced only when some object is placed in front of its light. This was not the case with the Old Sun. It had in itself the power to produce the alternation of light and darkness, illumination and obscurity because that was its process of exhalation and inhalation. . . . It was able to alternate light and darkness like inhalation and exhalation, because at that time the Sun was a sort of fixed star.

This quotation does not mean that the whole sublime glory of the Old Sun condition is also to be found in the present variable stars. For in the stars, luciferic beings also hold sway, and during the Old Sun stage of evolution these did not yet exist. In *Genesis: Secrets of the Bible Story of Creation,* lecture 4, Rudolf Steiner expressly says that the whole plant-like weaving in the gas-, warmth-, and light-ball of the Old Sun, this springing forth of gas in flower-like forms of light, today is no longer physically present anywhere in the whole universe as it was at that time. The breathing in and the breathing out of light, however, that was bound up with the experience of the archangels on the ancient Sun, we can look upon as essentially related to what still today is played out in the starry skies.

Now it is significant that the so-called "pulsation theory" of the origin of variability has been added to the hypotheses of the last decades. This theory supposes that with the short-period variables it is not a matter of a two-body system. Rather these gaseous or even liquiform glowing stars are disturbed in their balance by some external cause or other, start to fluctuate periodically, and thus have their outbursts of light. This explanation relates to what actually happens in the same way that the common scientific theories about blood circulation and the movement of the heart relate to the explanation of spiritual science. However, it shows us how through the facts themselves, one is led to the concepts that otherwise are applied to the human being, such as that of pulsation. In both cases one can come to a correct explanation only through adopting a spiritual point of view.

It is just in the last decade that science has undertaken really comprehensive investigations of the variable stars and the star world in general. These set forth in varied ways, sometimes even in statistical form, many relationships between the color, brightness, spectrum of the stars, as well as their positions and distribution over the whole sky in relation to the plane of the Milky Way. This vast material will someday enable us to grasp the starry heavens as an expression of a spiritual reality, as the archetype of the human being. Then for the first time it will acquire meaning, significance, order, and harmony. We have presented only a small part of the mass of scientific findings, only as much as we can now with certainty relate to the content of anthroposophical teachings. Everything else must await further research. Some day the chaos that still holds sway today in this enormous mass of facts will be divested of its materialism and will be changed into a cosmos of spiritual ideas, imaginations, and inspirations. Then this knowledge—the results of the immense scientific research work of the nineteenth and twentieth centuries—can pass over into the new mythology of the starry heavens of which we spoke. What we have thus far presented, however, should enable us to imbue ourselves to some extent with that mood of conse-cration in respect to the starry heavens that Rudolf Steiner describes in the booklet *Christmas* with the words:

> Today when a human being—influenced by an abstract science of astronomy—looks at the starry heavens, these are filled with abstract, material spheres. But these celestial spheres will again become for the human being the bodies of souls and spirits. Space will once more be permeated by spirit and soul. We will experi-ence the whole cosmos as warm and comforting just as we find the embrace of a friend warm and comforting, though of course we will experience the spirit of the cosmos as more majestic and sublime.

We are just beginning to have experiences, but even today they can certainly live within us.

April 1930

The World of the Stars VII

New Stars

WE WILL NOW EXAMINE the new stars, the final domain of the world of the stars. We do not mean to imply, however, that our survey can be considered at all exhaustive. Just as we have tried to see in the starry heavens the expression of something spiritual, we will view the new stars also in this light. In the often-cited lecture of June 4, 1924, in which Rudolf Steiner speaks of the "loving stroking" of the stars and of the "spirit-self" of the cosmos, he also refers briefly to the nature of the new stars:

> Now please think about the illumination of certain stars at definite times. This is something that, when explained only in terms of physical realities, is full of riddles. One can understand nothing with these explanations. Stars that were not there before light up and again disappear. Thus a "corpse" of short duration also exists in the universe. In epochs during which, so to speak, the gods want to work out of the astral world into the etheric world, there one sees these stars that light up and again quickly disappear.

We see from this that the new stars represent an impulse that the gods send into the universe. In the world of finished work therefore, which surrounds us and which no longer bears the divine-spiritual directly in itself, the new stars are a remaining expression of the deeds of the gods. They are a manifestation of the activity of spiritual beings, as in another way we have found to be the case with the comets. For this reason alone we cannot count the new stars among the "variables" as is done today in astronomy. Not only do their appearances lack a periodic element, but they must be seen as having a quite different spiritual nature. (In terms of spectrum analysis also, the new stars are completely a class unto themselves. They have such a characteristic spectrum that today several stars with this spectrum are looked upon as former novae, although their actual illumination had not been observed.)

We will first describe what modern science has to say about the phenomenon of the new stars. Here too, the use of the telescope and celestial photography has taught us significant things. We know that the name "new stars" is not quite apt (Rudolf Steiner avoided it) and that the expression "temporary stars" fits the case better. Nevertheless we do not want to eliminate from the name the idea of impulsiveness that is implied in the word "new."

Before the invention of the telescope people already knew of individual stars that suddenly lighted up and then disappeared from view. Then the telescope made it possible to view the stars for a time even after they had become invisible, so that they were thus known to remain in existence after disappearing for the naked eye. The nineteenth century brought for the first time complete information about the meaning of this aspect of the phenomenon. It has been possible to ascertain the magnitude (usually a very slight one) to which the stars decline after their lighting up (they continue with this degree of light sometimes with remarkable accompanying phenomena). But also, because the photographing of the entire heavens is being carried on systematically, there has been an opportunity to confirm the fact that on earlier photographs of a celestial region in which a new star has appeared, a tiny star had already been present in exactly the same place. This star was usually extremely faint, and had therefore perhaps not even been catalogued. Then in the space of a few days or even hours it had changed to a bright shining star. It has sometimes even been necessary to indicate the maximum brightness by a minus sign, for new stars can far exceed stars of the first magnitude in brilliance and must therefore be described as of magnitude 0.5, –1, –2 and so on. (The magnitude of Sirius is –1.6.) In this sense, therefore, such stars are really not "new," for they were there both before and after. A few stars, to be sure, have not been found on the photographs in this way. They must have been smaller than the smallest magnitude that could be photographed, perhaps of the sixteenth to the eighteenth magnitude. Whether individual stars were formerly not there at all cannot, of course, be determined.

In order to give a concrete example we will look at the new star in Perseus that appeared early in the twentieth century (*Nova Persei,* 1901).

It was later determined that previously it has been of the thirteenth–
fourteenth magnitude. Three days before the maximum it was still of
the eleventh magnitude; then, on February 21, it was discovered as a
star with a magnitude of two and one-half—above and to the right of
Algol. From this we gather that a few hours before it must still have
been below the range of visibility—(sixth magnitude). In a few days it
was as bright as Vega, and then sank again in the succeeding months
below the level of visibility—with fairly strong oscillations of brightness.
The accompanying diagram (Figure 71) depicts this part of its course.
One sees a powerful activity in the sudden brightening, then a tremulous
dying-down as the impulse from the astral world ceased to work.

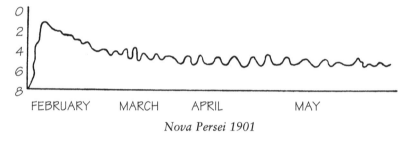

Nova Persei 1901

Figure 71

What followed has since then occurred with several other new
stars—an appearance in the immediate area of nebulous masses that
had not been seen before. Nebulae clouds and streaks formed themselves
into a kind of spiral and rapidly changed, so that the new star became
the center of an extensive and complicated field of nebulae rings, of
spiral nebulae, and so on. We can only mention this phenomenon and
do not wish to go deeply into scientific explanations. We have always
maintained that the actual ruling cosmic law is not a physical one. In the
universe live the etheric and the astral, and beyond them spirit-selfhood.
One mighty say that it is just this highest member of the cosmos that
participates in the coming about of the phenomena of the new stars.
The ordinary scientific explanations which all originate from a concept
of physical causation can lead only to a desolate materialism. In this
view, the new stars are the result of either a collision or an eruption. In
other words, they have either an external or an internal cause. The colli-
sions are either between two (preferably defunct) stars or between a star

already somewhat cooled down and a mass of cosmic dust. In this case, here the "dust" need not have merely earthly dimensions. According to another theory, the eruption occurs because glowing masses from the interior of the star break through the surface, which has cooled down to a kind of cinder shell. (One is reminded of coal fires under the Earth.) The nebulae clouds that can appear around new stars are supposed to be dark nebulae. These either were already present, but not yet illumined by the light of the new star, or are the nebulous matter coming out of the new star itself. We are here simply at one of those points where every non-spiritual explanation must be of no avail.

As to the region in which new stars mainly appear, we can say with certainty that they are nearly always to be found near the Milky Way. They appear frequently also in the Milky Way itself and there in the regions richest in stars, such as in the Swan, or in Sagittarius. Scorpius also has had several new stars. There are actually only two known exceptions of stars that have appeared far from the Milky Way. One was in the Northern Crown in 1866. The other flamed up in 1925 in the southern hemisphere—in itself a rare occurrence—almost at the other pole of the Milky Way. We will describe both later.

What is important and at the same time interesting about the new stars is their history. It seems that in earlier times they actually gave strong impulses that, apart from what they signify spiritually, have worked for the furtherance of astronomy. We know with certainty of a new star that was observed in 134 B.C. We know of it from Chinese sources. We know of it also from the Greek astronomer Hipparchus, although not directly from him, as his writings have nearly all been lost—but from the naturalist, Pliny the Younger. What Pliny said was somewhat as follows:

Hipparchus has never been appreciated for his true worth, for he has contributed more than any other to establishing the connections of the human being with the world of stars and has proved that our souls participate in the heavens. He discovered a star that appeared in his time, and by its movements was led to ask whether this phenomenon occurred frequently and also whether the stars we consider stationary do not in fact have movement. And so he was led to undertake a project that to the gods might seem foolhardy—to count the stars for the benefit of posterity. He gave names to all and invented instruments by which to record the position and magnitude of each star. He did this in such a way that it could be easily determined not only whether they faded away and arose, but also whether they increased or decreased or altered their position. In this way he bequeathed the heavens as a spiritual heritage for all human beings who might be able to make use of them.

Thus the appearance of a new star was the occasion for the making of the first star catalogue, which in turn through comparison with earlier observations led to Hipparchus's discovery of the precession of the vernal point as a scientific fact. Such a list of stars with their positions and degrees of brightness may appear abstract and dreary. But this star catalogue, on the basis of which Ptolemy later compiled his own, contributed much to the study of the starry heavens at a time when the planets were the main object of people's attention.

According to the Chinese records, the star must have been in Scorpius, but whether this is the same as the one seen by Hipparchus can no longer be established with certainty.

Now we find several new stars mentioned in the fourth as well as in the ninth century. It seems in general as if these phenomena are concentrated in certain periods—when "the gods desire to work out of the astral into the etheric world"—and then are much less frequent. Throughout the whole Middle Ages we scarcely hear of one nova except through the Chinese. The lack of a capacity for observation, characteristic of the western countries in the Middle Ages, may have caused the new stars to escape detection. People calculated a good deal—the planetary orbits for instance, from ancient or improved Ptolemaic tables, but they paid little attention to whether or not the result of the calculation corresponded to reality. That was still true of Copernicus. And so a new star was again needed to kindle the love of observation.

It was the famous new star in Cassiopeia that was seen by Tycho Brahe in 1572. Tycho from his youth had a strong inclination toward astronomy, but this science was not then considered a worthy occupation for a nobleman. So he might easily have entered upon a different career. Then, at the age of twenty-five he saw a radiantly bright new star. It may be said that this star made him an astronomer, and that all later astronomy, inasmuch as it depends upon observation, derived from it. Brahe wrote a paper about his discovery, yet pride again held

him back from letting the work be published, for this also did not befit
a nobleman. Only his annoyance at the foolish things that other people
wrote about this star brought him to the point of letting the book be
published. He became well known and some years later received from
the king of Denmark the island of Hveen, where he built his castle
Uraniborg, which was at the same time an observatory and an academy
school for practical astronomy.

Learned scholars and young
people from many countries went
there and studied the art of observation and various other things.
Tycho lived before the invention
of the telescope. His instruments
were actually not very different
from those with which Ptolemy,
for instance, had worked. Perhaps
it was just because of this that he
could develop the faculty of observation that had so long been lost

NOVA
1572

Figure 72

—following the planetary orbits over weeks, months, and years, and
the registering of individual stars. Stimulated by the star of 1572 he
completed a new catalogue of stars. From this point of view, in spite
of his system having been completely dropped, he is the true father of
modern astronomy.

It is exceedingly interesting to learn what Tycho said about the new
star. He had a thoroughly astrological, spiritual understanding of it. He
believed that the star was not to be measured by ordinary standards. Its
position on the vernal colure (the circle through the vernal and autumnal
points at right angles to the equator) was important since it actually
appeared "in the east" like the star of Bethlehem and, astrologically,
belonged to Aries. At first it was similar in appearance to Venus and
Jupiter and seemed to be of a friendly nature. Then it turned red like
Mars and became the bringer of wars throughout all Europe. (The terrible St. Bartholomew's Day massacre of French Huguenots on August
24, 1572, was still remembered by all). Tycho thought that only in 1592
would the star become active in the destiny of persons born in 1572. It
gave tidings of the end of the "grand trine" that was to follow at the
turn of the century.

At this point we will allow a short digression to explain something of the phenomenon of the so-called "trine period," which is also
very significant for spiritual science. The trine period is related to the
conjunction of Jupiter and Saturn, which in consequence of the slow
movement of these planets only takes place every twenty years. This
was always called in astrology the "great conjunction," and Rudolf Steiner
once said that this conjunction signified periods of renaissance. Naturally
there is not a renaissance every twenty years, but just here the "trine
period" plays a part. For the conjunctions take their course according to
a remarkable law. The zodiac has been divided from ancient times into
four trigons (three times four signs) which are related to the sequence of
the four elements of fire, water, air, Earth. (In terms of anthroposophical
teaching about the ether today we would say warmth ether, light ether,
chemical ether, and life ether. (Cf. Dr. Guenther Wachsmuth's book, *The
Etheric Formative Forces in Cosmos, Earth and Man,* volume 2, p. 15.)
Three such similar signs form a "trigon," for instance, Aries, Leo, and
Sagittarius belong to the fiery trigon; Pisces, Cancer, and Scorpio to the
watery trigon, and so on. Now the successive conjunctions of Jupiter
with Saturn proceed so that they occur in turn in the three signs of a
trigon, but against the direction of the zodiac. Thus, for example, the
conjunctions occur with an interval of twenty years—in Scorpio, Cancer, Pisces, Scorpio, Cancer, and so on. Meanwhile, however, the points
at which the conjunction takes place move within the signs themselves
somewhat forward in the zodiac. Thus after several such cycles the
Saturn-Jupiter conjunction leaves the trigon and moves to the next. Such
a period lasts about 200 years. In the four times 200 years, or 800 years,
the whole zodiac is traversed. Each of the "elements"—we can also say
each of the four kinds of ether—have in turn left their mark upon the
occurrence. In these 800-year periods we can see epochs of which Rudolf
Steiner spoke in the introduction to *The Riddles of Philosophy,* and also
in lectures, as being characteristic of the "course of development of the
philosophical endeavor of humanity." These are from the eighth century
B.C. to the Mystery of Golgotha; from then to 800 A.D.; and from 800
A.D. to 1600. About 1600, a "fiery trigon" began, followed since 1800
by an "earthy" one. (The 1921 Saturn-Jupiter conjunction was in the
sign Virgo. That occurring in the second half of 1940 will be in the sign
Taurus. The conjunction in 2000 in Taurus is the last in the "Earth"
trigon.) [See also Notes on the Text.]

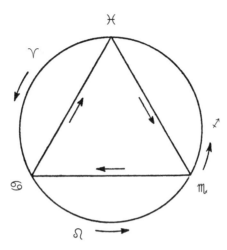

Figure 73

Here it is always a matter of the signs, not of the constellation. It is as if an etheric element intervenes here, determining an astral meeting of Saturn and Jupiter.

The end of the watery trigon that Tycho Brahe awaited, and for which the new star seemed to be a messenger, was in Pisces in 1583. This was the same year in which Galileo, as a youth of nineteen, saw the lamp swinging in the cathedral at Pisa, and went to formulate the law of the pendulum. In 1603 the fiery trigon began in the sign of Sagittarius. This time was very important in the history of astronomy and the heavens at that time were not lacking in signs.

Tycho Brahe's new star had already become invisible in 1574. In 1576, the first variable star, Mira Ceti, was observed by a former student of Tycho. On August 18, 1600, there appeared in the Swan a new star of the third magnitude, upon which Kepler, Tycho's colleague in his last days, wrote a treatise. In the centuries since, this star has certainly behaved differently from the way in which new stars usually do. On February 17, 1600, Giordano Bruno, the poet and proponent of the Copernican world view, had been publicly burned to death in Rome. In 1601, Tycho Brahe died in Prague. He left behind observations of the planet Mars, the results of many years of work. From 1602 Kepler worked with these and used them to discover his well-known laws. In 1603, the *Academia dei Lyncei* (Academy of the Lynx-eyed) was founded in Rome (Galileo was later a member). This was the first academy in the sense of modern science, and it has contributed an extraordinary amount to experimental natural science. On November 30, 1603 the period of the fiery trigon began with a conjunction of Jupiter and Saturn in Sagittarius. A year later, on October 9, 1604, another new star was discovered, this time in the Serpent Bearer between Scorpius and Sagittarius. This was in the Mars region of the zodiac where that planet stood, not far from where Jupiter and Saturn were still located. These two had been in conjunction in that area in the previous year. We should be aware that the 1603 conjunction in the sign Sagittarius thus took place in the constellation Scorpius. In 1604 then, as can be see in Figure 74, Saturn is at the end of Scorpius, and Jupiter is in Sagittarius.

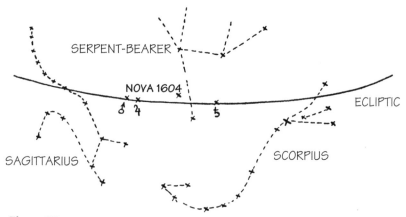

Figure 74

It is the same critical moment in world history—of which Rudolf Steiner has spoken—when at the request of Christian Rosenkreutz, the Buddha left the aura of the Earth in order to go to Mars. He went there to realize his gospel of love and compassion amidst a warlike, decadent race—if one may use such earthly expressions (see lecture December 18, 1912).

In 1606 the principle of the telescope was discovered, which Galileo perfected in 1609. He thereby added to the art of observation inaugurated by Tycho Brahe discoveries within the planetary world that seemed to entirely confirm the Copernican system.

At the same time however, there raged an intellectual battle kindled by the new star of 1604. One can say that it finally brought about the end of the domination of Aristotelianism in the realm of natural science, one that had lasted for nearly 2000 years.

Aristotle had taught the eternal changelessness of cosmic things, saying, for example, in his work *Concerning the Heavens*:

This first among all cosmic bodies is eternal, does not wax or
wane, and is immune against age, decay, and any alteration (1.3,6).
Things out there cannot become old, and there is no possibility of
any change coming to anything that is found there. Things that are
changeless and eternal retain for the entire duration of eternity the
most perfect existence and the fullest independence (1.9,11).

Hence the Aristotelians of that time concluded that a new star could
not be a star at all, but at most was a comet or another phenomenon
coming from the world "beneath the moon, that is, the domain of
change and eternal metamorphosis." (Strangely enough Hipparchus,
who was closely connected to the Alexandrian school, did not feel himself hindered by the Aristotelian teachings in respect of his new star.)

Tycho has based his observations of the new star entirely upon a
question: Does the star actually show, scientifically speaking, a clear
daily parallax—which is something like a perspective—by which in
consequence of the diurnal movement it sometimes is located higher,
sometimes lower in relation to the fixed stars? Nearly all the observing
astronomers at the time of Tycho looked for a parallax as large as possible, so that the star would be close to the Earth, would be, in other
words, sub-lunar. And for the most part they found what they wanted
to find. Only Tycho held to the point that his observations showed him
no parallax and that the new celestial objects must therefore be looked
for beyond the Moon, Sun, and planets. (Kepler expressed a similar
view in his treatise "The New Star in the Foot of the Serpent-Bearer").
Galileo had to fight this same battle. He describes it most graphically
in his *Dialogue upon the Cosmic Systems*. In the end, of course, the
actual observers won the day over the theoretical delusion of the inflexible "Peripatetics." These had not realized that they needed to develop
their master's methods in a way appropriate for the new spirit of the
times.

Then again there followed a period strikingly poor in novae. It was
only the nineteenth century that again produced more new stars, the first
being in the spring of 1848. But then the photographic camera as well as
the telescope began to play a role. New stars that are not at all visible
could be found, stars that are only of the tenth to twelfth magnitude at

their maximum illumination. We have already described the method of discovering these stars.

One small but important star was found on May 21, 1860 in Scorpius, a star that certainly had not been there on May 18. It appeared in a nebula, as is often the case with new stars. It reached the seventh magnitude, quickly faded again, and has since then disappeared. It is a rarity among new stars.

On May 12, 1866 a very bright star appeared in the Northern Crown and in four and one-half hours it had increased in brilliance from the fifth to the second magnitude. Within two hours it had already begun to decrease, although very gradually. It is now of the tenth magnitude.

Among the more recent new stars we will only mention Nova Persei of February 1901 and the Nova Aquilae (the new star in the Eagle) of June 1918. When we think over what was said in letter 4 of this year, at the beginning of the present letter we shall find it understandable that Rudolf Steiner connected these stars with the appearance on Earth of significant human individualities. It relates to an event that actually comes out of the astral world and must take place in the etheric world and at a definite time in prenatal life.

The course of development of this last star was very remarkable. It was first seen on May 25, 1925 and lit up to a powerful visible brilliance. It appeared in the constellation of the southern hemisphere that bears the name "The Painters Easel" (the star is therefore called Nova Pictoris). Its position was thus quite unique in the history of new stars. These usually appear in the neighborhood of the Milky Way, while this star was in the neighborhood of the south pole of the Milky Way. As the southern sky, containing so many stars, is less continuously observed than the northern sky, the star's appearance was entirely unnoticed for a long time. In any case, it was later found that the star appeared on older photographic plates as a star of the thirteenth magnitude. On April 13, 1925 it was already of the third magnitude, and had become plainly visible. In contrast to the stars mentioned above it thus increased in brilliance very slowly and perhaps had entered the range of visibility at the beginning of April. On June 9 of the same year it was almost of the first magnitude and then slowly declined to the ninth magnitude.

In January 1926 this star was seen surrounded by a deep reddish halo like a solar flare. In March 1928, it suddenly appeared as a double star. It had split apart—a phenomenon as yet unknown for a new star. In fact, the astronomers of the northern hemisphere did not want to believe their colleagues of the South who had observed it! People then talked a good deal of inconceivable cosmic cataclysms and recalled the fable of the frog who tried to inflate up to the size of an ox and then burst. This was because on the basis of the spectrum analysis it seemed that the star had not actually increased in temperature. Its immense increase in brightness (50,000 times, according to one calculation) could only be ascribed to an actual enlargement of surface that might be fatal to the star. However, those materialistic explanations need not confuse us. At the same time the star itself was surrounded by haze, as is often the case, so that for a time it presented the spectacle of two red stars surrounded by haze. Soon after this it divided itself yet a second time and then there were four stars: a brighter one in the middle, three smaller ones around it, all white in color and enfolded in a pink nebula. It must have been, according to the relatively few astronomers who could observe it, a wonderful sight. Rings then formed around the separate stars, and in the course of time the different parts drew yet further away from one another.

Here then at last we have been able to mention a few phenomena that are little more to us than the letters of a still very secret script. It is, at any rate, better to regard the letters in this way, than to speculate about them in a materialistic or other fashion.

We have to come to a certain conclusion in our considerations of the world of the stars. It has been evident that for this celestial world a spiritual perspective is absolutely necessary. We are here at one of those very points where without keeping in mind the spiritual background, and even concrete spiritual beings, we can come to no useful understanding. Everything else must then be built up on those foundations. Only so can astronomy be gradually led back to spirituality.

May 1930

The Copernican System

THE MODERN VIEW OF THE UNIVERSE insofar as it derived from modern astronomy reveals itself as being born out of terrestrial physics and mechanics and as containing no concept of the precedence of spiritual realities. This worldview dwells unconsciously within every human soul today, having been able to establish itself there over the centuries because of the authoritative position of natural science. A typical expression of this picture of the cosmos is contained in the words with which Sir A. S. Eddington opens the section on astronomy written by Miss Agnes Clerke in the new edition of the *Encyclopedia Britannica:*

> The Earth on which we live is the fifth largest planet belonging to one of the lesser stars. Perhaps it is less necessary now than it used to be to insist on the smallness of our planet. Scientific inventions and ease of travel seem to have brought different parts of the Earth near together, and we no longer hold an exaggerated idea of its immensity. But it is when we look up into the vault of the heavens that we realize the insignificance of the Earth in the scheme of the material universe. Our sight penetrates space beyond space revealing world beyond world of unimaginable grandeur; and the greatest of these orbs is but as a speck in the vast intervening void.

The "nothingness" of our Earth in the material cosmos is here expressly spoken of, and one can say that the spiritual majesty of the Earth remains unaffected. We know that Rudolf Steiner has often referred to the fact that the Earth could be the scene of the life of Christ, in spite of its relative smallness, and that this fact for Christian sensibility has been further emphasized by the birth's having taken place in a stable and not in a palace. But even if one were inclined to consider the Earth as the "fifth largest planet to one of the lesser stars" (by which our Sun is meant) there remains the other idea of yawning void in which the celestial bodies float forlornly as single specks of dust, separated from each other by inconceivable distances. "Like a few small peas strewn upon the ocean"—thus might we find the stars in the universe, and in place of the waters of the swelling ocean we must imagine just nothingness, or at most the hypothetical world ether, which for the most part is already rejected today.

This worldview bereft of spirit is only a few centuries old. But we must take the trouble to see how it arose, and on what suppositions it rests. Otherwise we cannot inwardly transcend it. Here, necessary events in world history, such as the emergence of the Copernican system, are closely interwoven with the deficiencies and misconceptions of this system. All those things based on light-years, star-distances, and so on, and presented with such certainty as realities, hang upon a very thin thread indeed.

The Copernican system supplanted the Ptolemaic. The essential thing here for the evolution of the human being is the spiritual difference that evokes an alteration in consciousness, not the inner "truth content" of the two systems. Rudolf Steiner drew attention to this fact of world history again and again.

We may refer to Letter 6 of Year One for a description of the Ptolemaic system. Of its spiritual foundation, Rudolf Steiner said in the Torquay lecture cycle, *True and False Paths in Spiritual Investigation,* that the Ptolemaic system is correct as seen from the sphere of the Moon, while Copernicus based his system only on the sphere of Earth. The Ptolemaic system is the geometric abstraction of a spiritual reality.

At the time of Copernicus, the Ptolemaic system was as yet entirely uncontested. Copernicus saw its defects, entertained doubts, and found (as he himself related) in the authors of classical antiquity—Cicero and especially in Plutarch—that in ancient times a system involving the movement of the Earth had been held by the Pythagoreans. For that was the great challenge: to think of the Earth as moving, to remove it from the center of the universe! Here play a part both the particular moment in world history that demanded this venture of the human spirit and also the destiny of Copernicus—his karma from ancient Egypt as well as his inner connection with Nicholas of Cusa. We will not, however, pursue this further at this time.

In the period immediately following Copernicus, his system—in terms of human sensibility—was something like a liberation from cosmic fetters.

But one may say that it also brought an immense desolation into human consciousness. The Copernican system has caused humanity to become used to looking at the planets as mere rolling globes without any ruling "planetary intelligence." But above all, the enormous distances to stars and the immense emptiness of the universe have become generally accepted ideas. One can say that not Copernicus himself, but those who came after him, should be blamed for this. To understand what transpired, we must examine the Copernican system more closely, especially the remarkable "third movement" to which Rudolf Steiner so often called special attention.

Copernicus in his well-known work, *On the Revolutions [of the Heavenly Spheres]*, gives as the first movement of Earth its rotation from west to east around its axis in the course of twenty-four hours. As the second movement, he gives the yearly revolution around the Sun, also from west to east—like the other planets when they are not retrograde. In connection with this movement the question arises: How does Earth's axis behave? As long as Earth is thought to stand still it is evident that the axis is always pointing toward the celestial North Pole. (Even in the Ptolemaic system, however, Earth's axis was not completely stationary. The precession of the vernal point was already recognized in this system, and this may also be conceived of as a turning of Earth's axis. (See Letter 11, Year One.) But if Earth itself moves, its axis can also take up different positions and turn in different directions. Now Copernicus had the beautiful thought that Earth in its movement around the Sun must always orient itself to the Sun, as the Moon does in relation to the Earth. He did not mean that Earth should always turn the same side toward the Sun, as the Moon does toward Earth. This does not happen because of the daily rotation. Rather Copernicus thought that throughout the year the axis of Earth must always be inclined toward the Sun. It would, he said, "follow the movement of the center," that is, describe such a circle around the Sun as Earth, or rather its central point, describes a circle around its own center. This is reproduced in figure 75. The circle that Earth describes around the Sun—the plane of the ecliptic ("the circle that passes through the center of the constellations of the zodiac," Copernicus called it) is shown here clearly as an ellipse. The axis is given in four positions, which may represent the four cardinal points of the year—the beginning of summer, autumn, winter, and spring. The arrow indicates the direction of Earth's revolution around the Sun. The axis would always point to the particular place in the sky where the Pole Star is.

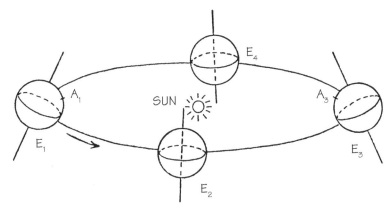

Figure 75

But Copernicus was aware that the system could not work this way:

Because, if they (the Earth's axis and with it the equator) persisted in an invariable direction and simply followed the movement of the center, no dissimilarity of day and night would arise. Rather it would always be solstice, or the shortest day, or the equinox; summer, winter, or any other season would always remain the same.

Point A_1 on the Earth, when in position one—which may correspond to the summer solstice—is turned toward the Sun, would also in position A_3 (winter solstice) be turned toward the Sun. We disregard here the daily rotation. Thus through the whole year, in terms of the season and of the lengths of day and night, it would be in the same relation to the Sun.

Copernicus felt strongly that the second movement described here is the "natural movement." However, since this cannot work, he introduced yet a *third movement,* which he called the "movement in declination." This causes Earth's axis always to remain parallel to itself while Earth is moving around the Sun. Point A (which if we like we may say is the location of the Goetheanum) moves after six months from A_1 to A_3, to the side turned away from the Sun (Figure 76).

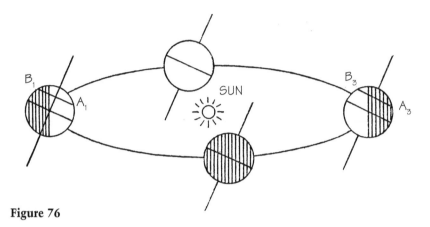

Figure 76

The daily rotation would bring it in twelve hours from A$_1$ to B$_1$ and also from A$_3$ to B$_3$. One sees that at B$_3$ during winter days the rays of the Sun fall at more of an angle than at A$_1$ during the summer. For Copernicus this was possible only if there were a third movement—the "movement in declination." According to his conception this allows Earth's axis to rotate in a backward direction exactly to the same extent as Earth's center has progressed in its path around the Sun. This is rendered in Figure 77—based on a comment of Copernicus—by the outline of a cone that has its apex at the center of the Earth.

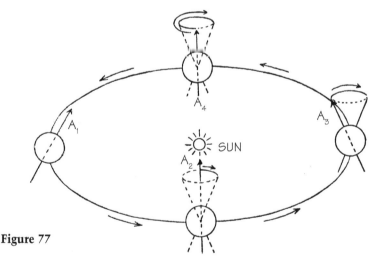

Figure 77

In the first position the axis is in the direction A$_1$ whether or not the third movement is assumed. In the second position it would be in A$_2$ if the "natural movement" alone took place. Through the third movement, however, the axis is brought back into a parallel position. In the same way on the right (winter solstice for the northern hemisphere) the axis is brought from A_3 in a semicircle to the parallel position while Earth itself has also moved in a semicircle around the Sun. Thereby the direction of the axial rotation is the same as that of the hands of a clock, and the Earth's rotation is counterclockwise. In this way, Earth goes to the fourth position and past this back to the first. Altogether then, the axis of the Earth in the course of the year describes a circle opposite in direction to that described by Earth itself. Therefore Copernicus says:

> It is thus clear how the two contrary movements, namely that of the center (of Earth) and the [ecliptic] declination (of the axis) force the axis of Earth to remain in the same inclination and in exactly a similar position [its positions in orbit staying parallel to each other].

The two movements, the second and the third, he called "almost equal." They are not exactly equal, for the precession causes a slight lag.

We know that Rudolf Steiner over and over again pointed out that science has let this third movement "fall under the table," and has therefore taken Copernicus seriously only in part. This disregarding of the third movement—which represents a backward rotation of the north-south axis around the ecliptic axis is the consequence of the celestial mechanics that arose later and is mainly associated with Newton, although beginnings can already be found in the works of Galileo and Kepler.

As one can see from the foregoing description, Copernicus was as little concerned as Ptolemy with forces, but only with mathematically conceived movements. The question, what force moves the planets in space, prior to Copernicus would either not have been asked, or it would have been answered in a spiritual sense: through heavenly intelligences or through the impelling force of God. The age of natural science first brought forward the quite abstract thought that a body once in movement needs no further force to keep moving. It goes forward eternally by virtue of its inherent "inertia." Such movements are certainly not to be found on Earth where, through the resistance of the ground, friction, and so on, every body soon comes to a standstill. But in cosmic space a body that has once received an impetus is supposed to continue in its direction and movement forever. (One does not speak of where the original impetus comes from. Thus Rudolf Steiner spoke of the Newtonian "push" that takes place at the beginning). According to Newton, therefore, the "natural" movement of the Earth around the Sun was not what Copernicus thought it to be—he derived this view from the Moon, and in part from his intuitive feeling for the relation of Earth to the Sun (cf. our first diagram). But the "natural" movement in the Newtonian sense is one in which Earth's axis remains parallel of its own accord, since no force drives it out of the direction it has assumed. Thus in the formulation of celestial mechanics, the third movement of Copernicus was dropped as superfluous. For that approach would have needed a special force or movement that causes Earth to move in the manner depicted in our first, hypothetical diagram.

Copernicus and Newton both agree that the direction of Earth's axis remains the same, that it always remains parallel to itself (Figure 76). Thus we must pay all the more attention to the hints that Rudolf Steiner gave, pointing again and again to this third movement and its unjustified suppression. He places special emphasis on that movement which Copernicus takes as his point of departure (if one omits the first movement, that of day and night). This does not imply that Copernicus's view, presented in Figure 75, is entirely correct. For we have learned that the Earth really *follows* the Sun in a lemniscate movement. But in just such a case there must be a kind of "movement in declination"—a continuous pointing of Earth's axis toward the same point in the sky—a rotation of Earth's axis around the ecliptic axis. Copernicus also believed this, that only through Earth's axis remaining fixed, remaining parallel to itself, is the succession of seasons possible.

But there is something else of significance here. If the axis of the Earth always remains parallel to itself, then it must describe a circle in the vault of the heavens that is a reflection in the course of the year of the circle that Earth in the Copernican system describes around the Sun. In the same way, in twenty-four hours each star describes an apparent circle from east to west, reflecting in reverse Earth's rotation from west to east. Thus with the annual movement, each star must seem to describe a little circle in the opposite direction to that in which Earth goes around the Sun. This is the well-known "annual parallax of the fixed stars."

One finds in astronomical books various schematic drawings of these parallaxes, which all exhibit certain imperfections. We will present

one here in order to describe this
hypothetical phenomenon purely
in terms of modern science.

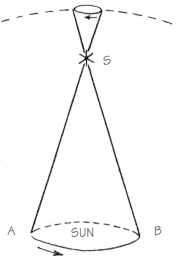

As Earth goes around the Sun,
we observe a star in relation to its
neighboring stars. In the course of
the year, this star shows a little
circular or elliptical movement.
Points A and B are two positions
of the Earth in its orbit six months
apart, and S represents the star.
We measure the angle A–S–B.
The more distant the star is from
Earth, or Earth's orbit, the smaller
the angle at S, and the smaller the
yearly parallax. That is the theory.

Figure 78

And with the planets such parallaxes can indeed be said to occur, appearing in the Ptolemaic theory as deferents for the inner planets, and as epicycles for the outer planets. (These are only the reflection of Earth's orbit, or with Ptolemy, of the Sun's orbit.) They thus take place in the course of 365 days.

Now if such effects of Earth's path were really to be seen for the stars as well as for the planets, the starry heavens in the course of the year would present a remarkable picture. The stars lying nearer would have to describe larger circles; the more distant, those lying further away, would have to describe smaller circles. Of all this, however, nothing is to be seen with the naked eye, and the astronomical instruments for centuries after Copernicus revealed no trace of such parallaxes.

Here for the first time appears the idea of stars being at a lesser or greater distance from the Earth, measured in a radial direction. In the Ptolemaic system all the stars were attached to the sphere of the fixed stars, and there was no talk of a definite distance from this "eighth sphere" to the Earth. In fact, Copernicus retained the sphere of the fixed stars. He did not break through the "crystal-heaven" of the Middle Ages. Nor did it occur to him to think of definite distances of the stars from Earth's orbit, for example. Thus Copernicus was not troubled by the question whether the stars really manifest the effect of the annual movement of Earth, which according to his theory must be the case. Copernicus writes:

> The fact however that there is no appearance of it (Earth's movement) in the case of the fixed stars proves their immeasurable distance. This by itself causes the path of the yearly motion or its image to disappear for our eyes.

Mathematically one would say: the angle at S is equal to zero degrees, and for Copernicus there is no parallax at all. Those who have come after him, however, have felt it necessary to look for a yearly parallax since people could not accept the stars as being at "an infinite distance." Tycho Brahe rejected the Copernican system and put his own in its place. He did this because he considered Copernicus to be refuted by the fact that no such parallax, no annual circling of any size—by any star—was to be found. In the seventeenth and eighteenth centuries people looked all the more eagerly for parallaxes. This search resulted in the discovery of all sorts of other movements of stars and of Earth, but not a single parallax was found. To these discoveries belongs the nutation we dealt with in the Letters of Year One, the annual "aberration of the light," and also the movement of the stars themselves. We cannot go into all these particulars here.

It was only in the nineteenth century that Bessel, the eminent and patient observer and measurer of the heavens, for the first time succeeded in proving a very tiny ellipse for a star in the constellation of the Swan that the star described in the course of a year. One must imagine a star that—if compared with a neighboring star—seems to show no parallax. This star does not always remain stationary in the course of the year, but in addition to the above-mentioned movements it describes an ellipse, whose major axis equals one-third of a second of an arc, that is, about $\frac{1}{6000}$ of the diameter of the Sun's disk! And this parallax is even one of the larger ones. It corresponds in terms of distance to almost eleven so-called light-years. (This follows from Figure 78 if one takes AB as the size of Earth's orbit in miles, this also being the result of a parallax calculation.) A "light-year" is the distance that light will travel in a year, the velocity of light being taken at 186,300 miles per second. In this way one arrives at [over sixty billion miles (60 million million)—U.S.A. 60 trillion] the distance of this star from Earth. The star lying nearest to us, the one with the greatest parallax, is nearly four light years distant. For the more distant stars, the parallaxes, inasmuch as they can be measured, go down to the vanishing point, and the distances become almost infinite. And yet all these stars sparkle for us in the one firmament. But, according to the results of the parallax measurements, the stars nearest to us are not the brilliant stars of the first magnitude, but are quite insignificant little stars.

We have here the origin of that oppressive picture of the universe set forth in the passage quoted at the beginning of this letter. In this view, Earth is of inconsequential size and the cosmos is vast and empty, because if the stars are so far away—perhaps a million light years away—then in spite of their numbers they are very thinly distributed. Thus instead of the sparkling starry sky, instead of the Milky Way bursting with stars, the void of the universe yawns before us. This, however, is the picture that has insinuated itself everywhere, bringing about all the attendant further consequences that—if they were true—would undermine every spiritual concept. If this picture were true, all that we can speak of concerning the effective working of the stars into the realm of Earth would be an illusion. It would be senseless to speak of the human soul and body being born out of the world of the stars and to have any kind of spiritual astronomy.

In themselves, these considerations of course say nothing about the truth or untruth of the materialistic-astronomical worldview. If it were true it would have to be accepted. But from our description one has perhaps been able to see how little founded in fact these parallaxes are. They have really been found only because through centuries people have compulsively looked for them, thinking they were absolutely essential to the Copernican system. And it is known that Nature always gives an answer that corresponds to the way a question is put. If one had assumed a real cosmic ether that reveals its boundaries in the blue vault of heaven and in which the "astral world" of the stars makes its impression, one would have asked in a different way and would have received a different answer. So with anthroposophy as a basis we can be convinced that this materialistic view of the world is not a reality but an illusion.

Here we may refer to the work of Dr. Wilhelm Kaiser, which indicates that the so-called yearly parallaxes of the fixed stars are non- existent, and which also explains from a spiritual point of view the yearly "aberration." (We cannot go into the details of it here.) At the mathematical conference at Easter (1930) Dr. Kaiser was able to report on the latest progress of this work.

Naturally a rejection of these minute parallactic circles or ellipses does not mean that for us the stars are "infinitely far away." Rather one ought not use a concept of distance that applies only to Earth. One ought to employ other, more spiritual conceptions, above all with regard to space.

So we see how a narrowly conceived Copernicanism carried to the extreme has helped further materialism, in fact has provided the foundation for it. The theory of Kant and Laplace [regarding the origin of the universe] and the Darwinism of the nineteenth century with their ideas of evolution devoid of spirit, would not have been possible if, as a result of Copernicanism, heaven and Earth, God and the human being had not been separated in such a fundamental way. It can be said that astronomy has always been the trail-breaker for materialism. We have referred to this on other occasions.

We have spoken a good deal here of how science has misinterpreted Copernicus. It would also be a misunderstanding to fail to see that what Copernicus brought about indeed had to come. And so Rudolf Steiner once called the time of the appearance of the great Copernicus, the great Kepler, Galileo, and "all those who in the first place had to direct human thoughts to the outer world" a "cosmic Maunday Thursday," which was followed by a Good Friday. The concept of immortality was laid in the grave [Steiner lectures "Things of Present and Past in the Human Spirit" —Berlin, 1916.] The cosmic Easter Sunday must now come and following it the cosmic Whitsuntide —the outpouring of the Holy Spirit in that very realm which is liable to fall a victim to darkness.

June 1930

Copernicus, Kepler, and Their Systems

The Movement of the Apsides I

WE HAVE DESCRIBED THE Copernican system to some extent as a theory, and we will now consider more closely Copernicus the man and his place in the spiritual evolution of humankind.

Copernicus was a spirit who had intimately experienced the worship of Osiris in ancient Egypt, and he carried this influence very strongly in his subconscious (*Universe, Earth and Man,* lecture II). Osiris for the Egyptians was the spiritual Sun, who also illumined the being of the human soul. We spoke of this in the letter on the threefold Sun, December 1927. Something that has been experienced spiritually at some time during the third post-Atlantean epoch has the tendency to emerge again in a materialized form in our fifth post-Atlantean epoch. In our epoch the emergence of a materialistic natural science is the primary event. In Steiner's *The Spiritual Guidance of the Individual and Humanity* the deeper causes of this phenomenon are given. This tendency thus lived in Copernicus, who stood just at the beginning of this new age. In terms of the threefold Sun, he sets the third, the external, physical Sun in the center of the planetary system—not the second Sun that had been revered among the Egyptians.

For Copernicus himself this was merely a simplification of the Ptolemaic system. It had become more and more clear that this system, in terms of mathematics, was inadequate. Since the time of Aristotle scientific thinking had held that such simplification was a prerequisite for validity. Rudolf Steiner himself referred to this in the Berlin Architekten-Haus lecture, "Copernicus and His Time in the Light of Spiritual Science" (February 15, 1912). We find this idea in Ptolemy also. He even apologizes for the fact that his hypotheses "are too artificial," saying that one may not compare the human with the divine, and that what seems simple in the heavens—for example, the invariability of the daily revolution—would be just the most difficult thing for the human being to bring about (*Handbook of Astronomy,* 13.2). Ptolemy also knew about the theory of the Earth's revolution around the Sun, a theory that had been known from the mysteries already long before his time. He says that its greater simplicity is in its favor, but on physical grounds holds it to be impossible. The early scientists still felt that they applied their concepts to the soul and spirit of the universe, to the divine. They accepted the sense phenomena just as these presented themselves.

In the age of Copernicus, however, human beings began to consider the sense phenomenon itself, to deal with it mathematically in some way or another. And it is significant that this first "critique of pure sense perception" involved a denial of what is given by the senses, in a rejection of the sovereignty of sense perception. For what Copernicus taught was not at all what the senses saw, but just the opposite. He taught, in effect—and since then natural science has done the same in all realms—that the external world is illusion or maya. However, he connected no concrete spiritual concepts with this. Spiritual science must bring that back again. (Cf. *The Spiritual Guidance of the Individual and Humanity.*)

Here again we see the remarkable fact that it is always in the field of astronomy that the lines of thought are first developed that then become standard in the other sciences. A straight path leads from the Copernican theory to the hypotheses of modern natural science, even though for Copernicus everything remained in the sphere of mathematics and did not enter the domain of physics. In his case, however, another remarkable circumstance came into play. This was the connection that lay between him and his predecessor, Nicholas of Cusa, of which Rudolf Steiner spoke in detail in the cycle of lectures: *The Origins of Natural Science* (December 1922–January 1923). Nicholas of Cusa died in 1464, nine years before the birth of Copernicus. He was not an actual reincarnation of Nicholas, but the astral body of Nicholas had been incorporated into his being. Thus there was a relationship of soul between the two. Nicholas of Cusa, in his work *Of Learned Ignorance,* stands humbly before the spiritual—which disappears in nebulous distances before his soul's vision—and at most ventures to express it in mathematical symbols. Copernicus, however, courageously applies geometry to the outer sense phenomena, to the world of stars. In such a short time the change from the old to the new occurred, a change that in terms of the spirit was a complete degeneration.

Tycho Brahe worked out of quite different impulses. He was, far more than Copernicus, a man dedicated to the observation of the actual sense phenomena. In his "system" he had the planets revolve around the Sun, but the Sun then revolves around the Earth. Rudolf Steiner has often said that though the system of Tycho was not accepted, our astronomical ephemerides are in fact based on it. Thus we in fact calculate according to Tycho, but we regard Copernicus as "true." Therefore we give the position of the Sun in relation to *Earth,* whereas for the planets we give the heliocentric coordinates, their positions with reference to the *Sun.* This corresponds to Tycho's system.

It is basically the relation of Earth and Sun that is the great problem in these systems. For Ptolemy, Earth with its surrounding spheres is the center of the universe, for now is the time of the Earth stage of evolution, and not of the Saturn or the Sun stage. Long before Ptolemy, humankind experienced spiritually the position of the Earth as being in the center of activities of the spiritual hierarchies, and the ancient planetary systems derived from this. When Copernicus placed the Sun in the center he actually dethroned the Earth. That means that in effect—and it would have appeared thus to a mystic of the Middle Ages—he had capitulated before the fact that through humanity, Earth has become involved in the Fall. The Earth no longer stands steadfast in the center of the universe, but is actually governed by the Sun. This is because humankind, as a result of the luciferic temptation, has not been able to be the true regent of the Earth. The Sun became "the unlawful prince of this world." (See the lecture of January 11, 1924.)

Yet this Sun has become the dwelling place of the Christ. Inasmuch as Copernicus pointed to the Sun as the center, he pointed to that direction from which the salvation of humanity must come. In fact, this salvation had in his day already long since come. Thus in a peculiar way, and for Copernicus—a pious man and a church official—totally unconsciously, the fertile and the dying elements are mingled together in the Copernican world view. The further evolution in this age made sure that it was the infertile aspect that was specially cultivated. Even today the seed germ of his system lies deeply hidden. It can first be awakened through anthroposophy, but then at the same time must undergo a metamorphosis, one that corresponds to the evolving human faculty of comprehending the spiritual together with the physical.

Kepler who, one might say, was spiritual, also came from ancient Egypt but had fewer Arabic influences in his understanding than Copernicus. Kepler was far more able to revive old impulses in a form vitalized by Christianity and not to materialize them. He totally defended the principle of the Copernican system against his patron and superior Tycho Brahe, but he used the observations of Tycho in order to ask himself quite concretely and without preconceptions how in fact the orbits of the planets around the Sun are formed. He had a strong creative fantasy in relation to space (we spoke of this in regard to his "moon dream" in Letter 7, Year Two) and in this respect he broke with the ancients much more definitively than did Copernicus. Copernicus had not gotten away from the dogma that only circular orbits were possible, and he also used the epicycles and such devices.

Kepler found empirically a nearly circular ellipse for the orbit of Mars. He drew it heliocentrically according to Tycho's observations—which are always geocentric. Thus he developed the first of his laws: "the planets describe ellipses around the Sun in which the Sun itself is one of the foci."

He felt, as Rudolf Steiner said in the *"Astronomy Course,"* that a planet must be much more alive, much more ensouled when it moves in an ellipse through the greater and lesser curvatures in its orbit, that this is a more active way than revolving in an unchanging circle. In his second law particularly he expressed this living planetary force.

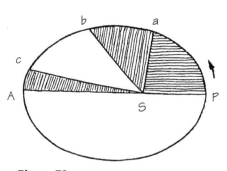

"The radius vector of the planet (i.e., the direction from it to the Sun) describes equal sectors in equal periods of time."

In other words, when for example the areas of *PSa*, *Sab*, and *ScA* are equal, the Earth will take the same amount of time—let us say thirty days—to travel from *P*

Figure 79

to *a*, from *a* to *b*, and later from *c* to *A*. It follows thus that the Earth, or any planet, moves faster when it is close to its perihelion (*P*) than when it is near its aphelion (*A*). The line from *P* to *a* is obviously greater than that from *c* to *A*. Thus in winter, when Earth is closer to the Sun, it travels faster than in summer. The difference in speed of course is in fact much less than is indicated by the diagram. Here the ellipse is exaggerated and drawn as a decided oval.

Rudolf Steiner in the *"Astronomy Course"* describes the greater living quality that is contained in these laws of Kepler:

> To the modern, purely quantitative point of view these are also only quantities. To someone like Kepler though, there was simply something in the expression of the elliptical that conveyed to him—as he thought of the curve—a greater vitality than the circle. When something or other moves elliptically it is more vital than when it only moves in a circle, for it must bring to bear an inner impulse in order to change the radius. When something moves only in a circle, it doesn't need to do anything to alter the radius. The revolving body must bring to bear a more intensive inner life if the radius vector has to be continuously altered. Therefore, simply in the sentence: "The planets move in ellipses around the central body and the central body is not in the center, but in a focus of the ellipse" was the implication that one is dealing here with a greater vitality than one meets in a body that moves in a circle.
>
> There is the further assertion that "the radius vectors describe equal sectors in equal periods of time." Here we have the transition from the line to the area. Please notice that! When just the ellipse is described to us at first, we remain in the line, in the curve. When we are directed to the path that the radius vector describes we are led to the area. This reveals a much more intensive relation to planetary motion. When the planet thus rolls along—if I may so express myself—it expresses something that lies not only within itself. It draws its tail after it, so to speak. The whole area that the radius vector describes belongs spiritually to the planet. One must point out further that in equal periods of time the planet possesses an equal extent of area. One must lay stress upon this fact, when one wants to describe what is happening to the planet.

Kepler's third law also sounds abstract at first. It was for Kepler the expression of the eternal harmony of the cosmos that expresses itself so eloquently in numbers: "The squares of the periods of revolution of the planets are proportional to the cubes of the larger semi-axes of their orbits."

Here are time and space—the life between the different planets—brought into connection with one another. We will not pursue this law further here. Rudolf Steiner said that this is the law that Newton has killed with his law of gravity: "The force of gravity of two bodies is in direct proportion to the product of their masses and in inverted proportion to the square of their distance." Newton's law can be derived from the third law of Kepler, except that there is no longer any life in it.

The first law of Kepler can also be useful to us in considering the last great cosmic rhythm, to which we will now turn our attention.

In addition to the movements already known to us, such as the daily and yearly revolutions and those of the precession and the nutation (all described in the letters of the first year), there is still the so-called movement of the apsides. This is connected with the great cosmic rhythm revealed in the geological epochs known as the glacial ages, and also in the ages of human history. Dr. Steiner has referred to this movement in several places in his lectures—always in connection with the precessional movement but without using its astronomical name. If we study this movement we will gain knowledge that is extraordinarily significant for the evolution of the Earth and humanity. Thus we will not hesitate to explain the phenomenon in a somewhat mathematical and astronomical way.

One can present the movement of the apsides equally well in a geocentric way, according to the Ptolemaic theory, as heliocentrically— according to Copernicus. In both cases one has of course only a mathematically abstract rendering of an active cosmic force. The Ptolemaic system adapts itself quite well to the rendering of this movement, although Ptolemy himself did not know of it. The discovery escaped him in some way, for the time that lay between him and his predecessor Hipparchus was long enough for him to have discovered the movement of the apsides. It was first found about 900 A.D. by an Arabian astronomer named Al-battani or Albategnius.

Ptolemy knew, as Hipparchus before him, that the four seasons are of unequal length. The time that the Sun takes to go from the vernal equinox past the summer solstice to the autumnal equinox is longer than that from the autumnal equinox past the winter solstice back to the vernal equinox. This is, of course, a matter of astronomical measurements. The four cardinal points correspond to the lowest and highest positions of the Sun in the zodiac (the beginning of winter and of summer) and the points of intersection with the equator that lie in between (the beginning of spring and of autumn).

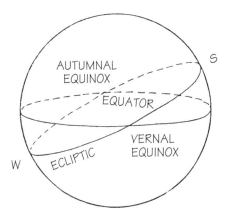

Figure 80

This fact, noted in early times, did not allow the Greek astronomers to make the center of the Sun's orbit, which for them was Earth, coincide with the center of the universe. In other words, they had to place Earth eccentrically in the circle of the ecliptic (the zodiac). Figure 81 illustrates the position at the time of Ptolemy (taken from Manitius's translation of Ptolemy). E is Earth. M would be the central point of the path of the Sun, of the center of the universe according to the ancients. The eccentricity—the distance from E to M—is exaggerated for the sake of clarity. The Sun goes around in the smaller circle, and the larger circle represents the zodiac. Now the Sun takes longer from point a (vernal equinox) past b (summer solstice) to c (autumnal equinox) than for the second half of the year (from c past d to a), for the arcs abc and cda differ in length.

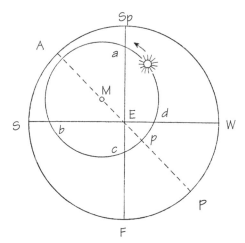

Figure 81

It is evident in such a diagram that there is a point at which the Sun and Earth are nearest to each other, namely in P on the zodiac corresponding to p on the ecliptic. (Both points, as seen from Earth, are in the heavens one and the same. Six months later, the two celestial bodies are farthest from each other—[the Sun] at point A. The former point is called perigee (point closest to Earth), the latter apogee (point farthest from Earth), and the line PA that connects the two is the line of the apsides.

P and A are naturally two precise, specific points in the zodiac just as the vernal equinox and the Moon's nodes have actual positions there as well. Ptolemy says, on the authority of Hipparchus, that in terms of the signs of the zodiac the apogee was in Gemini at 5° 30' and the perigee opposite to it at 5° 30' in Sagittarius. Hipparchus had indeed calculated these positions correctly. At the time of Ptolemy, nearly 300 years after Hipparchus, the apsidal line had moved nearly five degrees, which, however, Ptolemy did not notice. Al-battani found the apogee in twenty-two degrees of Gemini and concluded from this that the line of the apsides moves. Copernicus, using what Hipparchus and Al-battani had found, discovered the difference between the length of the first half of the year and the second half of the year (calculated from the beginning of spring). He calculated from this that the apogee had moved 10°41' in 1,580 so-called "Egyptian" years, that is, about one degree in 148 years. According to modern observations, the period of time is twice as long.

In terms of the Copernican system, things are the same as in the Ptolemaic, except that Earth and Sun have changed places. Also, instead of a perigee or an apogee one now speaks of a perihelion or aphelion [conventionally, the points at which the Earth is closest to and farthest from Sun]. We will hereafter for the sake of a consistent terminology speak mostly in terms of perigee, the point closest to Earth—in other words, Ptolemaically. The line of the apsides first gains special importance in the system of Kepler. It appears as the major axis of the ellipse on which Kepler makes Earth revolve around the Sun and within which the Sun is one of the two foci—that is, has an eccentric

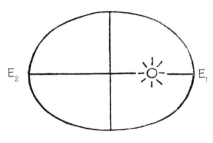

Figure 82

position. Figure 82 once again represents the ellipse as too strongly eccentric, as deviating too much from the circle. One sees plainly the point where the Sun is closest to Earth (E_1), where it is farthest away (E_2). The line E_1E_2 forms the major axis—called here the line of apsides, and at right angles to this is the minor axis of the ellipse. The major axis, and at the same time of course the minor axis, rotates in space with respect to the zodiac in a period that, according to modern observations, is about 110,000 years.

To represent this more concretely let us be clear about the fact that there is in the year a certain day on which the Sun and Earth are nearest to each other. The Sun stands then on the ecliptic at a certain point of the zodiac—the point at which it is normally found on that day of the year. This day is now one of the first days of January and the point lies therefore in the constellation of Sagittarius. Almost six months later the reverse is true. Earth and Sun are as far as possible from each other. One need not take this conception of near and far very literally. According to the purely spatial concept of modern astronomy, it is a matter of about 3 million miles difference in apogee and perigee. But one can quite imagine that the relative nearness of Earth and Sun corresponds to a stronger cosmic activity, and that the greater separation between Earth and Sun corresponds to a more estranged condition of the two celestial bodies. The perigee is also established quite externally (the ancients knew of the existence of the perigee from the difference [in day length] from the shortest to the longest or the longest to the shortest day). But apart from that, the perigee can be established from the observable fact that the Sun's disk appears larger in winter when it is closer to Earth than in summer when it is at the point of greatest separation. This difference is of course not noticeable with the naked eye and is measurable only with the help of good instruments. It has nothing to do with the apparent increase of size of the disk of the Sun at sunset and such things. We want to truly grasp the idea that the intensity of the relationship between Earth and the Sun, insofar as it is dependent on this movement, is continually changing in the course of the year and is at a maximum in January and a minimum in July.

One can thus indicate two points, one in Sagittarius and one in Gemini, at which what has been described takes place. Yet the movement of the apsides teaches us that these points gradually change their position, just as the cardinal points of spring, summer, autumn, and winter shift on account of the precession. However, the apsides move far more slowly and in the opposite direction, that is, *with* the signs of the zodiac. The whole ellipse of figure 82, which one must think of as surrounded by the zodiac at an indefinite distance, revolves with reference to the zodiac (figure 83). Thus the axes AP and KL gradually point to other points in the heavens, and the approach of Earth and Sun takes place under a star of the zodiac lying farther on. At the same time, however, the cross formed by the four cardinal points winter, spring, summer, and autumn also revolves as does the precession, *against* the direction of the zodiacal constellations and in the course of 25,920 years. In the drawing the position is given for our time, of course rather roughly.

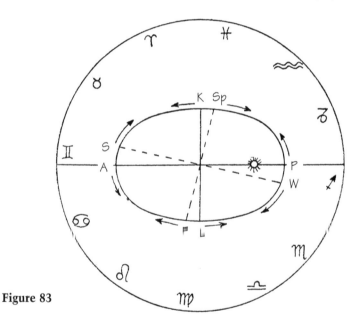

Figure 83

Another important fact is to be seen from this. With this movement toward each other of the cross of the ellipse-axes and of the "cross of the year," the single points P, A, K, L and W, Sp, S, F will meet with each other alternately. That is to say, again and again there will be a time when the cardinal points of the year will coincide with cross of the axes or the line of the apsides. For example the vernal equinox can coincide with the perigee (Sp on P). The autumnal equinox and the summer and winter solstices can do the same. The opposite cardinal point will then coincide with the apogee.

Let us suppose such a meeting of the vernal equinox and the perigee to have taken place at some time historically. Then an easily worked-out calculation will give us the period of time until such a meeting will occur again. One need only remember the well-known school exercise of the two hands of a clock following each other and from time to time covering each other, except that here the "hands" move toward each other. One hand takes 110,000 years, the other almost 26,000 years, moving almost four times as fast. The meeting comes about when the "large hand" (the one that goes faster) has completed almost four-fifths of a revolution. One thus arrives at a period of 21,000 years).[1]

If now after the vernal equinox the autumnal equinox coincides with the perigee, the so-called equinoctial line coincides again with the line of the apsides. This takes place in half of the total period, something over 10,000 years. Here we have the glacial epoch cited by Rudolf Steiner corroborated by the results of scientific research. And if we bear in mind the four conjunctions that are possible from each one of the cardinal points with the perigee, we then come to a period of 5,260 years. In just this period of time important cosmic conditions always arise, conditions that must be expressed in important earthly events.

We refer to the lecture cycle *Occult History*, where in the fifth lecture Rudolf Steiner mentions these things. Rudolf Steiner speaks there of

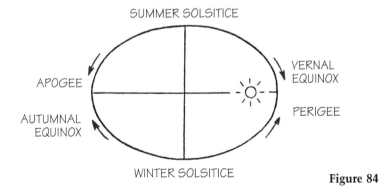

Figure 84

---

1. In another way it may be expressed mathematically thus: The apogee or the perigee—that means, therefore, the line of the apsides—moves 1°42.6' in 100 years. This movement is given by 0°19' of the actual apsides revolution and 1°23.6' which comes from the precession, together 1°42.6'. The siderial revolution of the apsides is therefore 110,000 years and its tropical revolution 20,900 years.

the hierarchies that have specially revealed themselves to humankind in the various cultural periods. In the fourth post-Atlantean epoch it was the spirits of form. They did not work directly into the inner nature of the human being, but through the kingdoms of nature. Human beings received their influence at that time indirectly, through the senses, so that they came to direct their attention entirely to the external world.

These spirits of form had also been active before the Atlantean catastrophe. But at this time human beings did not direct their attention to what met them externally. They were diverted from the outer world. And that came from the configuration of the cosmos:

We have a sort of boundary between the old influences of Atlantean times and those of the post-Atlantean times. The Atlantean catastrophe occurred at this turning point. There were occurrences that totally altered the face of our Earth in terms of the division of water and land. Such times and the changes they bring are connected with great occurrences in the heavens, which involve the position and movement of the cosmic bodies connected with the Sun. And in fact what takes place upon Earth in such a period is directed from the macrocosmic realm. It would take us too far afield today if I were to explain to you how these successive periods are governed, are marked out, by what modern astronomy calls the precession of the equinoxes. That is connected with the position of Earth's axis in relation to the ecliptic axis. It is connected with great occurrences in the heavens involving the configurations of the cosmic bodies close to us. Thus there are quite definite times when, because of the particular position of Earth on its axis in relation to the other celestial bodies of its system, the distribution of warmth and cold on Earth is quite different from what it is at other times. Climatic conditions change according to the position of Earth's axis in relation to the neighboring stars. In fact, in the course of something over 25,000 years our Earth's axis describes a kind of conical or circular movement. Thus after 25,000 to 26,000 years the Earth experiences the same conditions again in another form but on a higher level. But in between these great divisions of time there are always smaller ones. However, things do not proceed in a regular, uniform way. Rather, certain years are points of junction, deep incisions, in which important things take place. And here we may especially point out in particular, since it is extremely significant for the whole historical development of humanity on Earth, that in the seventh millennium B.C. there was an especially important astronomical point in time. It was important because the position of Earth's axis in relation to the neighboring stars expressed itself on Earth in climatic conditions that brought about the Atlantean catastrophe.

In the explanations preceding this quote we elaborated—explaining in astronomical terms—everything that Rudolf Steiner says here. One sees then with what exactness Rudolf Steiner presents these cosmic facts despite his somewhat flexible manner of expression. He says that the successive periods ". . . were governed, were marked out by what modern astronomy calls the precession of the equinoxes. But in between these great divisions of time there always lay smaller ones . . . so that certain years are points of junction, deep incisions, in which important things take place."

These divisions, these points of junction, are the result of the meeting together of the two axial crosses, the two pairs of clock hands that move toward each other and meet every 5,200 years. There remains to be explained what was said about the particular position of the axis of Earth at that time. Earth's axis stood at right angles to the minor axis of Earth's orbit (or ecliptic). At that time this coincided with the line joining the vernal equinox and the autumnal equinox, in other words, with the celestial equator. At each of the four meetings that take place about every 5000 years, Earth's axis is always at right angles to the

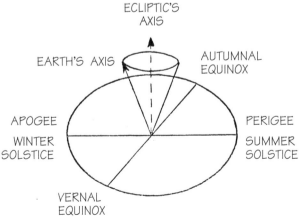

Figure 85

major axis (the apsides, coinciding with the line of the solstices) or to the minor axis (coinciding with the line of the equinoxes). If one is familiar with geometrical representation one can see from figure 85 that the cone that Earth's axis describes in 25,920 years is placed in the center of the ellipse, as are also the lines of the equinoxes and solstices.

Figure 86 gives the situation for the present day, and no such exceptional circumstances exist. The axis of the Earth and of the equator is, however, as always at right angles to the solstice line and to the equinoctial line.

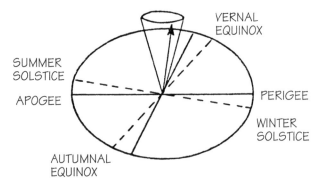

Figure 86

One can calculate that the configuration described that led to the Atlantean catastrophe first occurred 9,200 years before our era, and that it had its reflection in another configuration that took place 10,000 years later. Then the perigee no longer took place during the summer solstice, but during the winter solstice. That brought about the important set of celestial circumstances of 1250 A.D., of which Rudolf Steiner speaks in the same lecture. In the cycle "The Relationship of the Diverse Branches of Natural Science to Astronomy" (*"Astronomy Course"*), he further compares the two points of time—in the Atlantean and in the fourth post-Atlantean epochs—with a point of time coming just as long after, about 11,000 A.D. Then the conditions for a glacial epoch will be present again. Next time we will consider those moments in history, so important for the history of culture and of the world, that have here revealed themselves.

July 1930

The Movement of the Apsides II
Glacial Epochs

CONTINUING WITH OUR DESCRIPTION of the apsidal movement, we come to quite concrete points of time in which critical events in human evolution took place. Such a turning point lay in the tenth pre-Christian millennium, in the time of Atlantis. The perigee, the time of the greatest proximity of Earth and Sun, coincided with the summer solstice, and therefore the apogee coincided with the winter solstice.[1] A sort of counterpart of this took place during the Middle Ages, about 1250, when the perigee was reached at the time of the winter solstice, at Christmas time.

In these dry mathematical statements is symbolically expressed the entire difference between these two points of time. Most of the continent of Atlantis lay in the Northern Hemisphere, and during that time the point of the greatest proximity of the Earth and Sun was at midsummer (for the Northern Hemisphere). Summer is the time when Earth breathes out her soul into the cosmos and is lovingly held by the cosmic forces coming toward her. What occurs in the summer is like an embrace between Earth and heaven. Now let us imagine that this situation is extraordinarily enhanced by the Sun at that period being nearer Earth in summer than at any other time of the year. Thus this union of the soul of Earth and the soul of the Sun is especially intensive. But at the same time the apogee is at the winter solstice. This means that the winter represents, in its nature, an extreme, just as the summer does. The moment of the greatest distance of the Earth from the Sun occurs

---

1. The expressions: summer solstice, vernal equinox, and so on are always employed here for the Northern Hemisphere. They would be exactly the opposite for the Southern Hemisphere. They are also to be understood geocentrically, i.e., as the celestial phenomena are seen from Earth.

just when Earth is more withdrawn into itself than at any other time during the year. The "farthest cosmos." which is active in the winter in the formation of frost and snow, finds an Earth whose connection with the Sun is reduced to a minimum. This farthest cosmos of the starry world, of the zodiac, can penetrate Earth powerfully. So in those regions that stretch toward the north there must be powerful glacial activities. Because of the coincidence of the apogee with the winter solstice, and because of the equal division of the orbit of Earth around the Sun in respect to the year, conditions prevailed then that are similar to those at the North Pole today. There the year consists of one day and one night, each six months long, and cold and winter dominate.

The strong force of the Sun, evoked by the perigee at the summer solstice, must fight against the formation of ice from the south. And if the powerful frigidity of the northern regions abates, the melting power of the summer has an effect over time and the result will be inundations and catastrophes. This explains the Atlantean catastrophe in the seventh and eighth pre-Christian millennia.

This is just a summary description of what, considered macrocosmically, led to the Atlantean catastrophe, which appears in the karma of humanity as the Flood. In the tenth and ninth millennia B.C. glaciers covered much of Europe, extending far into the tropical regions of today. No culture could evolve. There was, as Rudolf Steiner called it, a desolation, a death of civilization. Humankind lived in the same conditions that prevail today in the polar regions. Because of the peculiar division of the year into a day and a night of six months each, human beings are affected by the cosmos in such a way that they become apathetic, and develop no particular cultural life. The influence of the changing seasons of the year works within the human organism—as is the case with a child in its first seven years. This influence, if not moderated by the daily short-term changes, can tear the soul element out of the operation of the organization.

So in the ninth millennium the position of Earth's axis divided the year over wide areas into winter and summer in a way resembling the present division of day and night at the North Pole. As those conditions began to change, the increasing force of the Sun could only lead to catastrophic inundations.

Other conditions than just the coincidence of the apsidal line with the line of the solstices bring about these events. Other great rhythms play a role. For example, the form of Earth's elliptical orbit, its so-called eccentricity, changes continually. Today it is very nearly a circle, which means that the two foci almost coincide with the center. (The distance from center to focus (the Sun) is, according to astronomical calculations, 2 $\frac{1}{2}$ million miles, with a major axis of 186 million miles). In earlier times this ellipse was more oval, the major and minor axes differing more from one another, and in consequence certain conditions that have to do with the seasons were more accentuated. According to the calculations of celestial mechanics the ellipse at about this time must have been at maximum eccentricity. Also, the angle of Earth's axis to the plane of the ecliptic, which today is 23°27', alters over long periods of time, so that Earth's axis comes into a different relationship with neighboring stars.

We will not go further into these relations here. One finds them— together with the precession and the apsides movement treated in detail in the essay "The Ice Age During the Period of the Flood and its Causes," by Franz Koflor, who was a geography teacher of Rudolf Steiner during his high-school years. Rudolf Steiner mentions this essay in his autobiography. (The essay was republished through the exertions of C. S. Picht in 1927. See also my remarks in *Das Goetheanum* of June 12, 1927.)[2]

Koflor took as his point of departure other works of that time, especially J. d'Adhemar's *Revolutions de la mer Deluges periodiques*. A few geologists in the middle of the nineteenth century, among them the well-known Lyell, came to the conclusion that one cannot consider geological epochs like the Ice Age without at the same time bringing the cosmos into consideration. To explain terrestrial phenomena they brought forward the four cosmic rhythms we have discussed— precession, the movement of the apsides, the change of the eccentricity of Earth's orbit, the change of the obliquity of the ecliptic. And it was this that made a great impression upon Rudolf Steiner when, just as he was graduating, he became acquainted with the essay of his teacher. He writes of this: "I grasped the import of this with great eagerness and developed a strong interest in the problem of the Ice Age."

---

2. Anyone reading the essay in connection with these letters must bear in mind that Koflor took it from the heliocentric standpoint as used in modern astronomy, in which the relations are all reversed. (He used the signs, too, where we use the constellations.)

The article by Rudolf Steiner on the Ice Age (in Pierer's *Conversations Lexikon,* 7th ed.) is written from this point of view. We quote here, from the article's final paragraph, the concise, comprehensive description of the cosmic causes of the glacial epochs:

> Because of the eccentricity of Earth's orbit, Earth does not always move with the same speed. It moves more quickly when nearer the Sun and more slowly when it is farther away. Therefore the hemisphere that has its winter during the time of perigee has a shorter winter than the other hemisphere. However, the axis of Earth alters its position with regard to the Sun, and hence that shorter winter will not always take place in the same hemisphere. Earth's axis describes a full revolution in 21,000 years and during this time winter and summer will twice be actually equal—once for the Northern Hemisphere and once for the Southern. For 10,500 years, however, the Northern—and for the same length of time, the Southern—Hemisphere will have longer winters. But when the winters in a hemisphere are essentially longer than the summers, then the average annual temperature can sink so low that a period of cold is possible. These differences can, however, according to astronomical calculations increase to a maximum of 36 days. [See Notes on the Text.]

After nearly 21,000 years, at the end of the twelfth millennium A.D. the glacial age will be recapitulated. The perigee will again lie in the summer solstice and again Earth's axis will be vertical to the minor axis of the orbit. Naturally other terrestrial and cosmic conditions will not have just remained the same. The wheel of the world will keep on rolling. But we will refer to the point in time that Rudolf Steiner (in his *"Astronomy Course"*) described as being at the other end of the revolution of the apsides.

> We therefore have, if we survey in this way the evolution of this part of Europe, in the tenth millennium before the Christian era a sort of glacial period in civilization, and we shall have it again about 10,000 years after that point of time. (January 6, 1921)

And it was explained how the point in the middle (point A in Figure 87) corresponds to the year 1250 of the Christian era.

This was a time of much inner agitation in the cultural life of humanity. The glacial epoch had to bring desolation to the organism of the Earth and was followed by the external agitation of the catastrophe of the Flood.

Figure 87

What is crucial here is the development of medieval Scholasticism, that unique conceptual system that in its metamorphosis has deeply influenced the entire further development of consciousness and of science. With the question of Realism versus Nominalism, and with the search for a proof of God, Scholasticism deeply stirred humanity in terms of its relation to the spiritual world. The spiritual world was entirely closed to the human soul about 1250. At the time of the Atlantean catastrophe, though, it revealed itself in the visible effects of the Flood. In *The Spiritual Guidance of the Individual and Humanity* Rudolf Steiner explains in detail how even human souls who had already reached high stages of development, if they were incarnated around 1250, "were compelled for a while to undergo a complete clouding of their direct view of the spiritual world." And in *Occult History* Rudolf Steiner points out how today we have the reverse of the great Atlantean catastrophe (lecture 5):

> This will naturally not be easy to notice. People of the post-Atlantean time, strongly conditioned as they are by what is physical, would be very much affected by a catastrophe in which portions of Earth are destroyed. But they will notice less when the spirits of form have a powerful influence on the human personality, but only a small influence on what takes place externally. This point in time, when what is naturally less noticed by human beings took place, was the year 1250 of the post-Christian Era. That year is an extraordinarily important year historically. It was the starting point for Scholastic philosophy, which today is too little appreciated. . . . But if we want fully to understand historical events we must take into consideration that such critical points in evolution always relate to certain positions of the stars. In 1250, the axis of our Earth was so positioned that the so-called little axis of the ecliptic was in a very special position in relation to the axis of Earth.

This was, as we know, a vertical position. We are reminded of the cosmic celestial configuration, of the critical points in evolution that take place every 5,200 years, always when the line of the apsides coincides with two cardinal points of the year lying opposite to each other. In the year 1250 the perigee was in the winter solstice, at Christmas time. We get the counterpart of the Ice Age, also in a cosmic sense. When the Sun comes near the Earth it finds the Earth soul withdrawn into itself. On the other hand, at the time when Earth expands its soul into the cosmos, the Sun's influence is diminished. Human beings are as if shut off from cosmic forces. They feel themselves thrown back into their inner being. What in the glacial epoch was a strong external activity of spiritual powers—of the spirits of form—works within the human being as a spiritual activity. In the *"Astronomy Course"* Rudolf Steiner refers more precisely to the configuration of the heavens, bringing into consideration the precession of the vernal equinox.

> We see the vernal equinox in the sign [here, means "constellation"] of Pisces at the time when humanity is spiritually agitated. In the Greco-Roman times it was in the sign of Aries, before that in the sign of Taurus, and so on. We come back approximately to Leo and to Virgo in that age when our region and much of the rest of Europe and also America were covered by glaciers. And when we find the vernal equinox in the sign of Scorpius we shall have a glacial age again in these regions. (January 1, 1921)

In fact, we find that in the year 9200 B.C. the vernal equinox was in Leo. For the other glacial age we find it in Libra, [having just been] "in the sign of Scorpius." In the year 1250 it was in Pisces. In order to bring together the various references in a consistent way, we will note the conjunctions of the perigee with the cardinal points, and give in each case the position of the vernal equinox (according to the constellations). We must think of these epochs, given in round numbers, as always following one another at intervals of 5200 years.

(1) Let us begin with the year *20,000* B.C. It is the time we can regard as the middle of the Atlantean epoch—in fact, as the middle of earthly evolution as a whole. From this time, we can expect a universe that operates according to certain laws, that is running its course in a mechanical way. The "world of finished work" is in place.

The celestial configuration corresponds to that of the year 1250. The *perigee* [in 20,000 B.C.] is in the *winter solstice,* which then was in Virgo. The *vernal equinox* was in *Capricornus.* In this very important time decisive events for human evolution took place. The diagrams for the epochs are made according to the Ptolemaic view. The zodiac is always drawn in the same position (with Pisces and Virgo as a horizontal line); Earth (E) is always eccentric, located toward the perigee; the four cardinal points are indicated by W, Sp., S, F. Thus we have Figure 88:

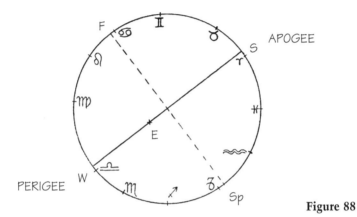

Figure 88

(2) In the year *14,500* B.C. we again have an extraordinarily significant configuration. The *perigee* was together with the *vernal equinox in Libra.* Rudolf Steiner spoke of this time in the important lecture of January 27, 1908. Coming from opposite directions, the line of the apsides and the equinoctial line meet in Libra for the first time in our earthly evolution. [See Figure 89.]

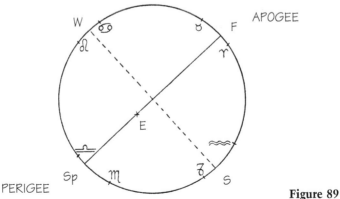

Figure 89

From that time on the human being takes part in the creation of cosmic processes. In this same lecture, Rudolf Steiner describes how forces continuously "rain down" upon Earth from out of the zodiac. These forces are the offering of the zodiac to the new planetary being that has now advanced to the earthly stage. These forces must however also reascend from Earth, for through human evolution on Earth a new zodiac will arise. "The mysterious working together of our Earth with the zodiac consists of this."

These zodiacal forces have been coming down since the Saturn stage of evolution,

> . . . and when the Earth was at its middle point the step was also already taken for the forces gradually to reascend. Those forces that are to be understood today as being in ascending evolution we bring together because they belong to the seven constellations— Aries, Taurus, Gemini, Cancer, Leo, Virgo, Libra. These are the seven constellations that correspond to the ascending forces. Five constellations correspond somewhat to the descending forces: Scorpius, Sagittarius, Capricornus, Aquarius, and Pisces. Thus, you see how forces rain down from the zodiac and ascend, and how the ascending corresponds to seven constellations, the descending to five constellations.

Before this point in time, however, up to the middle of the Atlantean epoch, six forces were in descent, six in ascent. The boundary lay in Virgo, Libra still belonging to the descending forces. Thus from the beginning of earthly evolution up to this time, and without humanity having anything to do with it, the first six constellations, the "light signs" of the zodiac, from Aries to Virgo, were changed from descending to ascending. The forces coming from Libra then first became ascending forces. We find the expression of this in the heavenly script, which indicates that at just this critical point, the vernal equinox was in conjunction with the perigee in Libra.

(3) 9200 B.C. We have discussed this position in detail. It is that of the Ice Age with the Flood that followed. The *perigee* was in the *summer solstice* in Scorpius, in that mysterious constellation of destruction and death, which is also considered a water sign. The *vernal equinox* was in *Leo*. Perhaps the most important of the three crosses of the zodiac is

this one formed by those constellations from which later the Chaldeans saw the four cherubim approaching: the bull, the lion, the eagle, and the human being (Aquarius). The eagle, as we know, has become Scorpius. [See Figure 90.]

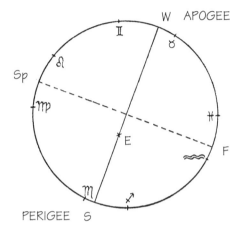

Figure 90

(4) *4000 B.C.* If in the celestial configuration just described we had that of the physical Flood, we come now to the time that Rudolf Steiner (in *Earthly and Cosmic Man,* lecture 7), has called a kind of spiritual Flood. The old clairvoyance disappeared more and more as the Kali Yuga, the Age of Darkness, drew near. It was not yet the beginning of the Kali Yuga itself, but to a certain extent its preparation. The *perigee* stands in the *autumn equinox,* and something like a shiver passes through human

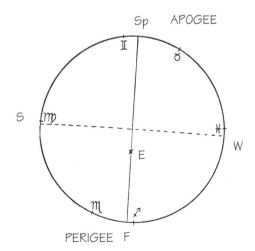

Figure 91

evolution. The perigee is still in Scorpius, for the line of the apsides takes almost 10,000 years to pass through a constellation. The vernal equinox has now entered Taurus. (We remember what was said in Letter 12 of Year One about the connection of the cultural periods with the zodiacal signs, the periods being reckoned from the middle of the constellation.) Although the vernal equinox already stands in Taurus in 4000 B.C., the third post-Atlantean culture period is reckoned only from the year 2907 B.C. (747 + 2160 B.C.). One sees from Figure 91 that the vernal equinox, coinciding with the apogee and moving backward from Gemini to Taurus, has not reached the middle of Taurus.

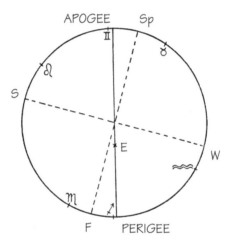

Figure 92

(4a) We have here as a kind of intermezzo the position in the year *3101 B.C.* at the beginning of the Kali Yuga, the time of great death for humanity, because the blackness of the "Age of Darkness" blotted out consciousness like a flood. The perigee does not coincide with one of the cardinal points. One sees that the *vernal equinox* is now in the *middle of Taurus,* and the third post-Altantean epoch is about to begin. The perigee has just entered the constellation *Sagittarius,* which corresponds to the human ego, and it is still in this constellation today. [See Figure 92.]

(5) *1250 A.D.* (Figure 93) We have already described this situation also. It is the opposite of what is explained under numbers two and seven. The perigee is in the winter solstice in Sagittarius and the vernal equinox in Pisces. Once more a diagram, corresponding to the others, depicts the configuration.

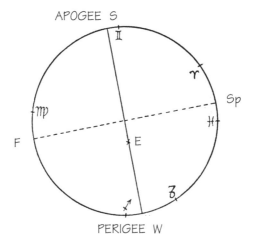

Figure 93

(5a.) *For our own time* the position is approximately as depicted in Figure 94:

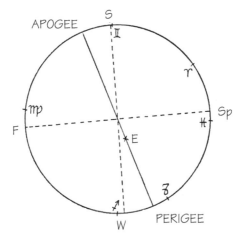

Figure 94

There now remain only but a few future celestial configurations to be noted.

(6) *6500 A.D.* (Figure 95) The perigee is in the *vernal equinox* just about to enter [the conventional constellation] Capricornus from Sagittarius. Rudolf Steiner has described this age as the time of the reunion of the Moon with Earth, a time of terrible catastrophes for those human beings who have not spiritualized their intellects. (See lecture May 13, 1921.)

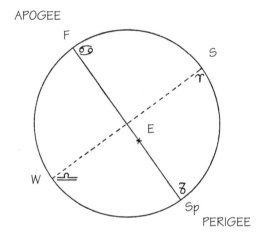

Figure 95

(7) *12,000* A.D. (Figure 96) This is the new Ice Age, differing from the other that took place 21,000 years before in that the *perigee* with the summer solstice will now be in *Capricornus,* while at that time it lay in Scorpius. One can call it a more hardened, a "less watery" Ice Age than that of Atlantean times. The *vernal equinox* will be in the constellation of Libra. It will then have left the dark signs, in which it has been since the time of the Mystery of Golgotha, and will once more enter the light signs. One can experience this symbol as a descent into the increasing hardening of the earthly and as an ascent, full of light and springtime, of the freed spirit into the brights

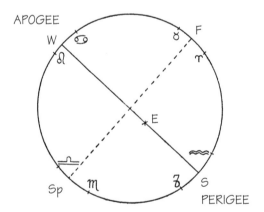

Figure 96

Thus we have tried to read the great world clock that is in the heavenly firmament. The diagrams, because of their small size and due to technical difficulties, reproduce only approximately what is based on quite exact calculations. Nevertheless, if one looks at them in succession one sees how the "hands" gradually advance and how in their meetings they continually bring about new combined positions. Thus they become a true heavenly script. Even something of the great world ages may be deciphered from this heavenly script, as we saw in the case of the approach of the Kali Yuga. We will occupy ourselves with this next time.

The World Ages

FROM EARLIEST ANTIQUITY the teachers of humankind have spoken of the great ages that have unfolded one after another in world history. This knowledge is one of the most widely disseminated treasures of wisdom from the time of the ancient atavistic clairvoyance. The ancient Indians had a special sense for everything rhythmic, everything taking its course cyclically. They regarded as history progress that went according to law and rhythmic necessity rather than accidental, unique occurrences that the western mind sees as history. (This is of course connected with the fact that the etheric body was the foundation of the ancient Indian culture.) These ancient Indians knew of world ages of varying lengths. This knowledge must be traced back to the wisdom-revelation of the seven holy rishis.

In later works concerning these cycles of time (as for instance, the *Surya Siddhanta,* or *The Sun Doctrine*), when the duration of the yugas or world ages is mentioned, enormous numbers are often given, numbers that can only be compared with the notorious "astronomical figures" of modern times. We know that such immense numbers are to be read in a way different from that of our modern decimal system. Each zero (0) actually denotes a past stage of evolution, period, or age. It is the egg from which the next stage of evolution proceeds. Much may have come from a later decadent time when the declining clairvoyant power brought a debased element into the visions. But the doctrine of the four great world ages is firmly established. They were named in Indian terminology the Krita, Treta, Dvapara, and Kali yugas. Rudolf Steiner also made use of these expressions (cf. *The Christ-Impulse and the Development of Ego-Consciousness,* lecture 3).

In the western tradition that arose from Grecian culture they have been called—this also based on a profound wisdom—the golden, silver, bronze, and dark, or iron ages. Sometimes a fifth age or fifth creation is added, and sometimes only three ages are spoken of. Still, when the ages are characterized according to their nature, the correspondence with Indian occultism is unmistakable.

In this teaching about the great ages is the knowledge—which in the ancient pre-Christian Orient was especially strong—that, since the ancient clairvoyance is disappearing more and more, evolution is on a descending course, that each age is poorer, less spiritual than the preceding one. This applies to the greater as well as the lesser periods. For the names of the ages are sometimes employed for the very great epochs that start from the beginning of our Earth's evolution. They have also been understood as shorter periods since each civilization also runs its course in such a way that one can always look upon the preceding one as the better and the more spiritual. The "original sin" works ever more deeply into humanity.

The ancient initiates looked back to a time when humanity lived together with the gods. The human being perceived as yet no physical environment, and rather was still closely connected with the spiritual world. That was the "Golden Age," the Krita Yuga, which in the Indian secret doctrine was also called Satya Yuga or the Age of Truth. We must seek this far back in human evolution—even before Atlantis, in Lemurian times. According to Rudolf Steiner's often quoted "Leading Thoughts" of October 26, 1924, it is the age that corresponds to the first stage of world evolution in which only spiritual beings are present. Although in this first age the temptation by the serpent and the expulsion from paradise had already taken place, for those who came later it was still the Golden Age, for human beings were still the companions of the gods, were guided by the divine will, and were not only given over to their own erring, sinful will.

Then came the next age, the Silver Age, during which already less was experienced directly out of the spiritual world. Nevertheless, human beings still knew much of the spiritual world through the memory of the prenatal state. They could still experience the impulse of the divine spiritual world. It was the Age of Revelation, the second stage of world evolution. It corresponds to most of the Atlantean age. It is therefore the Silver Age, for the old Atlantean time is a reflection of the Moon stage of evolution. As Treta Yuga, it takes its name from the three holy fires on the Indian sacrificial altar. It also expresses the revelation of the Trinity, which was still experienced by human beings.

Then followed the Bronze Age, witness to the great migrations before and during the Atlantean deluge, witness also to the mighty wars that the migrating peoples had to wage against the aboriginal races. It also included the ancient Indian and ancient Persian civilizations. The ego-consciousness awoke. The spiritual world, no longer directly known, lived only in memory and in longing. In the name Dvapara Yuga the fact that it is an age of doubt is revealed. With the awakening of the ego, doubt must enter the soul. That doubt then became elemental despair with the event that lay at the beginning of the age that followed the Dvapara Yuga—the Kali Yuga, the Black or Dark Age. (Here the eastern and western designations coincide.)

The Kali Yuga begins in 3101 B.C. and is characterized by the great war reported in the *Bhagavad Gita*, when blood relatives stood opposed to one another in the two armies—an occurrence unknown until then. Arjuna, a leader of the one host, is on the verge of breaking down in despair over the godlessness of such conduct. Then Krishna, the incarnated divinity, reveals to Arjuna that this outrage is necessary and can be met only by strength of soul. Arjuna arouses himself, the battle begins, and the Age of Darkness sets in. It came to an end in 1899.

Rudolf Steiner once gave specific figures for the duration of the world ages, by which we can faintly discern their relation to the connection with the cosmic rhythm of the line of the apsides (lecture, January 25, 1910, Karlsruhe). The Kali Yuga lasted exactly 5000 years. The figures that stand for the other world ages are all multiples of 5000. The Dvapara Yuga or Bronze Age lasted for 10,000 years, the Silver Age for 15,000 years, and the Golden Age for 20,000 years. These figures are related to the revolution of the line of the apsides and its coinciding with the cardinal points at intervals of about 5000 years.

We have here a cosmic rhythm, not a direct celestial configuration (for the difference between these, see letter 2, year one). The point of time, for instance, of the beginning of the Kali Yuga does not coincide with one of the great meetings of the "hands" of the world clock. However, in the duration of the age itself the coincidence of the rhythm of the precession and of the apsidial line is mirrored. These figures for the yugas, are all multiples of 5000 years. In them the connection with the "Platonic world year"—the revolution of the vernal equinox—stands out still more clearly than in the figures that H. P. Blavatsky gave for the yugas using Indian occultism as a basis. (*Secret Doctrine,* vol. 2). One must only keep in mind what was said earlier—that the many zeros do not indicate a decimal number. Blavatsky gives for the duration of the four successive yugas the figures: 1,728,000 (Krita), 1,296,000 (Treta), 864,000 (Dvapara), and 432,000 (Kali). She means by these, the great periods of time. Blavatsky also reckons the ordinary Kali Yuga as 5000 years. There we have again multiples of the length of the Kali Yuga, and if one takes this as 4320 years, it thus becomes one-sixth of the great world year of 25,920 years.

The periods given by Rudolf Steiner comprise altogether (if one includes the fifth age of 2,500 years) about 52,000 years, half of a siderial apsidal revolution. Such a length of time takes us back into ages when we cannot speak of an actual chronology. The "year" did not have a specific length as it does today. In these "years" and in the calculations we can base upon them, we have something that increasingly points to a mere rhythm, to an astral-etheric law. In the meeting every 5200 years of the two pairs of "clock-hands," we could still point to definite positions in the heavens where these actually take place in regular successive periods of time. Here, however, we have to reckon only with different multiples of these periods, without a definite position in the heavens.

On the other hand, we also lose the exact connection between the cultural periods, or "sub-races"—as they were named for the period of Atlantis—and the passage of time. This is because the year, if we go backward from the middle of the Atlantean age, changes in length. One need only consider that at the beginning of the Lemurian Age the Sun left Earth and that all the conditions that have since led to the length of the year at present were then quite different from what they were later. We can, in spite of this, apply the ordinary figures in calculating the Atlantean periods and the world ages. In doing so we bring about a certain parallelism between the world ages and the Lemurian, the Atlantean, and the post-Atlantean world periods. Thus, for example, we must count seven periods or sub-races of 2,160 years each for the old Atlantean epoch. This is 15,000 years in all, and the end of this lies at the beginning of the first post-Atlantean period. This is about 7200 B.C. if, as is usually done, we take the beginning of the first post-Atlantean period as 747 B.C. The following table results:

The Krita Yuga, or Golden Age, runs its course entirely in the Lemurian age. Duration 20,000 years.

The Treta Yuga, or Silver Age—the first 6,000 years are still in the Lemurian Age, the succeeding 9,000 in the Atlantean Age; in all 15,000 years.

The Dvapara Yuga, or Bronze Age began 6,000 years before the first post-Atlantean civilization and stretched over a further 4000 years, during the ancient Indian and ancient Persian cultural periods—in all, 10,000 years.

The Kali Yuga, or Dark Age, lasts from 3101 B.C. to 1899 A.D. Its duration is 5,000 years. In the second half of this period falls the Mystery of Golgatha.

After this comes another age, our own, which began three decades ago, and which will last 2500 years. In accordance with a term often employed by Rudolf Steiner, we may call it the Age of Light. In spite of all the hardships it has already given us and no doubt will provide in the future, we know what the light of this age is. We are in the age of resurrected spiritual faculties, of a newly awakened clairvoyance. This is, however a bright, clear, "exact clairvoyance," not the misty, dream-like clairvoyance of times past. The ego impulse has finally entered the human being. We can lift ourselves through our own strength, through our own endeavour, into the spiritual world. We can receive the grace of experiencing the gods' world of light, out of which we will draw our strength and guidance for our own soul life as well as for the social life of humanity.

We know also that this new faculty of clairvoyance, the seeing of pictures in the etheric world, will—already in its early stages—lead human beings to directly experience the Christ, in etheric form, in earthly life. At first only a few, then in the next centuries more and more human beings will have this experience.

Our consideration of the great cosmic rhythms led to our dealing with the world ages. It would not be arbitrary if we now turn our attention to the greatest of these, the "Age of Light." Rudolf Steiner himself gave the first indications concerning this event in connection with information concerning the world ages. The lectures given in the first months of 1910 deal with the two subjects in direct connection. [Also:]

... The occultist is able to point out that since the year 1909 or thereabouts what is to come is being prepared for, in a distinct and perceptible way, that since the year 1909 we are inwardly living in a very special time. It is possible today, if we do but seek him, to be very close to the Christ, to find him in a way quite different from what has been possible up to now. [*Cosmic and Human Metamorphoses*, Lecture 1, February 6, 1917]

We have in our considerations traveled the path from the maya of outer nature to the cosmic movements that reveal themselves in this maya on to the reality of the spiritual beings. The circle begun with these Letters three years ago closes.

Our point of departure was the mighty panorama Rudolf Steiner presented in the Helsingfors lecture cycle, concerning the coming forth of the celestial bodies from the spiritual beings of the hierarchies and the guidance of these heavenly bodies by higher and lower beings. The point of departure was that the world, the "world of finished work," is maya, a maya of the past. We sought to take this maya in its purest aspect, where it reveals itself as sense phenomena. Thus we considered celestial phenomena and cosmic movements from the point of view of sense appearance. To really understand these phenomena and movements, we had to return again and again to the spiritual origin of the universe. The entire world of finished work is nothing but a heavenly script for this. We saw the human soul bound up through death and rebirth with the starry heavens, and we saw the warfare being waged in heaven between spiritual powers of the most varied sorts. Finally, we considered the great cosmic periods that together unroll before us the grand picture of human evolution, in which the picture of our age and the near future has a place.

We have again reached spiritual beings. This means that we have come to the primary being of human evolution, who once came down from cosmic heights; who has given to Earth its meaning; who "was in the beginning"; by whom "all things were made"; and who could speak of himself to humanity the words: "Lo, I am with you always, even unto the end of the world," and also the words: "Heaven and Earth shall pass away but my words shall not pass away." The new Earth will be incarnated in the new Jupiter existence, and this "Earth," as well as heaven, will at that time bear the mark of the spirituality or the non-spirituality of our present stage of human evolution. So concrete and real are the interrelationships that are known to spiritual science and that scientific astronomy today wants to seek only in physical materiality.

Rudolf Steiner said, "The science of astronomy is that science which, sooner than all others, may be restored to spirituality." From what we could present here out of the history of astronomy one can affirm the necessity as well as practicability of such an undertaking. We have also pointed out the ideas that especially today form a barrier against the spiritual point of view. These ideas have created the modern, utterly materialistic worldview of scientific astronomy, one bereft of divinity and spirit. Those who desire such a spiritualized astronomy must affirm that much, very much still remains to be done to replace the materialistic worldview with that presented by the spiritual investigator. The spiritual picture, however, can already live in the hearts and souls of those who have made anthroposophy the foundation of their life. From these hearts it can ray forth into the world and work to create the future.

Notes on the Text

The following observations are offered for those with an interest in technical details relating to the subject. They may prove helpful in clarifying certain aspects of what the book presents. Also, many years have passed since the original Letters were written, and a certain amount of astronomical updating, etc., has been included. Some material has been left undisturbed and helps to retain the character of the early versions.

YEAR ONE

Letter 2

Mercury is too small to be seen on the face of the Sun without a telescope or other optical aid. Looking at the Sun with or without such aid requires the use of a safe solar filter to darken the Sun's disk and avoid eye damage. Astronomers often use #14 welder's glass. Smoked glass is not considered today to be a safe filter.

Letter 5

The symbols for the astronomical *constellations* of the zodiac are the same as the symbols used for the astrological *signs* of the zodiac. But constellations and astrological signs do not coincide in the sky. Vreede (and Steiner) sometimes use the terms "constellation" and "sign" interchangeably, and in a general sense, though Vreede emphasizes their technical difference in the text. Further, in the Footnote on page 45, "Scorpius" refers to the astronomical star constellation of the Scorpion; the term "Scorpio" would refer to the differently-located astrological "sign." Likewise with the constellation of "Capricornus" and the sign of "Capricorn."

For observational experience, in the course of a year the Sun moves round an axis which passes through the poles of the ecliptic. In the course of a year the stars, from month to month, move round an axis which passes through the poles of the celestial equator.

In the calendar in common use, dates for the beginnings of the four astronomical seasons (spring equinox, summer solstice, autumn equinox, and winter solstice) can vary in different years and from different locations by at least one day. But the Church calendar, used for the determination of Easter, has its spring equinox fixed at March 21. See also Note for Letter 7.

Letter 6

Isaac Newton was born on Christmas Day 1642 by the old Julian calendar then in use in England. By the Gregorian calendar, which was not introduced there until 1752, he would have been born on January 4, 1643.

Letter 7

Concerning the establishment of the Easter Festival, the Church calendar (as indicated in *The Book of Common Prayer*) does not use the actual astronomical full Moon in its calculations, but an ecclesiastical full Moon which is the fourteenth day of the lunar month. The Church calendar also keeps March 21 fixed as the spring equinox when calculating the date of the Easter Festival. "Astronomically," however, Easter can be defined as the first Sunday after the full Moon which falls on or after the spring equinox. Therefore there are instances when the ecclesiastical (celebrated) Easter date differs from the "astronomical" date. During the 20th century this happened eleven times—in 1900, 1903, 1923, 1924, 1927, 1943, 1954, 1962, 1967, 1974, and 1981. The first such discrepancy in the 21st century will be in 2038, when the celebrated ecclesiastical date of Easter Sunday will be April 25, and the "astronomical" date March 28.

Letter 8

When reckoning planetary and other positions for the early part of the 20th century, it should be noted that before 1925 the astronomical day began at midday (00 hours). On January 1, 1925, the beginning of the astronomical day (still written as 00 hours) was moved back 12 hours to coincide with the civil day beginning at midnight. Almanacs using differing time systems can render different dates for the same phenomena.

It has been discovered that Galileo saw and recorded the planet Neptune in the early morning of December 28, 1612, but did not quite realise it was a planet, though he suspected it might have movement.

Uranus is *just* visible to the naked eye at certain favorable periods.

Letter 9

A maximum of seven normally visible eclipses (i.e., not including penumbral eclipses of the Moon) can be seen in one year, being a mixture of solar and lunar eclipses. These take place during (usually) two "eclipse seasons" or periods. A solar eclipse must happen when new Moon occurs within 15 degrees 23 minutes of a Moon node; a lunar eclipse (not penumbral) must happen if full Moon occurs within 9 degrees 39 minutes of a Moon node.

Letter 10

In one saros period of 18 years 10 or 11 days, an average of 70.6 eclipses, comprising solar and lunar eclipses, take place (excluding penumbral Moon eclipses). In a succession (series) of saros periods moving from pole to pole over hundreds of years, a solar series has from 70 to 85 eclipses; a lunar series from 39 to 59 eclipses.

Letter 11

According to conventional astronomy, the precession of an equinox takes about 25,800 years to make one cycle of 360 degrees along the ecliptic. A more precise calculation gives 25,770 years. The March or September equinox moves one degree in about 71.6 years. This expresses the east to west movement of the intersection of the plane of the celestial equator with the ecliptic. This east to west movement among the stars is thus also reflected by the celestial equator's pole, which describes a top-like motion round the pole of the ecliptic. Copernicus described the movement as being "in precedence" or westwards; it can be seen as the direction toward which the zodiacal constellations "go ahead" in their daily, monthly or yearly movements.

For details of Hipparchus' discovery of precession see, for example, J.L.E. Dreyer's *A History of Astronomy from Thales to Kepler*, Chapter 9.

Letter 12

With the precession of the equinoxes through the usual, unequal-length constellations of the zodiac, the spring Sun spends sometimes less and sometimes more time in a constellation than the average of just over 2,000 years.

The summer solstice moved into the astronomer's constellation of Taurus in 1989. A conventional star map for epoch (reference date) A.D. 2000 will show this new position.

Because the calendar has no year zero or minus years, 747 B.C. plus 2160 years brings one to A.D. 1414. However, the astronomer uses a year zero, and the year –747 (equivalent to 748 B.C.) plus 2160 years reaches the date A.D. 1413.

The Julian Calendar made the seasonal year 11 minutes 14 seconds too long. The seasonal year moves with precession.

In astronomical language, the equinoxes "precess" and the lunar nodes "regress"—though both in the same direction!

YEAR TWO

Letter 1

In a clear, dark sky, Mercury looks white. But it is often in or near the sunset or sunrise glow, and then looks red.

Mercury crossed into the sign of Libra on September 20, 1913. Its ecliptic longitude thus reached 180 degrees. It crosses the celestial equator on the same day if its path is ideally seen as coincident with the ecliptic. On the 20th it had a (descending) equatorial declination of around 1 degree north.

Letter 10

The constellation of the "Unicorn" (Figure 41) is usually given its Greek-derived name "Monoceros" on English star maps. It is a modern constellation, for Europe at least, with no bright or named stars. A depiction of it was made on a celestial globe by the Dutch theologian and cartographer Petrus Plancius in 1613, and some authorities attribute the invention of the constellation to him.

Steiner's lecture course *The Relationship of the Diverse Branches of Natural Science to Astronomy* was given in Stuttgard from January 1 – 18, 1921. It is often abbreviated to the *"Astronomy Course,"* hence the quotation marks when this version of the title is used here, along with the fact that Steiner himself emphasized that the *relationship* aspect of the title was important in light of an increased tendency to specialization and separation among the sciences. The task of these lectures was to "build a bridge from the different fields of scientific thought to the field of astronomy, that astronomical understanding may appear in the right way in the various fields of science." (Lecture 1).

Letter 11

The comet of 1843 (1) is presented according to descriptions by the astronomer Camille Flammarion. The comet was first seen in the Southern Hemisphere on February 5. It only became widely known from the perihelion stage onwards.

Astronomically, a distinction is made between a meteor (ordinary "shooting star") and a meteorite. A *meteor* is a flash in the night sky caused by small particles of matter (meteoroids), often about the size of grains of sand. They are usually considered to be related to cometary material which burns up in the Earth's atmosphere, often in the form of "showers." Any iron connected with them is perhaps of a "homeopathic" nature. A *meteorite* is a piece of stony or iron material which falls to Earth after passing through the atmosphere, often as a bright fireball. Most meteorites are understood to be fragments of asteroids rather than comprising cometary material.

It is now known that Jupiter has 25 retrograde moons and has rings.

Letter 12

Vreede's drawing of Figure 45 in the 1928 English version of Letter 12, shows the Comet of 1744 with five tails. The edges of the tails were emphasized into ten lines. Figure 45 in the present text is a different rendering, but also has its justification in that the comet was variously described as having from five to eleven tails. Often called after the Swiss astronomer de Cheseaux (although it was first discovered by someone else) the comet put on its spectacular display in the eastern dawn sky in March, 1744.

Today, the Perseid meteor shower is at its maximum around August 12 and 13.

YEAR THREE

Letter 1

The comet of 1862 (Comet Swift-Tuttle) which is associated with the Perseid meteors, returned in 1992.

The comet of 1866 (Comet Tempel-Tuttle) which is associated with the Leonid meteors, has returned periodically since 1899.

In this context, Vreede also refers to Comet Tempel (1) which appeared in 1879, had a period of around six years, and "disappeared" for a long time. See also "Endnotes" to the 1980 edition of the Letters in *Antronomie und Anthroposophie* – Philosophisch-Anthroposophischer Verlag, Dornach, Switzerland.

The Perseid meteor shower was recorded in China in A.D. 36. The Leonid meteor shower was reported in A.D. 585.

Today the meteoric fall of "immense size" in Siberia in 1908 is called the "Tunguska event" and is understood to have been an asteroid or small comet exploding before reaching the ground.

Letter 4

When the Italian astronomer Schiaparelli began detailed telescopic observations of Mars in 1877, he noted what had already been called "channels" (canali), and while introducing further names involving the surface of Mars (he also spoke of "seas" and "continents") he "made it quite clear, in publishing his results, that such terms were for convenience only and did not represent terrestrial actuality." (*The Biographical Dictionary of Scientists*; Peter Bedrick Books, NY). In *Worlds in the Sky* (University of Arizona Press) William Sheehan stated in 1992: "We now know that there never were any true canals; they were an illusion due to perceptual effects by which complex details are seen under symbolic forms."

Letter 6

Today, six stars of the Pleiades cluster are considered visible to the naked eye. Legend refers to seven, perhaps due to an earlier greater brightness of one of them, Pleione.

Letter 8

The New Star of 1600 in the constellation of Cygnus was first noted by the Dutch mapmaker and astronomer Willem Janzoon Blaeu, who inserted it on a celestial globe the following year. The star was reported to remain visible for two decades, disappearing sometime in the 1620s.

The Jupiter-Saturn conjunction of A.D. 2000 was the "last" of a series in an "Earth sign" of the zodiac (Taurus), although in 1980/81 the Jupiter-Saturn conjunction already took place in the next (air) sign of the trigon period.

Astronomically, the constellation of Ophiuchus (The Serpent Bearer) extends over an ecliptic area between Scorpius and Sagittarius. The conjunction of Saturn and Jupiter on November 30, 1603, took place in Ophiuchus. Mars and Jupiter were in conjunction in Ophiuchus a year later, on October 9, on the evening in which the Supernova ("new star") of 1604 was first seen (from Italy) as it stood just above these two planets. Observers confirm the new star was not there on the previous night. By the time Kepler saw the star on October 17, the planets had spread apart. The star was reported as brighter than Jupiter around when Kepler saw it, and, though later decreasing in brightness, remained visible for a year. (The radio remnant of this "Kepler's Supernova" has been positioned at 17h 30m 38.6s; -21deg. 28' 52" [epoch 2000]. Ref. computer program *"Guide 8.0"* – http://www.projectpluto.com).

Letter 9

Annual stellar parallax has certainly been sought, and, as Vreede says, has consequently been found. Disproving it would seem to be a similar process. As she emphasizes, if a different type of question had been asked, a different type of answer would have been found.

Letter 11

The quotation "Because of the eccentricity. . . . . 36 days." follows the rendering of this passage given in the 1980 edition of Vreede's Letters – *Astronomie und Anthroposophie*.

Letter 12

The "Leading Thoughts" are in *Anthroposophical Leading Thoughts* by R. Steiner (Rudolf Steiner Press, London, 1973).

Kali Yuga traditionally began in the year 3102 B.C., when there was a gathering of the five planets, Mercury to Saturn, plus Sun and Moon, within a span of about 41 degrees. That year was the same as the "minus" year –3101, which is sometimes confused with the B.C. numbering. The year –3101 plus 5000 years of Kali Yuga (including a year zero, which is not in the B.C./A.D. calendar system) arrives at the date A.D. 1899.

The lecture of January 25, 1910, appears in *The True Nature of the Second Coming* (Anthroposophical Publishing Company, London,

1961.) There, Steiner's response to questions after the lecture has an Endnote containing the lengths of the Yugas as given by Vreede.

—N.D. (January, 2007)

INDEX

Lightning Source UK Ltd.
Milton Keynes UK
UKHW030837090919
349451UK00003B/174/P